NATURAL GAS
ENGINEERING

NATURAL GAS ENGINEERING

Editor
Selvin Fernandes

DISCOVERY PUBLISHING HOUSE
INDIA

Published by:

DISCOVERY PUBLISHING HOUSE

4383/4B, Ansari Road, Darya Ganj

New Delhi-110 002 (India)

Phone : +91-11-23279245; 23253475; 43596065

Mobile : +91 9811179893 / +91 9871656464

E-mail : discoverybooksindia@gmail.com

orderdphbooks@gmail.com

namitwasan9@gmail.com

web : www.discoverypublishinggroup.com

Natural Gas Engineering

Edited by: **Selvin Fernandes**

Consider:

PREFACE

Natural gas is an important source of energy and chemicals that play a crucial role in meeting the world's increasing demand for cleaner and more sustainable energy. It is considered one of the cleanest, safest, and most versatile energy sources available. However, the process of exploring, producing, and utilizing natural gas requires careful engineering and understanding of the gas and its surrounding environment. Even small advancements in this process can have a significant impact on the gas industry.

This book presents the latest advancements in emerging technologies related to natural gas. It includes research articles from various scientific disciplines that focus on new developments in natural gas engineering. The topics covered include gas exploration, production, processing, and transmission. The book also includes key review papers written by experts from both industry and academia. The global transition towards decarbonization and a low-emission economy in the coming decades highlights the importance of natural gas as a crucial energy source. The demand for natural gas and liquefied natural gas (LNG) is expected to rise, particularly for substituting power generation processes that currently rely on coal. Natural gas is often used in areas where renewable energy sources cannot be effectively applied, making it a complementary energy source.

Given the urgent need to diversify energy sources due to the accelerating greenhouse effect and global warming, efforts must be made to explore alternative energy options. This book is motivated by the rapidly changing global energy landscape and the potential opportunities offered by the flexibility and performance characteristics of natural gas. The gas sector plays a vital role in ensuring a sustainable energy future, contributing to environmental protection, economic growth, and security. The existing gas infrastructure is also valuable for ensuring energy reliability, supporting the integration of renewable gases, and facilitating the incorporation of more renewables into the overall energy system.

In recent years, there has been a growing focus on improving the management of gas grids. The book addresses novel optimization and control techniques specifically designed for gas grids and natural gas applications. These emerging techniques aim to enhance the efficiency and effectiveness of gas grid operations. This book is intended for readers interested in the field of natural gas engineering, including professionals, researchers, and students seeking a comprehensive understanding of the principles, processes, and technologies involved in the extraction, transportation, and utilization of natural gas resources.

The editor of the book has gathered information from trustworthy and scientifically backed sources to give readers the most up-to-date and accurate information possible. The book is a collection of articles written by experts from all over the world, and the editor is grateful for their valuable input. The knowledge and expertise shared by these experts are insightful and will be beneficial for the readers.

Editor

CONTENTS

1

Catalytic Natural Gas Utilization on Unconventional Oil Upgrading

Peng He and Hua Song

Department of Chemical and Petroleum Engineering, University of Calgary, Calgary, Alberta, Canada

ABSTRACT

The upgrading of unconventional oil using methane, the principal component of natural gas, is a promising alternative method to the conventional hydrotreating process, which consumes naturally unavailable H2 at high pressures. Methanotreating is an economically attractive process with abundant and readily available raw materials to accomplish the upgrading of bio-oil and to attain improved oil quality. The application of methane as the H donor avoids the energy consumption and CO_2 rejection during the reforming of methane to produce H2. More product oil is also obtained through the incorporation of methane into the product oil. Ag/ZSM-5, Zn/ZSM-5 and Ag-Zn/ZSM-5 have been employed to upgrade bio-oil under methane environment to achieve increased oil yield and H/C molar ratio, suppressed total acid number and unsaturation degree of the product oil. Ag-Zn/ZSM-5 is used to catalyze the methanotreating of heavy oil to attain lower viscosity accompanied with good stability and compatibility, which are critical for the pipeline transportation of heavy oil to downstream refineries. Higher gasoline and diesel fractions, increased H/C molar ratio, lower total acid number are witnessed upon the upgrading in the presence of Ag-Zn/ZSM-5 under methane environment. The mechanism studies practiced in the literature using methods including solid-state NMR and FTIR have revealed at least two reaction pathways, i.e., carbenium pathway and alkyl pathway, to accomplish the activation of methane, which is crucial for the involvement of methane in the following upgrading reaction steps. The reaction thermodynamics and reaction intermediates have also been explored by computational approaches by researchers. These observations and achievements will encourage more researchers to develop more catalyst systems and attain improved catalytic performance in the unconventional oil upgrading using natural gas.

Keywords: *Natural gas, Unconventional oil, Methane activation, Bio-oil, Biomass, Heavy oil, Zeolite, Catalytic upgrading, Mechanism study, Theoretical calculation*

INTRODUCTION

The utilization of unconventional oil is attracting attention as the energy demand is growing rapidly driven by the urbanization all over the world, while the reserve of conventional petroleum is decreasing. The past decade has witnessed a dramatic change brought by unconventional oil to the petroleum industry. For instance, the technology breakthrough in the extraction of shale oil is one of the dominating factors that drive the crude oil price to drop from above 100 USD per barrel in 2014 to below 30 USD per barrel in 2016. Besides shale oil, other unconventional oil resources such as bio-oil and heavy oil could also be the alternative energy source of the conventional petroleum and meet the ever surging demand of human society due to their huge scale of potential reserves.

Bio-oil is receiving increasing attention since it is the only renewable source of hydrocarbon that can be used for liquid fuel [1] and chemical production [2–6] owing to its low cost, ready availability, resource abundance and environment-friendliness [7]. It is often produced from the pyrolysis of biomass, which destructs biomass in the absence of air/oxygen generating liquid bio-oil, syngas and biochar [8]. However, the obtained bio-oil often faces problems such as hydrogen deficit, high oxygen content and the presence of contaminants including sulfur, chlorine and trace metals. The low H/C molar ratio is closely related to the high concentration of unsaturated contents in the bio-oil, resulting in the instability when exposed to light, oxygen or heat above 80°C, rendering stability issues while storage and transportation [9]. The high oxygen content in the bio-oil makes the produced bio-oil of low heating value, impeding its application as substituent for traditional liquid fuel to power the world. In order to deal with these drawbacks, various processes have been explored to remove or chemically modify the undesired components to obtain upgraded bio-oil [10–14], among which hydrodeoxygenation is most widely employed [10–12] to improve the quality of bio-oil in terms of higher energy dense, enhanced stability and suppressed causticity. The process, however, has to consume expensive H_2 at high pressures (typically 70–140 atm and even above 200 atm) [15, 16]. The involvement of naturally unavailable H_2, and the stricter requirements of the reaction units to tolerate high pressure, will eventually escalate the operating cost [15]. The upgrading of bio-oil by catalytic cracking on zeolites at atmosphere pressure without hydrogen has also been explored to produce aromatics [14, 17], which still suffers from the low yield and high coke deposition due to the low H/C molar ratio [18]. Co-feeding with some hydrogen-rich feedstocks such as waste oil, plastics and alcohols can provide hydrogen to the reaction system and improve the quality of bio-oil [19–22]. These co-fed materials, however, are not naturally available on a large scale. Therefore, an economically attractive method with abundant and readily available raw materials to accomplish the upgrading of bio-oil and to attain improved quality is greatly desired.

Another unconventional oil with sufficient potential availability is heavy oil, such as bitumen extracted from Canadian oil sand. There are an estimated 174 billion barrels of bitumen reserves in Canada. In Alberta alone, the bitumen production reached 2.3 million barrels per day in 2014. Compared with conventional petroleum, the deficiency of heavy oil is owing to the low H/C molar ratio, high impurity content, high viscosity, high asphaltene content and high density [23]. Heavy oil was formed from conventional oil, degraded by bacteria upon the migration towards the surface region. Some light hydrocarbons were consumed during the biology reaction process. As a result, heavy oil is deficient in hydrogen and has high asphaltene content. For instance, the hydrogen to carbon molar ratio is often below 1.5 versus a value close to 2.0 in conventional reservoirs [24]. The heavy oil reservoirs are rich in several countries such as Canada and Venezuela, while the downstream refineries are in other countries including the United States. Therefore, the transportation of heavy oil from the oil fields to refineries is critical for its further upgrading and application in industry. The extracted bitumen from steam-assisted gravity drainage (SAGD) processes in Canada has an average density of 1.0077 g/cm^3, API gravity of 8.9, and a dynamic viscosity of 2×10^5 to 2×10^6 cP at atmospheric conditions [25]. Such a high viscosity makes it challenging to transport heavy oil, especially through pipelines. Dilution of heavy oil is widely practiced to meet pipeline specifications for transport to refineries. Solvents such as naphtha or gas condensates (1:2 ratio of diluent:bitumen, known as dilbit) and synthetic crude oil (SCO) (1:1 ratio of SCO:bitumen, known as synbit) are used to increase the API gravity of the diluted bitumen to 22. Pipeline transport requires a fluid density of <0.940 g/cm^3 and dynamic viscosity of <330 cP (at 7.5–17°C) [25, 26]. Therefore, the complete elimination or significant reduction in diluent usage is highly desired from a financial and operating standpoint as well as from an environmental perspective.

In order to reduce the viscosity, thermal cracking is widely carried out to break down the carbon chains into short ones. Despite the reduced viscosity due to the carbon chain breakage into smaller molecules, the olefin content of the product oil will inevitably be lifted. Olefins contained in the produced oil are oxidatively and thermally unstable and may gradually form polymeric deposit during storage and transportation [27]. Therefore, hydrotreating processes are used to remove the olefin contents and reduce the sulfur and nitrogen content of the oil. But similar to hydrogen oxygenation process on bio-oil, such process is faced by the cost brought by the consumption of naturally unavailable hydrogen as well as the high pressure during the operation.

In industry, more than 50% hydrogen is obtained through the reforming of methane, the principal component of natural gas, such as steam methane reforming of methane. The reforming of methane is a highly endothermic reaction and often requires high operating temperatures (>800°C) and pressures (1.5–3.0 MPa) to attain high equilibrium conversion of CH_4 towards H_2. The involvement of such a naturally unavailable hydrogen source will inevitably result in a significant cost for hydrotreating process. Another drawback of this process is that the carbon from methane has to be ejected as CO_2 to recover H_2, resulting in more greenhouse emission. If CH_4 could be used as the hydrogen source directly in the hydrocracking processes, the operating cost could be lowered, since the cost of methane reforming is saved. In this scenario, rather than ejected as CO_2, the carbon from methane will be incorporated into the product oil to produce more synthetic oil and attain more profit. If the upgrading under CH_4 atmosphere could be achieved at a lowered pressure, the cost of this process would again be reduced since the cost owing to the materials and connections of the reaction units is decreased.

One of the obstacles of the application of methane in oil upgrading is its inert structure. The energy of the C–H bond in methane is the highest among all hydrocarbons. In order to activate the C–H bond of methane for successive upgrading steps, catalysts with high activity and stability should be formulated. Over the past decades, these catalysts that have been intensively studied under variable conditions including oxidation and non-oxidation conditions, shedding light on the oil upgrading using methane. Among them, MIF-type zeolite (ZSM-5)-based catalysts exhibit outstanding methane activation capability under non-oxidation condition, which is more feasible for oil upgrading compared with oxidation condition. These catalysts are prepared by loading active metal species on ZSM-5 framework with variable acidity. At a temperature range of 350–400°C and pressure range of 10–50 bar, these catalysts can catalyze methane to upgrade unconventional oil to achieve the olefin saturation, deoxygenation, desulfurization, denitrogenation and demetallization. These studies open a door for upgrading unconventional oil with natural gas under fairly mild operating conditions instead of expensive hydrogen under rather stringent ones.

PRODUCTION TECHNOLOGY OVERVIEW

Upgrading Technology of Bio-oil

Bio-oil is often collected from the pyrolysis of biomass, such as canola straw [28], saw dust [29] and agricultural residues [6], due to the convenient apparatus set up and relatively low capital cost [9]. Bio-oil is produced by heating up the biomass rapidly to a high temperature, typically 450–550°C, for a short period of residence time in the absence of oxygen, followed by the liquid product collection upon condensation [8, 30]. Such a fast pyrolysis process would significantly augment the liquid product yield and suppress the formation of gas product and char [8]. As a sustainable hydrocarbon resource with abundant availability and carbon-neutral nature, bio-oil has drawn attention to be the potential reservoir that provides fuels and chemical feedstocks. The obtained bio-oil is a complex mixture composed of acetic acid, acetaldehyde, water, furfurals and phenolics [31]. The low energy density due to the large amount of oxygenated functional groups and the complex of the product matrix impedes the application of bio-oil as fuels or chemical feedstocks directly. Therefore, lots of efforts have been made to improve the quality of bio-oil in terms of product yield, suitable selectivity, stability, compatibility with conventional fuels, reduced corrosivity and so on.

Nowadays, there are mainly three processes for bio-oil upgrading [30]. In the first one, bio-oil is first produced then upgraded by catalytic cracking, hydrotreating, steam reforming, etc [32]. For instance, the liquefaction oil can undergo the conventional petroleum catalytic hydrotreating method to attain higher yield of hydrocarbons upon deoxygenation [33–35]. Some researchers also put efforts on the catalytic conversion over certain fractions of bio-oil, which is separated from bio-oil by methods rather than distillation of oils. For example, the pyrolysis can be conducted at multiple stages with specific temperatures, resulting in several batches of bio-oil product with different compositions [32]. Upon the fractionation of bio-oil, each fraction can be upgraded more efficiently comparing with the upgrading of bio-oil. Upgrading through reactions such as ketonization of small carboxylic acids [36], aldol condensation of furfurals followed by hydrogenation [37], alkylation [31] and hydrodeoxygenation [38] of phenolics can be carried out with corresponding high activity catalyst systems, respectively.

The other two processes, called in-bed and in situ pyrolysis, respectively, were divided based on the position of the catalyst within the reactor, while the bio-oil produced by pyrolysis is upgraded in vapor phase at high temperatures [30]. Compared with upgrading after condensation, such vapor phase upgrading is more feasible for industrial application due to the reduced number of operating units. During the in-bed catalytic pyrolysis, biomass and catalyst are mixed together, so the pyrolysis and upgrading are carried out simultaneously. The inorganic components of biomass such as silica, Na, K, Mg and Ca ions might contribute to the upgrading of bio-oil [9]. In the in situ process, the biomass is first cracked to produce pyrolytic vapors, and then the vapors pass through catalyst beds for upgrading. Compared with in-bed process, in this process, the produced bio-char and spent catalyst can be easily separated. Many catalyst systems have been developed to upgrade bio-oil. The co-fed H_2 can enhance the quality of bio-oil by removing the oxygenated function groups via H_2O and CO_2. Many catalyst systems have been developed to achieve desired quality of the bio-oil. Hydrotreating catalysts similar to those used in petroleum industry such as Ni, Co and Mo loaded on silica and alumina supports have been used for the upgrading of bio-oil [9, 39, 40]. Catalysts based on neutral support materials including Ru/C, Pd/C and Pt/C are also used to suppress the coke formation [39, 41]. Other support materials such as ZrO_2, CeO_2, zeolites such as USY [42] and MSU [43] are also used to upgrade bio-oil to increase the product yield and formation of hydrocarbons. Among the catalysts employed, ZSM-5-based catalysts have been widely employed to upgrade bio-oil [12, 30], which might be due to the aromatization capability of ZSM-5 [44].

The in situ pyrolysis apparatus can be modified to execute the bio-oil upgrading using methane, i.e., methanotreating, by replacing H_2 with CH_4, and charging the corresponding catalysts. The flow diagram of a typical reactor system [29] is displayed in Figure 1. The biomass, such as saw dust and flex straw, is grounded and sieved into small particles, and then put into the reactor. The biomass particle and the catalyst bed are sandwiched between three layers of quartz wool in the vertically oriented reactor. The feed gas is introduced downstream to react with the vapor product from pyrolysis. The product is then condensed and collected.

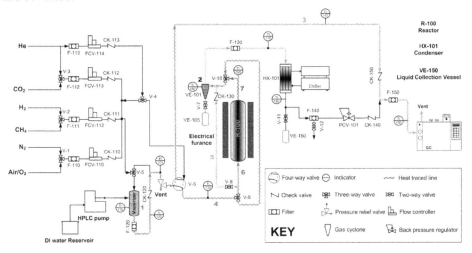

Figure 1. Process flow diagram of a typical multifunctional reactor system. Adapted with permission from Ref. [29].

It is reported that when Ag/ZSM-5 is charged as the catalyst and sawdust are used as the biomass feedstock, the introduction of CH_4 to the feed gas increases the oil yield from 4.07 to 4.85 wt%. As is displayed in Table 1, the quality of the collected oil is also improved. For instance, the H/C molar ratio is increased from 1.29 to 1.76. The contribution due to introduction demonstrates the synergistic effect among methane, biomass pyrolysis and the Ag/ZSM-5 catalyst. When CH_4 is fed without biomass, however, no significant conversion is observed, implying that the presence of biomass is critical to trigger the upgrading process, which relies on the synergetic effect between biomass, methane and the catalyst. It is worth noting that when ZSM-5 is modified by phosphorous and cerium, the oil yield is boosted along with a high H/C molar ratio of 2.26. The improved oil quality might be attributed to the suppressed cracking capability of the catalyst, which reveals a potential direction to optimize the catalyst and achieve a better catalytic performance.

Table 1. Saw dust pyrolysis performance under various environments

Trials	Oilayield (%)	Water formed (mg/g)	Oil quality		
			H/C molar ratio	O content	O/C molar ratio
Inert	5.47	97.0	1.62	5.25	0.226
Inert, Ag/ZSM-5	4.07	135.6	1.29	0.18	0.009
30% H_2	4.17	73.4	1.46	3.41	0.145
30% H_2, Ag/ZSM-5	3.42	100.2	1.45	0.45	0.024
30% CH_4	4.68	119.0	1.38	0.22	0.009
sole 30% CH_4, Ag/ZSM-5	4.85	128.3	1.76	0.07	0.003
30% CH_4,Ag/P-Ce-ZSM-5	6.89	110.9	2.26	7.35	0.356
30% CH_4, Ag/ZSM-5	0	0	—	—	—

[a] Moisture-free liquid collections with boiling point <150°C.

Adapted with permission from Ref. [29]. Copyright 2014 American Chemical Society.

Besides modifying ZSM-5 by silver, the methane catalyzed bio-oil upgrading is also realized by low cost metals [45]. Among Fe, Co, Cu, Mn, Zr, Ni, Ce and Zn, Zn shows the best catalytic performance on bio-oil upgrading when loaded on ZSM-5, in terms of H/C molar ratio, O/C molar ratio and acidity of the product oils. When 5%Zn/ZSM-5 is engaged as the catalyst, the H/C molar ratio of the product oil is increased from 1.92 to 2.20, which is obtained under CH_4 environment without catalyst, indicating the incorporation of methane molecules into the product oil.

A relatively low total acid number (TAN) of 30.63 mg KOH/g is witnessed along with a low O/C atomic ratio of 0.10, compared with 61.31 mg KOH/g and 0.16 when no catalyst is used under CH_4 environment. The reduced acidity is attributed to the removal of the carboxylic acid groups during the methanotreating. The influence of Zn loading on the catalytic performance is evaluated by varying the loading amount of Zn at 1, 2, 5, 10 and 20 wt%. As is shown in Figure 2, the liquid yield increases as the Zn loading is increased to 5%, but start to decrease at 10 and 20%. The H/C molar ratio, on the other hand, reaches the maximum value when the Zn loading is 10%.

By analyzing the products obtained using HZSM-5 and Zn/ZSM-5 with variable metal loading amount, it is concluded that during the reaction ZSM-5 framework promotes the deoxygenation and improves the quality of bio-oil, while the Zn species dispersed on the framework facilitate CH_4 activation and allow it to be incorporated into the carbon chain of the bio-oil, rendering an enhanced quantity of bio-oil.

The upgrading process can also be extended to other fields. For example, the expanding municipal solid waste (MSW) generated during the urbanization all over the work is causing growing environmental risk and management costs. The utilization of MSW in a similar manner as biomass not only disposes of the waste but also supplies the hydrocarbon fuel and chemicals. Therefore, the conversion of MSW into bio-oil upon upgrading under methane environment is drawing attention [28].

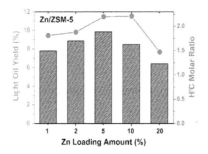

Figure 2. Influence of Zn loading amount on catalytic performance of Zn/ZSM-5. Reprinted from Ref. [45].

When MSW is used as the feedstock, the product oil collected over 1%Ag-5%Zn/ZSM-5 sees an oil yield of 12.73% in the presence of methane. The successful application of the catalytic conversion of MSW into fuels and chemicals under methane might change the landscape of waste management, leading to environmental and economic benefit. It is also worth noting that when MSW is engaged as the feedstock, the presence of 1%Ag-5%Zn/ZSM-5 would enhance the quality of bio-oil compared with 1%Ag/ZSM-5 and 5%Zn/ZSM-5. Transmission electron microscopy (TEM) images (Figure 3) coupled with energy dispersive X-ray spectroscopy (EDX) analysis collected over the 1%Ag-5%Zn/ZSM-5 catalyst demonstrate that Ag_2O particles with bigger sizes (about 10–20 nm) are surrounded by the smaller ZnO particles (<10 nm). The synergetic effect due to the two metal species should contribute to the improved catalytic performance.

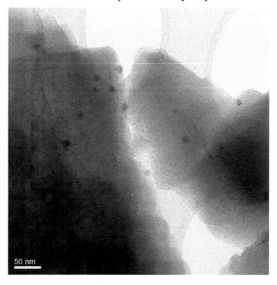

Figure 3. TEM image of 5%Zn–1%Ag/ZSM-5. Reprinted from Ref. [28].

Upgrading Technology of Heavy Oil

Hydrotreating is commonly performed to upgrade heavy oil in petroleum industry while hydrodesulfurization, hydrodenitrogenation, hydrodeoxydation and hydrodemetallization take place simultaneously in the presence of catalysts and substantial hydrogen supply. The catalytic hydrotreating capacity in the US is as large as 17.3 million barrels per day in January, 2015, according to the statistics released by the US Energy Information Administration. Olefins, generated during the breaking down of the large molecules in the previous thermal cracking step, are eliminated as hydrogen is added to the unsaturated bonds of olefins [46]. Among the hydrotreating catalysts, catalysts based on Mo_2S promoted with Co or Ni have been intensively investigated for decades due to their good catalytic activity in the hydrotreating processes [47–50]. For instance, the reactivity of the Co-promoted Mo_2S catalyst is believed to be closely related to the Co-Mo-S structure, where the promoter atoms are located on the edge of the MoS_2 clusters [51]. However, MoS_2 promoted hydrotreating process would consume a large amount of hydrogen, which is not naturally available. As is discussed in the previous section, if methane, the principal component of natural gas, can be employed as the H-donor to accomplish methanotreating of heavy oil, the upgrading process can be more profitable and environmental friendly.

Methanotreating of heavy oil has been explored to produce partial upgraded heavy oil, i.e., a product oil with reduced viscosity accompanied along with higher H/C molar ratio, suppressed acidity, improved stability and compatibility, by engaging Ag-Zn/ZSM-5 as the catalyst [52]. As is displayed in Table 2, when Ag-Zn/ZSM-5 is charged as the catalyst under an initial CH_4 pressure of 5 MPa, the viscosity of the product oil is remarkably reduced from 848,080 mPa (cP) to 413.7 cP, approaching the pipeline transportation requirements [53]. Despite a lower viscosity is witnessed when H_2 is employed in the reaction, the liquid product yield is higher when CH_4 is used, which is assigned to the incorporation of methane molecules into the product. The stability and compatibility of the collected product oil are evaluated through spot test. The obtained spot test images (Figure 4) show that the oil product collected under CH_4 environment with the Ag-Zn/ZSM-5 charged (Figure 4e) exhibits the best stability and compatibility which approach those of the product from the H_2 run (Figure 4f) making it more suitable for pipeline transportation.

Table 2. Performance of bitumen upgrading under various environments at 5.0 MPa and 380 °C for 150 min

Trial	Atmosphere	Coke yield (wt.%)	Liquid yield (wt.%)	Viscosity (cP at 25°C)
Bitumen	—	—	—	848,080
–	N_2	0.60	94.5	1718.3
–	CH_4	0.55	96.5	1617.1
HZSM-5	CH_4	0.80	93.8	1374.4
Ag-Zn/ZSM-5	N_2	0.86	92.9	1276.0
Ag-Zn/ZSM-5	CH_4	0.75	97.8	413.7
Ag-Zn/ZSM-5	H_2	0.62	93.1	280.2

Adapted from Ref. [52] with permission from the Royal Society of Chemistry.

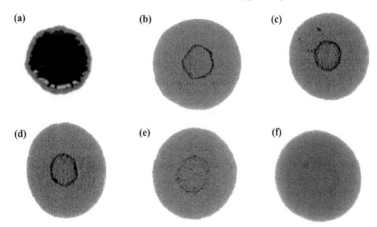

Figure 4. Stability test of (a) heavy oil feedstock and oil products collected under (b) N_2, (c) CH_4, (d) CH_4 with ZSM-5, (e) CH_4 with the Ag-Zn/ZSM-5 catalyst, and (f) H_2 with the Ag-Zn/ZSM-5 catalyst. Adapted from Ref. [52] with permission from the Royal Society of Chemistry.

Besides viscosity and stability, gasoline and diesel fractions of the oil samples also get significantly improved upon the methanotreating. Because the heavy oil will eventually be converted to gasoline and diesel in downstream refineries, an increased gasoline and diesel fraction in the product oil would lessen the burden of downstream refineries and make the partial upgrading more profitable. The gasoline and diesel fractions of the bitumen feedstock and the product oils gained under variable conditions are presented in Table 3. In the bitumen feedstock, there is litter gasoline and a small fraction of diesel (11.96%). After upgrading under various conditions, such as thermocracking under N_2 or CH_4, and catalytic upgrading under N_2 or CH_4, the fraction of gasoline and diesel is increased. However, among the oils in comparison, the highest total gasoline and diesel fraction of 36.77% and the highest gasoline fraction of 13.38% are achieved upon the upgrading in the presence of methane and the catalyst Ag-Zn/ZSM-5, demonstrating the carbon chain breakage and rearrangement capability of the catalyst under CH_4.

Table 3. Gasoline and diesel fractions of the oil samples collected before and after bitumen upgrading under various environments at 5.0 MPa and 380°C for 150 min

Trial	Atmosphere	Gasoline (wt.%)	Diesel (wt.%)	Total gasoline and diesel (wt.%)
Bitumen	–	0.19	11.96	12.15
–	N_2	6.88	20.81	27.69
–	CH_4	6.95	23.74	30.69
HZSM-5	CH_4	6.47	25.26	31.73
Ag-Zn/ZSM-5	N_2	6.28	26.57	32.85
Ag-Zn/ZSM-5	CH_4	13.38	23.39	36.77

Adapted from Ref. [52] with permission from the Royal Society of Chemistry.

Other properties of the oil including density, total acid number (TAN), water content, averaged molecular weight and asphaltene content are critical for the pipeline transportation. Therefore, they are also important criteria for the industry application of the partial upgrading. These parameters of the bitumen feedstock and product oils are summarized in Table 4. After upgrading in the presence of methane and Ag-Zn/ZSM-5, the density is lowered from 1.0275 to 0.9668 g/cm^{30}, corresponding to an API of 14.7. The reduced density is consistent with the increased gasoline and diesel fraction. These improved parameters can be attributed to the cracking capacity of the catalyst under CH$_4$, which is further evidenced by the averaged molecular weight of the product oil. The lowest molecular weight (330 g mol^{-1}) belongs to the oil product obtained under CH$_4$ with the Ag-Zn/ZSM-5 present. Among the product oil samples in comparison, the increased water content is accompanied by the reduced TAN. When upgrading occurs under the environment of methane with the facilitation of the catalyst, TAN is dramatically scaled down from 2.59 to 0.03 mg KOH/g, which results from the hydrodeoxygenation reactions that consume carboxylic and hydroxyl groups during methanotreating. The content of asphaltenes, the major contributor to the high viscosity of bitumen and the most difficult component in bitumen to be upgraded, of the various oil products is also compiled in Table 4. The methanotreatment witnesses a profound effect on the asphaltene content from 22.04 to 12.32%, which is a 44.1% reduction with respect to that of bitumen feedstock. This phenomenon is one important factor that contributes to the viscosity reduction in the product oil.

Table 4. Properties of the oil samples collected before and after bitumen upgrading under various environments at 5.0 MPa and 380°C for 150 min

Oil sample	Liquid product properties				
	Density (g/cm^3)	TAN (mg KOH/g)	Water content (wt.%)	Molecular weight (g/mol)	Asphaltene content (wt.%)
Bitumen	1.0275	2.59	0.159	700	22.04
N$_2$	0.9957	0.51	0.147	527	16.81
CH$_4$	0.9871	0.24	0.162	541	16.12
CH$_4$+ZSM-5	0.9762	0.26	0.171	524	14.84
N$_2$+ Ag-Zn/ZSM5	0.9755	0.39	0.158	458	14.43
CH$_4$+ Ag-Zn/ZSM5	0.9668	0.03	0.185	330	12.32

Adapted from Ref. [52] with permission from the Royal Society of Chemistry.

The element composition of the product oils are listed in Table 5 for comparison. When Ag-Zn/ZSM-5 is present with CH$_4$, the highest H/C molar ratio of the product oil is obtained at 1.65, compared with 1.52 in bitumen feedstock. The increased H/C obtained over this reaction condition verifies the participation of methane in the reaction and implies its incorporation into the product oils. Besides, the H/C molar ratio is closely related to the saturation degree of the product oil, which plays an important role in its stability. Therefore, a high H/C molar ratio is favorable for the storage and transportation of the product oil. The increased H/C molar ratio is also accompanied with decreased nitrogen and sulfur content, indicating a spontaneous denitrogenation and desulfurization, which will ease the work load of oil upgrading in downstream refineries.

Table 5. Elemental analysis of oil samples collected before and after bitumen upgrading under various environments at 5.0 MPa and 380°C for 150 min

Oil sample	Carbon (wt.%)	Hydrogen (wt.%)	H/C molar ratio	Nitrogen (wt.%)	Sulfur (wt.%)
Bitumen	81.09	10.29	1.52	1.85	6.48
N$_2$	81.96	10.44	1.53	1.74	5.58
CH$_4$	81.88	10.28	1.51	1.78	5.81
CH$_4$+ZSM-5	81.93	10.19	1.49	1.84	5.74
N$_2$+Ag-Zn/ZSM5	81.66	10.48	1.54	1.73	5.89
CH$_4$+Ag-Zn/ZSM5	81.34	11.18	1.65	1.72	5.58

Adapted from Ref. [52] with permission from the Royal Society of Chemistry.

CATALYST STRUCTURE AND OPTIMIZATION

The key to upgrade unconventional oils lies on the catalyst that can effectively activate methane. The catalyst should possess the capacity to rearrange carbon chains. Several catalysts have been successfully employed to upgrade bio-oil and heavy oil using methane, such as Ag/ZSM-5, Zn/ZSM-5 and Ag-Zn/ZSM-5. Their catalytic performance, which has been discussed in the previous section, is closely associated with their unique structures. Therefore, the structure characterization is fundamental to get a better understanding of the reaction mechanisms, leading to a rational design of the catalyst formula to achieve improved catalytic performance.

1%Ag/ZSM-5

1%Ag/ZSM-5 has been used to upgrade the bio-oil generated by the fast pyrolysis of biomass in vapor phase [29]. It is prepared by the incipient wetness impregnation of HZSM-5 with AgNO$_3$ solution, followed by calcination at high temperatures for 3 h [29]. One structure parameter that has profound influence on the catalytic performance is the dispersion of the active metal, which can be promoted by optimizing the precursor solution concentration (Figure 5a) and calcination temperature (Figure 5b). When the precursor concentration is 0.1 mol/L and the calcination temperature is 600°C, the magnitude of Ag dispersion is maximized.

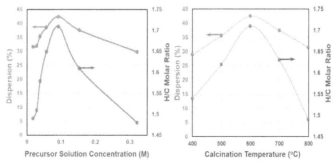

Figure 5. The Ag dispersion and H/C atomic ratio as a function of (a) AgNO$_3$ concentration (calcination temperature is 600°C) and (b) calcination temperature (AgNO$_3$ precursor concentration is 0.1 M) used for Ag/ZSM-5 synthesis. Adapted with permission from Ref. [29].

The Ag particles are widely dispersed throughout the catalyst surface with an averaged diameter of 13 nm (Figure 6a). Another approach to improve the catalytic performance of the catalyst is by introducing promoters to the catalyst. When the support is modified by phosphorous and cerium, the morphology of the catalyst is changed dramatically (Figure 6b). The irregularly shaped zeolite support is surrounded by many needle-shaped rods agglomerated into small clusters, which are mainly composed of cerium oxide with small decoration of phosphorus oxide, accompanied by the presence of silver species. As a result, significantly enhanced H/C ratio as well as oil yield is witnessed upon the structure modification (Table 1).

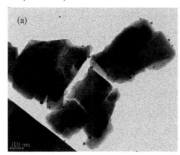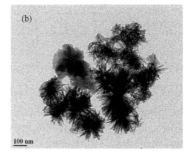

Figure 6. TEM images of the fresh catalysts of Ag/ZSM-5 (a) and Ag/P-Ce-ZSM-5 (b). Adapted with permission from Ref. [29].

5%Zn/ZSM-5

Besides 1%Ag/ZSM-5, 5%Zn/ZSM-5 is also used to upgrade the bio-oil [45]. As is discussed in the previous section, the loading amount of Zn is selected to be 5wt% based on the oil yield and H/C molar ratio of the product oil (Figure 2). The XRD patterns of HZSM-5 and the catalysts are displayed in Figure 7. When Zn loading is 1, 2 and 5%, no additional peak is observed, indicating the Zn species is well-dispersed. When Zn loading is increased to 10%, the diffraction peaks due to ZnO crystalline start to appear and become noticeable when the loading is increased to 20%. The averaged particle sizes of ZnO are calculated to be 15.9 and 38.4 nm, respectively. The TEM image of 5%Zn/ZSM-5 (Figure 8) shows that the ZnO particle size is below 10 nm. The smaller particle size and better dispersion should benefit and contribute to the outstanding performance of 5%Zn/ZSM-5.

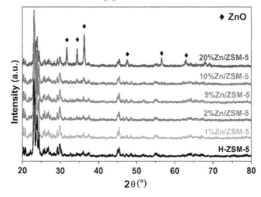

Figure 7. XRD patterns of H-ZSM-5 and Zn/ZSM-5 catalysts. Adapted with permission from Ref. [29].

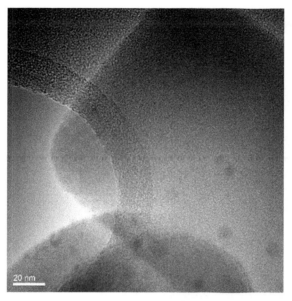

Figure 8. TEM image of 5%Zn/ZSM-5 catalyst. Adapted with permission from Ref. [29].

Ag-Zn/ZSM-5

By combining Ag and Zn to modify HZSM-5, Ag-Zn/ZSM-5 has been employed to upgrade bio-oil and heavy oil [28, 52]. The XRD pattern of 1%Ag-5%Zn/ZSM-5 is present in Figure 9. At this loading amount, no additional peak besides those belonging to the HZSM-5 support is observed, indicating that the metal particles are well-dispersed. The averaged particle size of Ag and Zn oxide species are determined from the TEM coupled with EDX images (Figure 3). The element composition of the particles can be determined by the EDX spectra (Figure 10). It is demonstrated that Ag_2O particles with bigger sizes (about 10–20 nm) are surrounded by the ZnO particles with smaller sizes (<10 nm).

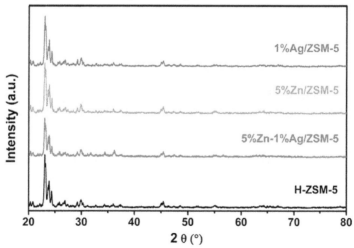

Figure 9. XRD patterns of the catalyst samples. Reprinted from Ref. [28].

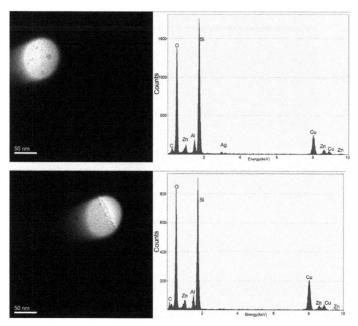

Figure 10. TEM–EDX results of different area for 5%Zn–1%Ag/ZSM-5. Reprinted from Ref. [28].

XRD patterns and TEM images of the 1%Ag-10%Zn/ZSM-5, which is used to catalyze the methanotreating of heavy oil, are also acquired to investigate the behavior of the catalyst during the upgrading. Figure 11 shows the XRD spectra of HZSM-5 and Ag-Zn/ZSM-5 acquired before and after the reaction with n-butylbenzene, a model compound to represent heavy oil, under N_2 and CH_4.

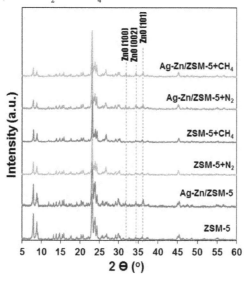

Figure 11. XRD patterns of ZSM-5 and Ag-Zn/ZSM-5 before and after n-butylbenzene upgrading at 3.0 MPa and 380°C for 150 min. Adapted from Ref. [52] with permission from the Royal Society of Chemistry.

It is noticed that diffraction peaks of Ag species are not discernible owing to its low loading and high dispersion. Also, the patterns of HZSM-5 remain unchanged upon metal loading and reaction, indicating that the catalyst structure remains intact after the introduction of metal species and the reaction. The diffraction peaks of ZnO, on the other hand, become smaller and wider after reaction, implying the reduction in Zn species and improved dispersion during the reaction.

The improved dispersion of ZnO is evidenced on the TEM image (Figure 12) acquired over Ag-Zn/SM-5 after the reaction under CH_4, while significant agglomeration of ZnO is witnessed under N_2. The improved ZnO dispersion assisted by CH_4 might be the reason for the catalytic upgrading performance under CH_4 environment.

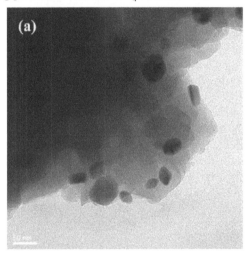

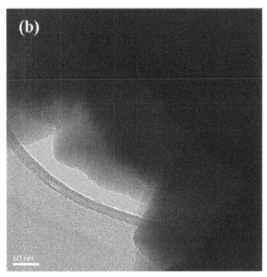

Figure 12. TEM images of spent Ag-Zn/ZSM-5 collected after catalytic n-butylbenzene cracking under the environment of (a) N_2 and (b) CH_4. Adapted from Ref. [52] with permission from the Royal Society of Chemistry.

REACTION MECHANISM STUDY

The mechanism study of the reaction pathway is crucial for the rational design of the catalyst formula to achieve improved catalytic performance. Several methods have been carried out to probe the reaction pathway and approach the detailed information during the reaction.

Diffuse reflectance infrared Fourier transform (DRIFT) spectroscopy is employed to study the heavy oil upgrading mechanism on the surface of 1%Ag-10%Zn/ZSM-5 [52]. The FTIR spectra of the surface species on the catalysts at a series of stages of the reaction are collected. By comparing the spectra collected with and without methane, the interaction between the catalyst and methane are revealed. Considering the complex nature of the heavy oil matrix, styrene is chosen as the model compound to represent the reactive compounds in heavy oil during the methanotreating. The DRIFT spectra acquired from the styrene temperature-programmed desorption (TPD) experiment under N_2 (blue line) and CH_4 (red line) environment are displayed in Figure 13. The peaks assigned to various bonds are labelled by dots with different colors. The blue dot represents C–H stretching at 3015 cm^{-1} due to the presence of methane in the gas phase. The brown dot represents the peaks due to C–O bending derived from styrene adsorption on the surface of Ag-Zn/ZSM-5, which decay much faster when CH_4 is present. This phenomenon implies that when CH_4 is present, the adsorbed styrene surface species would react with CH_4 and leave the catalyst surface. Similarly, the peaks due to the vinyl groups and aromatics also get smaller under CH_4 compared with the N_2 counterpart. And the reduced peak intensity is more significant at higher temperatures, i.e., 400 and 500°C. Such observations evidence the interaction between CH_4 and the styrene surface species on Ag-Zn/ZSM-5 and show that the reaction is more active at higher temperatures.

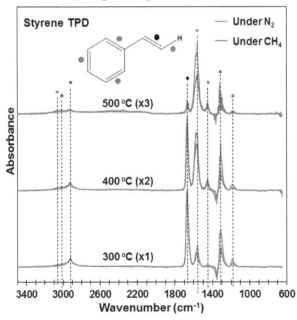

Figure 13. DRIFT spectra collected at different temperatures during styrene saturation under various gas environments over Ag–Zn/ZSM-5. Adapted from Ref. [52] with permission from the Royal Society of Chemistry.

The reaction taking placing on the catalyst is also investigated by X-ray photoelectron spectroscopy (XPS). The spectra of the fresh and spent Ag-Zn/ZSM-5 obtained after the upgrading of n-butylbenzene under CH_4 and N_2 environment are presented in Figure 14. On Figure 14a, the peaks due to Ag 3d shift towards higher binding energy, indicating the reduction in the Ag species, which is one part of the upgrading process. The decreased amount of Ag and Zn species upon the reaction is also witnessed in Figure 14a and b. It could be due to the diffusion of the metal species into the inner pores. Nevertheless, higher concentrations of Ag and Zn remain on the surface of the catalyst when CH_4 is present, which might be correlate to the better performance under CH_4 environment. The reduction in O concentration is also seen after the loading of metal species (Figure 14c), which might be due to the occupation of oxygen sites by the metals. After the reaction, the remaining oxygen concentration is higher with the presence of CH_4, which can be correlated to its better catalytic performance.

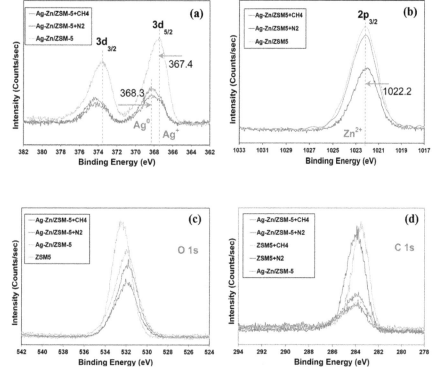

Figure 14. XPS spectra of HZSM-5 and Ag-Zn/ZSM-5 before and after n-butylbenzene upgrading at 3.0 MPa and 380°C for 150 min under different environments at (a) Ag 3d, (b) Zn 2p, (c) O 1s, and (d) C 1s regions. Reproduced from Ref. [52] with permission from the Royal Society of Chemistry.

The mechanism is probed by the GC-MS analysis of the product oil obtained by the upgrading of n-butylbenzene over various conditions. The results are shown in Table 6.

It is clear that the portion of benzene in the product is significantly increased when Ag-Zn/ZSM-5 is charged in the presence of CH_4. It can be attributed to the aromatization of methane under the non-oxidative environment, which has been studied intensively [54–59]. There are at least two possible pathways, i.e.,

Table 6. Composition of liquid products and conversions of n-butylbenzene and methane at 5.0 MPa and 380°C for 150 min

Compound	Liquid product distribution/conversion (wt%)					
	N_2	CH_4	ZSM-5, N_2	ZSM-5,CH_4	Ag-Zn/ZSM-5, N_2	Ag-Zn/ZSM-5, CH_4
Benzene	0.58	0.61	29.50	28.98	37.86	45.88
Methylbenzene	30.34	31.33	1.70	1.28	2.33	2.28
Ethylbenzene	1.36	1.32	2.32	4.10	0	0.82
Styrene	19.59	19.78	0	0	0.71	0.12
Isopropylbenzene	0	0	8.94	9.79	1.74	1.35
N-propylbenzene	0	0	0	0	5.97	5.51
Pentylbenzene	3.05	2.95	1.76	4.00	3.39	2.16
Heptylbenzene	0	0	9.00	7.37	15.56	13.22
Octylbenzene	0	0	3.66	1.74	20.74	16.26
Nonylbenzene	0	0	0	2.75	3.81	2.59
Butylbenzenea	0.89	0.81	88.71	86.43	21.94	25.04
Methanea	–	0	–	0	–	10.84

ª Conversion.

Adapted from Ref. [52] with permission from the Royal Society of Chemistry.

$$C_xH_y + CH_4 \xrightarrow{\text{catalyst}} \text{C}_6\text{H}_6 + H_2$$

and

$$CH_4 \xrightarrow{\text{catalyst}} \text{C}_6\text{H}_6 + H_2$$

It is observed that styrene is the primary product of the thermocracking

$$\text{(n-butylbenzene)} \xrightarrow{\text{heat}} \text{(styrene)} + \text{(benzene)}$$

It is also interesting to note that the ratio between isopropylbenzen and styrene, and that between n-propylbenzene and styrene, are 2.5 and 8.4 when the catalyst is charged under N_2 environment. The ratios are increased to 11.3 and 45.9 when CH_4 is present. The higher ratios are due to the addition of CH_4 into the vinyl group of styrene:

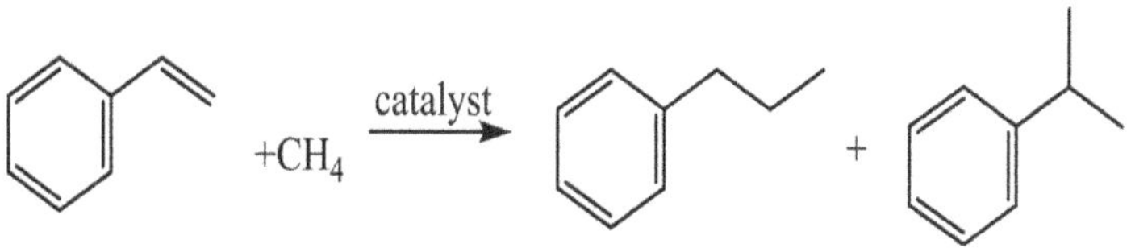

Another interesting observation is that ethylbenzene, which is absent under N_2 environment, appears when CH_4 is present. It can be because that the H_2 formed during the CH_4 dissociation is added to styrene:

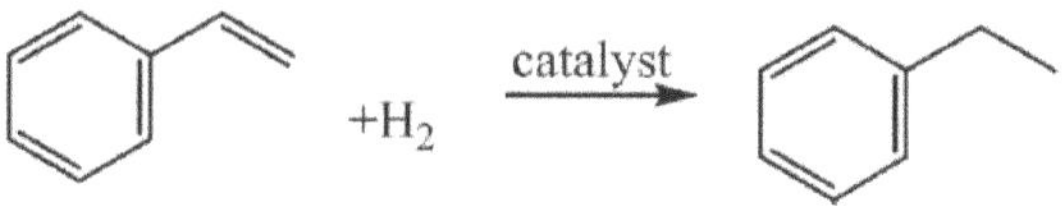

Based on these observations and interpretations, the overall reaction can be summarized to be

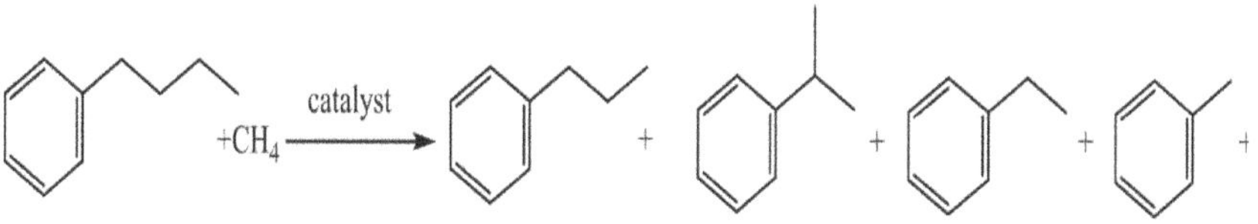

The reaction mechanism is proposed as Figure 15.

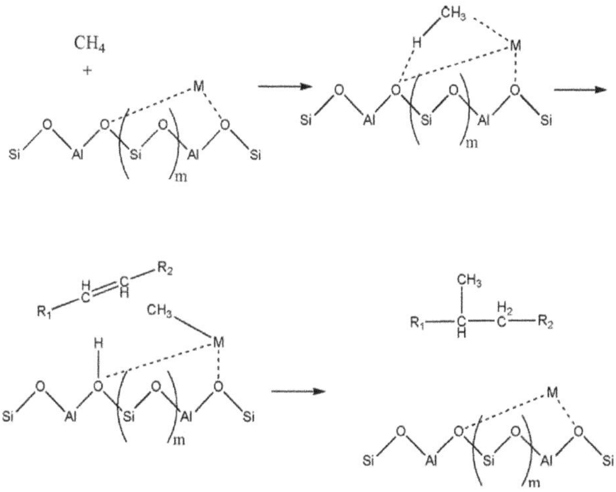

Figure 15. The hypothetical reaction mechanism of methane activation and addition to the broken pieces formed during hydrocarbon cracking over Ag–Zn/ZSM-5 (M = Zn^{2+} or Ag^+). Reproduced from Ref. [52] with permission from the Royal Society of Chemistry.

The reaction mechanism of oil upgrading using methane is also approached from the perspective of methane activation, which is the key step involved. By simplifying the feedstock system, the revolution of methane can be tracked more accurately. Among the methods, solid-state NMR (SSNMR) has been widely used to probe the reaction intermediates [60–63]. For instance, Gabrienko et al. [64] has used ^{13}C-enriched methane and ethylene as the feedstock to study the reaction between them. The NMR spectra acquired on upon the reaction between $^{13}CH_4+CH_2=CH_2$, $^{13}CH_2=CH_2+CH_4$, and $CH_4+CH_2=CH_2$ are displayed in Figure 16. The peak at 109 ppm is assigned to the ethane π-complex while the signal at 128 ppm is due to the benzene rings of simple alkyl-substituted aromatics adsorbed on zeolite catalysts. By comparing the spectra acquired upon $^{13}CH_2=CH_2$ adsorption and those obtained in the presence of CH_4, it is clear that the introduction creates additional peaks at 623 K (Figure 16e), including those belonging to aromatic species. It also significantly enhances the signal intensity due to benzene rings at 823 K (Figure 16f). By comparing the spectra acquired using $^{13}CH_4+CH_2=CH_2$ and $CH_4+CH_2=CH_2$ (Figure 16i, l), it is worth noting that when ^{13}C-enriched methane is present, the signal intensity due to benzene rings is increased dramatically, indicating that a large fraction of benzene product molecules origin from methane. Also, it is noticed that when $^{13}CH_4$ is present with ethene, the peak intensity due to aromatics is much stronger than that obtained when $^{13}CH_4$ is fed without ethene. Such observation indicates that the conversion of methane into aromatics is significantly improved by co-fed ethene.

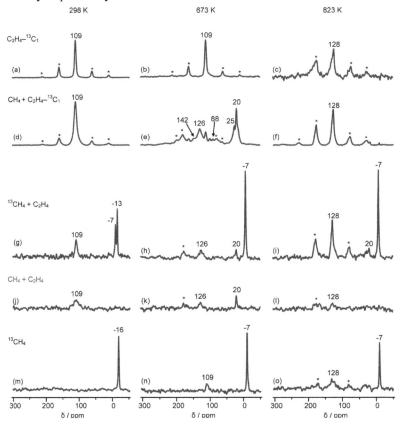

Figure 16. ^{13}C CP/MAS NMR spectra of methane and ethene adsorbed on Ag/H-ZSM-5 at room temperature and heated for 15 min at 673–823 K. Ethene-$^{13}C1$ was heated at 298 (a), 673 (b), and 823 K (c). Methane and ethene-$^{13}C1$ were heated at 298 (d), 673 (e), and 823 K (f). Methane-^{13}C and ethene were heated at 298 (g), 673 (h), and 823 K (i). Methane and ethene were heated at 298 (j), 673 (k), and 823 K (l). Methane was heated at 298 (m), 673 (n), and 823 K (o). Spectra g–o were acquired under identical conditions, with 3000 scans and a repetition time of 2 s. Asterisks denote the spinning side bands. Adapted with permission from Ref. [64].

The authors also propose a possible reaction mechanism (Figure 17) to describe the reaction between methane and the catalyst. The hydrogen from methane reacts with H from the brønsted acid sites with the assistance of the Ag active sites.

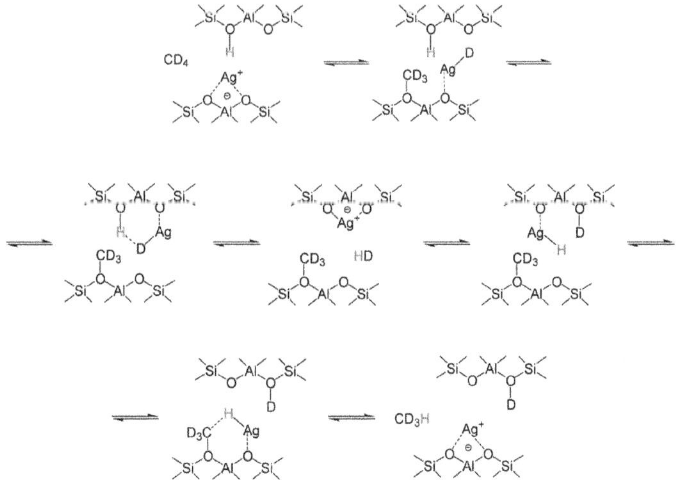

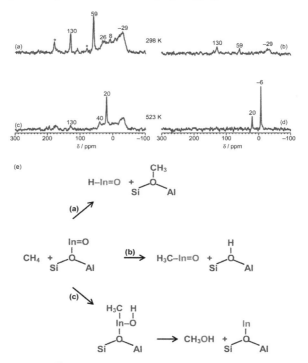

Figure 17. The mechanism of the H/D exchange between methane and brønsted acid sites on Ag/H-ZSM-5 zeolite. Adapted with permission from Ref. [64]. Copyright 2013 American Chemical Society.

Figure 18. ^{13}C CP/MAS and ^{13}C MAS NMR spectra of surface species generated from methane-^{13}C on InO+/H-ZSM-5 zeolite with co-adsorbed benzene: at ambient temperature (a and b) and after heating at 523 K (c and d). Pathways of methane transformation on InO$^+$/ HZSM-5 zeolite (e). Adapted with permission from Ref. [65].

Similar methods have been practiced on other catalysts that demonstrate outstanding methane activation activity including In/ZSM-5 [65]. By elevating the temperature and acquire the corresponding SSNRM spectra (Figure 18), the intermediates from the evolution of methane is identified. Accordingly, the reaction pathway is interpreted Figure 18e. Methane dissociates on the In=O site on the catalyst to form H_3C-In=O and brønsted OH groups. The H_3C–In=O then reacts with the In=O site to form H_3C-O-In=O site, which results in benzene, toluene and acetic acid molecules.

Besides SSNMR, the reaction mechanism is also probed using other methods. For instance, Liu et al. [66] employed a variety of characterization methods including FTIR, temperature-programmed reduction in H_2 (H_2-TPR), temperature-programmed desorption of NH_3 (NH_3-TPD) to study the evolution of methane on Zn/ZSM-5. The proposed reaction pathway is demonstrated in Figure 19. The dissociation of CH_4 involves an intermediate of H–CH_3–O–Zn four-member ring (Figure 19a). The bond between H and CH_3 would be broken, and the positively charged CH_3 group is bonded to the oxygen belonging to the zeolite framework (Figure 19b), followed by the aromatization steps (Figure 19c).

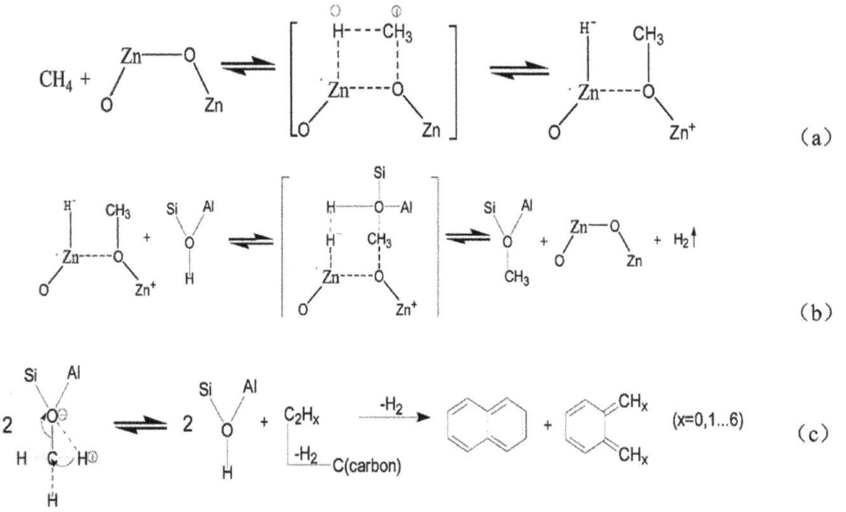

Figure 19. Mechanism of CH_4 conversion to aromatic compounds over 2Zn/HZSM-5. Adapted with permission from Ref. [66].

In addition to the aromatization of methane, other reactions such as the reaction between methane and CO_2 [67] and the one between methane and CO [68] have also been studied using SSNMR. The methane activation pathways in these scenarios help reveal the activation mechanism of methane. Two methane dissociation pathways, i.e., alkyl and carbenium pathways [61], have been revealed. In one scenario, upon the cleavage of C–H bond in CH_4, the negatively charged CH_3 piece is attached to the active metal, while H is bonded to the oxygen on the catalyst. This pathway is denoted "alkyl pathway". In the other one, CH_3 is bonded to an oxygen atom and positively charged. Therefore, it is denoted "carbenium pathway".

COMPUTATIONAL APPROACHES

The theoretical calculation is a powerful tool to understand and interpret the reaction pathway taking place. The obtained information will guide the rational design of the catalyst to achieve better performance on the oil upgrading using methane. As is demonstrated in previous sections, such feedstock and product matrix are highly complex. Therefore, the theoretical calculation is mainly explored over simpler systems such as the evolution of methane alone. Xu et al. [63] carried out the calculation using the Gaussian 09 software package. $Al_2Si_6O_9H_{14}$ is used as the cluster model to represent the structure of ZSM-5. The negative charges of the cluster are balanced by the positively charged Zn^{2+}, Zn^+ and Zn–O–Zn clusters. The energy gaps between each intermediate are displayed in Figure 20. It is noticed that the energy of the structure H_3C-O-zeolite is the lowest. Accordingly, this structure is the most stable and possibly the key intermediate during the methane activation and dissociation. This observation also confirms the methane dissociation step in the mechanism proposed by Liu et al. [66] displayed in Figure 19.

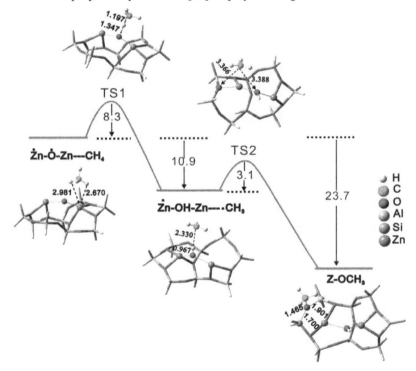

Figure 20. Homolytic cleavage reaction pathway from DFT calculation for the activation of methane on Zn–O–Zn cluster in open shell to produce methoxy intermediates. Calculated energies (kcal mol⁻¹) and selected interatomic distances (Å) are indicated. Adapted from Ref. [63] with permission from the Royal Society of Chemistry.

Mo/ZSM-5 has been intensively studied for methane activation and conversion [69–71]. It has been determined that the active sites on the catalyst are closely related to the molybdenum carbide species [72]. In order to identify the anchoring sites of Mo carbide nanoparticles that catalyze the dehydroaromatization of methane, Gao et al. [73] compared the infrared vibrational spectra for surface OH groups before and after the introduction of Mo species. The anchoring modes of Mo carbide nanoparticles, however, cannot be accurately determined through the IR spectroscopy. DFT cluster calculations and with hybrid quantum mechanical and molecular mechanical (QM/MM) periodic structure calculations are employed to evaluate them. The structures of Mo_2C_x (x = 1, 2, 3, 4, and 6) and Mo_4C_x (x = 2, 4, 6, and 8) nanoparticles are identified by the calculation results. It is also interesting to note that Mo carbide nanoparticles with a C/Mo ratio >1.5 are more stable on external Si sites according to the calculation results. They tend to migrate from inner pores of the zeolite to the external surface. Therefore, in order to minimize such migration, the researches pointed out that the C/Mo ratio for zeolite supported Mo carbide nanoparticles under hydrocarbon reaction conditions should be maintained below 1.5.

Computational calculation has also been used by many other researchers to gain a better understanding of the reaction thermodynamics [74, 75], reaction intermediates [76–79] and select the most active metal species [80]. This approach should be further developed to obtain more details of the reaction and guide the rational design of the catalyst.

ECONOMIC CONSIDERATIONS

Natural gas, including its recently largely discovered form (shale gas), is abundant in North America. Currently, the utilization of natural gas is often limited to fuels and feedstock used in reforming to produce hydrogen. As a fuel, the application of natural gas is impeded by the difficulties in the liquefaction process. It is challenging to ship the natural oversea to customers in Europe and Asia. As a result, the value of natural gas is significantly underestimated compared with other hydrocarbon resources. According to the Annual Energy Outlook by the US Energy Information Administration in 2015, the price of natural gas is below \$3.73 per million British thermal units (MBTU), while that of gasoline is above \$10.77 per MBTU.

The proposed unconventional oil upgrading using methane, the principal component of natural gas, offers an effective approach to increase the value associated with natural gas by incorporating methane into the synthetic oil molecules. It not only enhances the productivity of the product oil but also converts the low value added methane into high value added commodities, making the process more profitable.

FUTURE DEVELOPMENT

The key to achieve effective upgrading of unconventional oils using natural gas is to deliver at least a catalyst formula that could effectively active methane, crack and rearrange the carbon chains oil molecules and incorporate the cleaved methane pieces into the oil molecules under a relatively low pressure. To be more specific, the catalyst should be able to catalyze the methane dissociation, as well as the addition of the CH_x and H_{4-x} moieties towards the unsaturated bonds of the oil molecules. Olefins in the product oil, which lead to instability issues, could also be diminished by the conversion to aromatics, which requires the aromatization capability of the catalysts to complete this dehydroaromatization process. It has been evidenced that the activation of methane is assisted by the presence of higher hydrocarbons such as ethane and propylene. Therefore, the catalyst should be able to maximize such synergetic effect.

It is also observed that upon the C–H bond cleavage, the CH_3 species may be bonded to the active metal or the oxygen of the framework, depending on the nature of the catalyst. In order to facilitate the activation of methane, the formula of the catalyst should be carefully designed to lower the energy of these intermediates. The optimization of the catalyst might be achieved by tuning the species and concentration of the active metal, surface acidity, as well as the morphology of the support materials including the pore size distribution.

REFERENCES

1. Alonso DM, Wettstein SG, Dumesic JA. Bimetallic catalysts for upgrading of biomass to fuels and chemicals. Chem Soc Rev [Internet]. 2012;41(24):8075-98. Available from: http://xlink. rsc.org/?DOI=c2cs35188a

2. Liu D, Chen EY-X. Organocatalysis in biorefining for biomass conversion and upgrading. Green Chem [Internet]. 2014;16:964-81. Available from: http://pubs.rsc.org/en/ content/ articlehtml/2013/gc/c3gc41934g

3. Tuck CO, Perez E, Horvath IT, Sheldon RA., Poliakoff M. Valorization of biomass: deriving more value from waste. Science. 2012;337(6095):695-9.

4. Van Putten RJ, Van Der Waal JC, De Jong E, Rasrendra CB, Heeres HJ, De Vries JG. Hydroxymethylfurfural, a versatile platform chemical made from renewable resources. Chem Rev. 2013;113(3):1499-597.

5. Zakrzewska ME, Bogel-Łukasik E, Bogel-Łukasik R. Ionic liquid-mediated formation of 5-hydroxymethylfurfural-A promising biomass-derived building block. Chem Rev. 2011;111(2):397-417.

6. Gallezot P. Conversion of biomass to selected chemical products. Chem Soc Rev [Internet]. 2012;41(4):1538-58. Available from: http://pubs.rsc.org/en/Content/ArticleHTML/2012/ CS/ C1CS15147A

7. Zhang L, Liu R, Yin R, Mei Y. Upgrading of bio-oil from biomass fast pyrolysis in China: A review. Renew Sustain Energy Rev [Internet]. Elsevier; 2013;24:66-72. doi:10.1016/j. rser.2013.03.027

8. Bridgwater AV. Review of fast pyrolysis of biomass and product upgrading. Biomass Bioenergy [Internet]. Elsevier Ltd; 2012;38:68-94. doi:10.1016/j.biombioe.2011.01.048

9. Dickerson T, Soria J. Catalytic fast pyrolysis: A review. Energies. 2013;6(1):514-38.

10. Bridgwater AV. Production of high grade fuels and chemicals from catalytic pyrolysis of biomass. Catal Today. 1996;29(1-4):285-95.

11. Gutierrez A, Kaila RK, Honkela ML, Slioor R, Krause AOI. Hydrodeoxygenation of guaiacol on noble metal catalysts. Catal Today. 2009;147(3-4):239-46.

12. Thangalazhy-Gopakumar S, Adhikari S, Gupta RB, Tu M, Taylor S. Production of hydrocarbon fuels from biomass using catalytic pyrolysis under helium and hydrogen environments. Bioresour Technol [Internet]. Elsevier Ltd; 2011;102(12):6742-9. doi:10.1016/j. biortech.2011.03.104

13. Horne PA, Nugranad N, Williams PT. Catalytic coprocessing of biomass-derived pyrolysis vapours and methanol. J Anal Appl Pyrolysis. 1995;34(1):87-108.

14. Carlson TR, Cheng Y-T, Jae J, Huber GW. Production of green aromatics and olefins by catalytic fast pyrolysis of wood sawdust. Energy Environ Sci [Internet]. 2011;4(1):145-61. Available from: http://pubs.rsc.org/en/content/articlepdf/2011/ee/c0ee00341g\nhttp:// xlink. rsc.org/?DOI=C0EE00341G

15. Wright MM, Daugaard DE, Satrio JA, Brown RC. Techno-economic analysis of biomass fast pyrolysis to transportation fuels. Fuel [Internet]. Elsevier Ltd; 2010;89(Suppl. 1): S2-10. doi:10.1016/j.fuel.2010.07.029

16. Graca I, Lopes JM, Cerqueira HS, Ribeiro MF. Bio-oils upgrading for second generation biofuels. Ind Eng Chem Res. 2013;52(1):275-87.

17. Zhang H, Zheng J, Xiao R. Catalytic pyrolysis of willow wood with Me/ZSM-5 (Me = Mg, K, Fe, Ga, Ni) to produce aromatics and olefins. BioResources. 2013;8(4):5612-21.

18. Zhang H, Cheng Y-T, Vispute TP, Xiao R, Huber GW. Catalytic conversion of biomassderived

feedstocks into olefins and aromatics with ZSM-5: the hydrogen to carbon effective ratio. Energy Environ Sci. 2011;4:2297.

19.   Zhang H, Zheng J, Xiao R, Shen D, Jin B, Xiao G, et al. Co-catalytic pyrolysis of biomass and waste triglyceride seed oil in a novel fluidized bed reactor to produce olefins and aromatics integrated with self-heating and catalyst regeneration processes. RSC Adv [Internet]. 2013;3(17):5769. Available from: http://xlink.rsc.org/?DOI=c3ra40694f

20.   Zhang H, Nie J, Xiao R, Jin B, Dong C, Xiao G. Catalytic co-pyrolysis of biomass and different plastics (polyethylene, polypropylene, and polystyrene) to improve hydrocarbon yield in a fluidized-bed reactor. Energy Fuels. 2014;28(3):1940-7.

21.   Li X, Li J, Zhou G, Feng Y, Wang Y, Yu G, et al. Enhancing the production of renewable petrochemicals by co-feeding of biomass with plastics in catalytic fast pyrolysis with ZSM-5 zeolites. Appl Catal A Gen [Internet]. Elsevier B.V.; 2014;481:173-82. doi:10.1016/j.apcata.2014.05.015

22.   Zhang H, Carlson TR, Xiao R, Huber GW. Catalytic fast pyrolysis of wood and alcohol mixtures in a fluidized bed reactor. Green Chem [Internet]. 2012;14(1):98-110. Available from: http://xlink.rsc.org/?DOI=C1GC15619E\nhttp://www.scopus.com/inward/record.url?eid=2-s2.0-84855852575&partnerID=tZOtx3y1

23.   Speight JG. Heavy Oil Production Processes. Elsevier; 2013.

24.   Speight JG. Petroleum Refining Processes. Marcel Dekker, Inc.; 2002.

25.   Belyk G, Burgart D, Jablonski B, Heida J, Kaiser T, Bernar R, et al. Heavy Oil 101. Participant Handbook. Canadian Heavy Oil Associations; 2013.

26.   Mech M. A Comprehensive Guide to the Alberta OilSands. 2011.

27.   Bolland JL. Kinetics of olefin oxidation. Q Rev Chem Soc [Internet]. 1949;3(1):1-21. Available from: http://xlink.rsc.org/?DOI=qr9490300001

28.   Xiao Y, He P, Cheng W, Liu J, Shan W, Song H. Converting solid wastes into liquid fuel using a novel methanolysis process. Waste Manag [Internet]. Elsevier Ltd; 2015;49:304- 10. doi:10.1016/j.wasman.2015.12.017

29.   He P, Song H. Catalytic Conversion of Biomass by Natural Gas for Oil Quality Upgrading. 2014;

30.   Tan S, Zhang Z, Sun J, Wang Q. Recent progress of catalytic pyrolysis of biomass by HZSM-5. Chin J Catal [Internet]. Dalian Institute of Chemical Physics, the Chinese Academy of Sciences; 2013;34(4):641-50. Available from: http://www.sciencedirect.com/ science/article/ pii/S1872206712605312

31.   Nie L, Resasco DE. Improving carbon retention in biomass conversion by alkylation of phenolics with small oxygenates. Appl Catal A Gen [Internet]. Elsevier B.V.; 2012; 447-448:14-21. doi:10.1016/j.apcata.2012.08.041

32.   Pham TN, Shi D, Resasco DE. Evaluating strategies for catalytic upgrading of pyrolysis oil in liquid phase. Appl Catal B Environ [Internet]. Elsevier B.V.; 2014;145:10-23. doi:10.1016/j.apcatb.2013.01.002

33.   Elliott DC. Historical developments in hydroprocessing bio-oils. Energy Fuels. 2007;21(3):1792-815.

34.   Laurent E, Delmon B. Influence of water in the deactivation of a sulfided Nimo GammaAl2O3 catalyst during hydrodeoxygenation. J Catal. 1994;146(1):281-91.

35.   Al-Sabawi M, Chen J, Ng S. Fluid catalytic cracking of biomass-derived oils and their blends with petroleum feedstocks: A review. Energy Fuels. 2012;26(9):5355-72.

36.   Martinez R, Huff MC, Barteau MA. Ketonization of acetic acid on titania-functionalized silica monoliths. J Catal. 2004;222(2):404-9.

37. Barrett CJ, Chheda JN, Huber GW, Dumesic JA. Single-reactor process for sequential aldol-condensation and hydrogenation of biomass-derived compounds in water. Appl Catal B Environ. 2006;66(1-2):111-8.

38. Zhao C, He J, Lemonidou AA, Li X, Lercher JA. Aqueous-phase hydrodeoxygenation of bio-derived phenols to cycloalkanes. J Catal [Internet]. Elsevier Inc.; 2011;280(1):8-16. doi:10.1016/j.jcat.2011.02.001

39. Wildschut J, Mahfud FH, Venderbosch RH, Heeres HJ. Hydrotreatment of fast pyrolysis oil using heterogeneous noble-metal catalysts. Ind Eng Chem Res [Internet]. 2009;48(23):10324-34. doi:10.1021/ie9006003

40. Baldauf W, Balfanz U, Rupp M. Upgrading of flash pyrolysis oil and utilization in refineries. Biomass Bioenergy. 1994;7(1-6):237-44.

41. Damartzis T, Zabaniotou A. Thermochemical conversion of biomass to second generation biofuels through integrated process design—A review. Renew Sustain Energy Rev [Internet]. Elsevier Ltd; 2011;15(1):366-78. doi:10.1016/j.rser.2010.08.003

42. Ma Z, Troussard E, Van Bokhoven JA. Controlling the selectivity to chemicals from lignin via catalytic fast pyrolysis. Appl Catal A Gen [Internet]. Elsevier B.V.; 2012; 423-424:130-6. doi:10.1016/j.apcata.2012.02.027

43. Pattiya A, Titiloye JO, Bridgwater AV. Evaluation of catalytic pyrolysis of cassava rhizome by principal component analysis. Fuel [Internet]. Elsevier Ltd; 2010;89(1):244-53. doi:10.1016/j. fuel.2009.07.003

44. Al-Khattaf S, Ali SA., Aitani AM, Žilková N, Kubička D, Čejka J. Recent advances in reactions of Alkylbenzenes over novel zeolites: the effects of zeolite structure and morphology. Catal Rev Sci Eng [Internet]. 2014;56(Sep):333-402. Available from: http://www. tandfonline.com/ doi/abs/10.1080/01614940.2014.946846

45. He P, Shan W, Xiao Y, Song H. Performance of Zn/ZSM-5 for in situ catalytic upgrading of pyrolysis bio-oil by methane. Top Catal [Internet]. Springer, US; 2016;59(1):86-93. doi:10.1007/s11244-015-0508-4

46. Topsoe H, Clausen BS, Massoth FE. Hydrotreating catalysis. In: Catalysis—Sciences and Technology [Internet]. Berlin, Heidelberg: Springer Berlin Heidelberg; 1996 cited 2016 Mar 24.. p. 344. Available from: http://linkinghub.elsevier.com/retrieve/pii/ S0166983400801335

47. Kimura N, Iwanami Y, Konno S, Corporation E. Regenerated Hydrotreatment Catalyst. US8795514B2, 2014.

48. Zakharov I, Startsev A. An ab initio molecular orbital study of the hydrogen sorbed site in Co/MoS2 catalysts. J Phys Chem B [Internet]. 2000;(V):9025-8. Available from: http:// pubs.acs. org/doi/abs/10.1021/jp001354f

49. Breysse M, Portefaix JL, Vrinat M. Support effects on hydrotreating catalysts. Catal Today [Internet]. 1991;10(4):489-505. Available from: https://abingdonsharedfiles.box. com/s/ p5c2yhfpvqi3r754qqr7h1p2gnw9plds

50. Jossens LW, Munson CL. Mild Hydrotreating/Extraction Process for Low Sulfur Gasoline. US6228254B1, 2001.

51. Lauritsen J. Atomic-scale structure of Co–Mo–S nanoclusters in hydrotreating catalysts. J Catal [Internet]. 2001;197(1):1-5. Available from: http://www.sciencedirect.com/science/ article/pii/S0021951700930884

52. Guo A, Wu C, He P, Luan Y, Zhao L, Shan W, et al. Low-temperature and low-pressure non-oxidative activation of methane for upgrading heavy oil. Catal Sci Technol [Internet]. Royal Society of Chemistry; 2016; doi:10.1039/C5CY00947B

53. Tsaprailis H, Zhou J. Properties of Dilbit and Coventional Crude Oils [Internet]. Alberta

Innovates; 2014. 93 p. Available from: http://www.ai-ees.ca/media/10927/properties_of_dilbit_and_conventional_crude_oils_-_aitf_-_final_report_revised.pdf

54.   Choudhary VR. Low-temperature nonoxidative activation of methane over H-galloaluminosilicate (MFI) zeolite. Science [Internet]. 1997;275(5304):1286-8. Available from: http://www.sciencemag.org/cgi/doi/10.1126/science.275.5304.1286

55.   Guo X, Fang G, Li G, Ma H, Fan H, Yu L, et al. Direct, nonoxidative conversion of methane to ethylene, aromatics, and hydrogen. Science [Internet]. 2014;344(6184):616-9. Available from: http://www.sciencemag.org/content/344/6184/616

56.   Choudhary TV., Aksoylu E, Wayne Goodman D. Nonoxidative activation of methane. Catal Rev [Internet]. 2003;45(1):151-203. Available from: http://www.tandfonline.com/ doi/ abs/10.1081/CR-120017010

57.   Baba T, Abe Y. Metal cation-acidic proton bifunctional catalyst for methane activation: Conversion of 13CH4 in the presence of ethylene over metal cations-loaded H-ZSM-5. Appl Catal A Gen. 2003;250(2):265-70.

58.   Weckhuysen BM, Wang D, Rosynek MP, Lunsford JH. Conversion of Methane to Benzene over Transition Metal Ion ZSM-5 Zeolites. J Catal [Internet]. 1998;175(2):347- 51. Available from: http://www.sciencedirect.com/science/article/pii/S0021951798920115

59.   Borry RW, Kim YH, Huffsmith A, Reimer JA., Iglesia E. Structure and density of Mo and acid sites in Mo-exchanged H-ZSM5 catalysts for nonoxidative methane conversion. J Phys Chem B [Internet]. 1999;103(28):5787-96. Available from: http://pubs.acs.org/doi/ abs/10.1021/ jp990866v

60.   Luzgin M V., Rogov VA, Arzumanov SS, Toktarev AV., Stepanov AG, Parmon VN. Understanding methane aromatization on a Zn-modified high-silica zeolite. Angew Chem Int Ed. 2008;47(24):4559-62.

61.   Luzgin MV., Gabrienko AA, Rogov VA, Toktarev AV., Parmon VN, Stepanov AG. The "alkyl" and "carbenium" pathways of methane activation on Ga-modified zeolite BEA: 13C solid-state NMR and GC-MS study of methane aromatization in the presence of higher alkane. J Phys Chem C. 2010;114(49):21555-61.

62.   Luzgin MV., Rogov VA, Arzumanov SS, Toktarev A V., Stepanov AG, Parmon VN. Methane aromatization on Zn-modified zeolite in the presence of a co-reactant higher alkane: How does it occur? Catal Today. 2009;144(3-4):265-72.

63.   Xu J, Zheng A, Wang X, Qi G, Su J, Du J, et al. Room temperature activation of methane over Zn modified H-ZSM-5 zeolites: insight from solid-state NMR and theoretical calculations. Chem Sci. 2012;3(207890):2932-40.

64.   Gabrienko AA, Arzumanov SS, Moroz IB, Toktarev A V., Wang W, Stepanov AG. Methane activation and transformation on Ag/H-ZSM-5 zeolite studied with solid-state NMR. J Phys Chem C. 2013;117(15):7690-702.

65.   Gabrienko AA, Arzumanov SS, Moroz IB, Prosvirin IP, Toktarev AV., Wang W, et al. Methane activation on in-modified ZSM-5: the state of indium in the zeolite and pathways of methane transformation to surface species. J Phys Chem C. 2014;118(15):8034-43.

66.   Liu BS, Zhang Y, Liu JF, Tian M, Zhang FM, Au CT, et al. Characteristic and mechanism of methane dehydroaromatization over Zn-based/HZSM-5 catalysts under conditions of atmospheric pressure and supersonic jet expansion. J Phys Chem C. 2011;115(34):16954-62.

67.   Qi G, Xu J, Su J, Chen J, Wang X, Deng F. Low-temperature reactivity of Zn+ ions confined in ZSM-5 zeolite toward carbon monoxide oxidation: insight from in situ DRIFT and ESR spectroscopy. J Am Chem Soc. 2013;135(18):6762-5.

68.   Wang X, Xu J, Qi G, Li B, Wang C, Deng F. Alkylation of benzene with methane over ZnZSM-5 zeolites studied with solid-state NMR spectroscopy. J Phys Chem C [Internet].

Royal Society of Chemistry; 2013;117(8):4018-23. doi:10.1039/C4CC03621B

69. Abdelsayed V, Shekhawat D, Smith MW. Effect of Fe and Zn promoters on Mo/HZSM-5 catalyst for methane dehydroaromatization. Fuel [Internet]. Elsevier Ltd; 2015;139: 401-10. doi:10.1016/j.fuel.2014.08.064

70. Ismagilov ZR, Matus EV., Tsikoza LT. Direct conversion of methane on Mo/ZSM-5 catalysts to produce benzene and hydrogen: achievements and perspectives. Energy Environ Sci [Internet]. 2008;1(5):526. Available from: http://pubs.rsc.org/en/content/ articlehtml/2008/ee/ b810981h

71. Wang D, Lunsford JH, Rosynek MP. Characterization of a Mo/ZSM-5 catalyst for the conversion of methane to benzene. J Catal [Internet]. 1997;169(1):347-58. Available from: http://www.sciencedirect.com/science/article/pii/S0021951797917127

72. Cook B, Mousko D, Hoelderich W, Zennaro R. Conversion of methane to aromatics over Mo2C/ZSM-5 catalyst in different reactor types. Appl Catal A Gen. 2009;365(1):34-41.

73. Gao J, Zheng Y, Fitzgerald GB, de Joannis J, Tang Y, Wachs IE, et al. Structure of Mo 2 C x and Mo 4 C x molybdenum carbide nanoparticles and their anchoring sites on ZSM-5 zeolites. J Phys Chem C [Internet]. 2014;118(9):4670-9. Available from: http://pubs.acs. org/ doi/abs/10.1021/jp4106053

74. Baba T, Sawada H. Conversion of methane into higher hydrocarbons in the presence of ethylene over H-ZSM-5 loaded with silver cations. Phys Chem Chem Phys. 2002;4(15):3919-23.

75. Rane N, Kersbulck M, van Santen RA, Hensen EJM. Cracking of n-heptane over Brønsted acid sites and Lewis acid Ga sites in ZSM-5 zeolite. Microporous Mesoporous Mater. 2008;110(2-3):279-91.

76. Miao S, Wang Y, Ma D, Zhu Q, Zhou S, Su L, et al. Effect of Ag+ cations on nonoxidative activation of methane to C2-hydrocarbons. J Phys Chem B. 2004;108(46):17866-71.

77. Pidko EA, Hensen EJM, Van Santen RA. Dehydrogenation of light alkanes over isolated gallyl ions in Ga/ZSM-5 zeolites. J Phys Chem C. 2007;111(35):13068-75.

78. Hensen EJM, Pidko EA, Rane N, Van Santen RA. Water-promoted hydrocarbon activation catalyzed by binuclear gallium sites in ZSM-5 zeolite. Angew Chem Int Ed. 2007;46(38):7273-6.

79. Li L, Li GD, Yan C, Mu XY, Pan XL, Zou XX, et al. Efficient sunlight-driven dehydrogenative coupling of methane to ethane over a Zn+-modified zeolite. Angew Chem Int Ed. 2011;50(36):8299-303.

80. Fellah MF, Onal I. C-H bond activation of methane on M- and MO-ZSM-5 (M = Ag, Au, Cu, Rh and Ru) clusters: a density functional theory study. Catal Today [Internet]. Elsevier B.V.; 2011;171(1):52-9. doi:10.1016/j.cattod.2011.04.001

2

Natural Gas and CO_2 Price Variation: Impact on the Relative Cost-efficiency of LNG and Pipelines

Marte Ulvestad and Indra Overland

Norwegian Institute of International Affairs (NUPI)

ABSTRACT

This article develops a formal model for comparing the cost structure of the two main transport options for natural gas: liquefied natural gas (LNG) and pipelines. In particular, it evaluates how variations in the prices of natural gas and greenhouse gas emissions affect the relative cost-efficiency of these two options. Natural gas is often promoted as the most environmentally friendly of all fossil fuels, and LNG as a modern and efficient way of transporting it. Some research has been carried out into the local environmental impact of LNG facilities, but almost none into aspects related to climate change. This paper concludes that at current price levels for natural gas and CO_2 emissions the distance from field to consumer and the volume of natural gas transported are the main determinants of transport costs. The pricing of natural gas and greenhouse emissions influence the relative cost-efficiency of LNG and pipeline transport, but only to a limited degree at current price levels. Because more energy is required for the LNG process (especially for fuelling the liquefaction process) than for pipelines at distances below 9100 km, LNG is more exposed to variability in the price of natural gas and greenhouse gas emissions up to this distance. If the prices of natural gas and/or greenhouse gas emission rise dramatically in the future, this will affect the choice between pipelines and LNG. Such a price increase will be favourable for pipelines relative to LNG.

Keywords: *Natural gas, Liquefied natural gas, Pipelines, Greenhouse gases, Pricing*

INTRODUCTION

The natural gas from large fields is normally transported by one of two means: either by pipeline or in the form of liquefied natural gas (LNG) [1]. In recent years, the production of LNG has risen rapidly as new facilities have been brought online, increasing its share of internationally traded natural gas to 30% in 2011 [2]. For the period 2005–2020, LNG production is expected to continue growing at a clip of 6.7% per year [3].

The building of new LNG facilities has often resulted in local resistance due to fears over the risk of explosions. Interestingly, however, there has been limited discussion of the environmental impact of LNG in terms of greenhouse gas emissions. This question is becoming increasingly pertinent as natural gas is cast as the transitional fossil fuel for a low-carbon world: worse than renewable or nuclear energy, but better than coal and oil. LNG is relatively abundant, the necessary technology exists, and much of the infrastructure needed for its exploitation is already in place. If natural gas is part of the medium-term solution to reducing greenhouse gas emissions and this is going to lead to increasing amounts of it being moved around the globe as LNG, the emissions aspect of LNG will become increasingly salient. In Norway, for example, the new LNG facility at Melkoya is the country's fourth largest source of greenhouse gas emissions [4].

Regardless of the mode of transport for natural gas, some of the gas is used to generate the energy required to transport the rest of the gas. In pipelines, a portion of the gas is burned in order to run the turbines that force the rest of the gas through the pipeline to the consumers. In an LNG plant, a portion of the gas is burned in order to generate enough energy to cool the rest of the gas. When natural gas reaches a low of −161°C (−260°F), it shrinks into a liquid that takes one 600th the amount of space of the gaseous form, becoming far more economical to ship [5,6].

Since both pipelines and LNG involve the burning of a portion of the gas, they also result in the emission of greenhouse gases. The market value of the gas that is burned as well as the cost of the resultant emissions will vary over time. Any major natural gas extraction project that has to choose between pipelines or LNG thus also has to take into account whether such future price variations may change the relative cost of the two infrastructure types. Some of the largest natural gas fields currently slated for extraction are located at distances from markets where such choices between pipelines and LNG need to be made, including those in the Barents Sea, on the Yamal Peninsula and possibly in the Persian Gulf.

CURRENT ASSUMPTIONS IN THE LITERATURE

LNG and pipelines differ in their cost structures. Whereas the cost of pipelines tends to rise steeply and linearly with distance, the cost of LNG has a high initial threshold but a lower increase with distance [6]. When choosing between these two options for transporting natural gas from a new field, a break-even point somewhere between 3000 and 5000 kilometres is often mentioned in the literature [7]. For the transport of natural gas over shorter distances, pipelines are assumed to be cheaper, whereas transport using LNG is normally more cost-effective for distances longer than this.

The literature offers several different formulations of this break-even point. Tongia and Arunachalam note that, due to the expense of building LNG facilities − such as tankers, re-gasification facilities and reception and storage terminals − pipelines will have a lower cost over shorter distances of around 2000 miles (3219 kilometres) or less [8]. According to Cornot-Gandolphe *et al.* [9], in 2003 the break-even point was around 4500 km at a price level of $1.60/MMBtu ($1.90/MMBtu in 2010). The same year, Quintana [10] argued that LNG is the best option for markets located more than 4000 kilometres away from the gas field and which have a volume of more than 16 MMm^3/day.

In a 2009 report, Paul Stevens argued that the cost of LNG had risen significantly, and that the break-even point had therefore risen to around 5000 km [1]. Further nuancing the comparison of LNG and pipelines, Mäkinen [11] claimed that, 'In general, LNG becomes economically feasible in contrast to 3000 to 4000 kilometres of land pipe or 2000 km of offshore pipe.' The break-even point will differ from project to project, depending on the geography, logistics and legal and political factors involved [11].

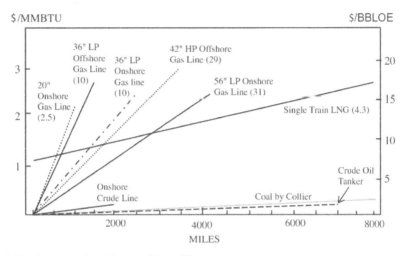

Figure 1. Break-even points. *Source* of data: [6].

Note: Figures in brackets show gas delivery capability in BCM

The literature says little about the analysis and data upon which these break-even points are based. This leaves several important questions unanswered: are both construction and operating costs taken into account? If the price of natural gas rises, will the transport of natural gas as LNG still be cheaper than pipeline transport over distances greater than 4000 kilometres, taking into account the fact that the LNG chain consumes more gas than do pipelines? Are costs related to CO_2 emissions included in the calculations? This article aims to fill the void in the literature represented by these questions, by developing a formal model for estimating the impact of natural gas and greenhouse gas price variation on the overall cost of the two transport options.

The prices of natural gas and greenhouse gas emissions are, however, only two out of many factors that determine the cost of LNG and pipelines. In order to understand their impact on overall costs, we must view these prices in the context of the other factors upon which the overall costs depend, in particular the amount of natural gas and the distance it must be transported. As the comparative advantages of LNG and pipelines change in accordance with these factors, we need to understand their impact before examining how variation in the prices of natural gas and greenhouse gas emissions plays into the relative cost-efficiency of LNG and pipelines.

In addition to the various factors that affect the cost structure of LNG and pipelines that we will cover here, there are many other factors which might affect the choice of transport method, for supplier and importer: taxes, capital charge, interest rates, insurance, the economic lifetime of capital, the flexibility of the LNG spot marked, demand and supply security, the risk of terrorist attacks, and the value of scrap metal at end of capital's lifetime. Putting a general price on these conditions is difficult, so they are not included in this analysis – but they remain important for the decisions made about such infrastructure. Before developing a model for comparing LNG and pipelines, it is necessary to explain some of the basics of pipelines and LNG. We start with pipelines, as this is the older, baseline technology.

PIPELINE ECONOMICS

The costs of pipelines and LNG can be divided into capital (construction) expenditure (CAPEX) and operating expenses (OPEX). CAPEX consists of pipe materials, installation and coating of the pipe, the building of compressor stations, construction management and right-of-way clearance. OPEX include compressor station fuel, pipe repairs, environmental permits and administrative costs [12].

Both construction and operating costs may vary significantly from one region to another. Differences in terrain, climate, labour costs, population density and the degree of competition between different natural gas provinces make pipeline economics highly project-specific [9]. Pipeline planners are therefore often hesitant to generalise the costs of constructing pipelines. A pipeline that runs through a dense urban area might cost five times more than a pipeline of the same length and diameter crossing a rural area [13]. The generic model for estimating the impact of variations in natural gas and emissions costs developed in this article will therefore have to be adapted when applied to individual cases.

Pipeline CAPEX

This article focuses on onshore pipelines, which are more common and normally less expensive than offshore pipelines. Several approaches will be used in this section in order to make an estimation of the costs of transporting natural gas by pipeline. The estimation will mainly follow the 'cookbook' approach developed in Jung *et al.* [14] for East Asian projects, drawing on Kubota [15]. This is combined with a formula for cost per pipe diameter per distance as suggested by the Canadian Energy Pipeline Association [16], while pipeline data from the USA published by Parker [13] are used to discuss the costs of constructing and operating natural gas pipelines.

Pipeline construction costs depend mainly on the cost of material (carbon steel), cost of labour, pipeline length and diameter and the number and capacity of the compressor stations. The data published in the *Oil & Gas Journal* were derived from the US Federal Energy Regulatory Commission and are divided into four categories: material, labour, right of way and miscellaneous costs [17]. The latter category includes surveying, engineering, supervision, administration and overhead, interest, contingencies and allowances for funds used during construction, and regulatory filing fees [18].

The capital costs (C) for a common onshore pipeline can be calculated by means of the following equation:

$$C = \$52,675\mu\delta + (\$3 \times 10^7)\alpha + \$3091c$$

The costs of constructing the pipeline are calculated by multiplying a constant cost by the diameter (μ) measured in inches, and by the length of the pipeline (δ) measured in km. α is the number of compressor stations and c is the total capacity of the compressor stations, measured in horsepower. Jung *et al.* [14] used \$21,300 as the cost per inch per kilometre for a common onshore pipeline in 2000. The estimated costs used in Jung *et al.*'s report [14] are more than 10 years old, and may no longer be valid for new projects. The costs of labour, materials or other components may have risen, or new cost-reducing technology may have been introduced to the market. We will ignore the last problem because, as pipeline transport is less complex, there have been only small cost reductions for pipeline transport compared to LNG in recent years [9] . The cost estimates from 2000, however, do need to be revised in view of the increased costs of vital inputs. In the USA, actual costs per pipeline mile rose by an average of 247.3% from 2001 to 2010, rising from approximately $1,310,000 per mile to $4,550,000 per mile in the same period. This increase was caused mainly by higher costs of labour and materials [18]. In the absence of more reliable data, we will use these figures to revise the figures from Jung *et al*.'s [14] report.

Nevertheless, price levels may have changed differently, depending on the country in question. The figures used by Jung *et al.* [14] are for a 'Common Onshore Pipeline', and it is unclear upon which country's prices the estimates are based. For example, the USA, Russia and Japan have seen the price level of investment (PPP over investment) develop in different directions over the past decade. In the USA, 2000–2007, the price level of investments decreased by 11.7% (although it has probably increased sharply since then) and in Japan by 32.8%, whereas in Russia the price level of investments increased by 124.1% during the same period [19]. But it is nevertheless important to revise the pipeline costs from 2000 to make them comparable with the revised LNG costs.

It is possible to check the accuracy of these estimates by comparing them with a proposed pipeline where the estimated costs are more or less current. We have estimated the costs of the Nabucco pipeline by entering the pipeline details (diameter of 56 inches, 11 compressor stations, distance 3893 km) into the equation below [20,21]. The equation calculates a total construction cost of almost $16.8 billion – a figure much higher than the estimated €7.9 billion ($11.5 bn) stated on the Nabucco project website [22]. According to Webb [23], however, the oil and gas company BP has produced a new estimate of €14 billion ($20 bn) for the same construction costs. These differing estimates exemplify the difficulty of determining pipeline construction costs.

Compressor stations constitute a large percentage of total construction costs. Jung *et al.* [14] use a fixed cost per compressor station (α) and then a variable cost per unit of horsepower. We assume that average distance between the compressor stations is 200 km [24] and that average capacity per compressor station is 110 MW. The latter assumption was made after a comparison of several proposed Russian pipelines and their capacities [25].

Parker [13] uses construction cost projections for over 20,000 miles of pipelines in the USA to generalise the construction costs for a pipeline of a given length and diameter. Parker concludes: 'Materials costs account for approximately 26% of the total construction costs on average. Labour, right of way, and miscellaneous costs make up 45%, 22% and 7% of the total cost on average, respectively.' These shares are estimated on the basis of US data for the years 1991–2003. The data refer to pipelines between 4 and 42 inches in diameter, which is less than many of the long-distance pipelines in Russia. For example the diameter of the pipeline running from Yamal to Europe is 56 inches (1420 mm) [26]. The small pipeline size is a problem, as pipeline diameter determines the share of the total costs within the four construction cost categories. For example, for a 4-inch diameter pipeline, materials account for 15% of total construction costs, but this figure rises to 35% for a pipeline 42 inches in diameter [13].

The cost of labour often differs significantly between countries or regions, as does the cost of materials (steel not least), which are never exactly the same throughout the world [27]. Furthermore, pipeline construction costs do not remain static within a country. Therefore, the relative share of construction costs depends on a range of interlinked factors with, for example, material or labour costs fluctuating as wages or steel prices change.

Figure 2 shows the average breakdown of construction costs in the USA for the period 2009/2010.

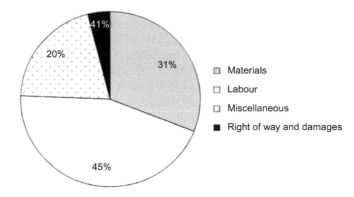

Figure 2. Pipeline construction cost components. *Source* of data: [18].

Here, the cost of materials differs markedly from the 26% share mentioned by Parker [13] above. The reason is that Parker's data are from 1991–2003, whereas the data presented in the figure are from July 2009–June 2010. Figure 3 below shows the development of the share of material and labour costs in the USA over the past 10 years.

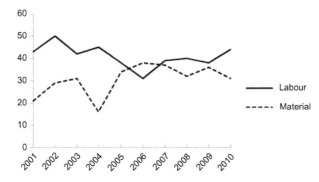

Figure 3. The share of the two major cost components in pipeline construction, 2001–2010. *Source* of data: [18].

According to Chandra [28], steel may account for as much as 45% of the total cost of a typical pipeline. It is possible to estimate the cost of steel in the overall share of construction costs in greater detail by using the Figure 3 graph above, Figure 5, and the US Carbon Steel Plate Prices from Figure 7 fig7 below. The estimates show that steel accounted for 5.6% of total construction costs from 2001 to 2003. The share rose markedly in 2004, due to a steep increase in steel prices, and was as high as 14.5% of total costs from 2005 to 2008. This may even be an underestimate.

Pipeline OPEX

A pipeline has annual operating costs such as fuel for the compressor stations, repair costs, SCADA and telecommunications, lease and rental, wages and administrative costs [12]. Operating costs are relatively project-specific, but may be broken down into two categories: operating costs as a fixed percentage of the construction costs and fuel.

Operating costs for a typical onshore pipeline can be estimated as follows:

$$O_p = C\tau + \left(1 - (1 - \ell)^{\frac{\vartheta}{\eta}}\right)Np$$

N is the volume of natural gas, measured in cubic meters per year, p is the price of natural gas, measured in dollars per cubic meter, and η is the number of kilometres between the compressor stations. The operating cost as a share of the capital costs (τ) is 3.5% for a common onshore pipeline. The percentage of the natural gas used as fuel in the compressor stations (ℓ) is 0.4% per every 100 miles (according to Jung *et al.* [14]). The reason why authors use the term 'every 100 miles' is probably that they account for compressor stations every 100 miles on average. But 100 miles (161 km) between the compressor stations seem short compared with long-distance pipelines like the proposed Nabucco pipeline and the Altai project. The Nabucco pipeline route is 3893 km long, with an estimated 11 compressor stations [20,22]: thus, the average distance between compressor stations will be 354 km. Furthermore, the Altai gas pipeline will be over 2600 km long and will have 10 compressor stations [25], corresponding to one compressor station every 260 km. In contrast, the Gryazovets–Vyborg pipeline will have a compressor station every 131 km, and the Ukhta–Torzhok pipeline every 198 km on average. The estimated distance between the compressor stations (η) will therefore be 200 km, as mentioned in Whist's article [24].

LNG ECONOMICS

The production and transport of liquefied natural gas is a three-step process: first liquefaction of the natural gas, then tanker transport and finally re-gasification. Here we will ignore the transport of natural gas from the field to the liquefaction plant, which is usually situated on the coast, because this stage is necessary for both pipeline and LNG transport and will not make a difference in the comparison[29]. The costs of LNG projects are difficult to generalise because they vary significantly from location to location, and depend on whether the project is greenfield or an expansion of an existing plant [30].

Figure 4. The LNG chain.

The liquefied natural gas is made in a liquefaction plant where the gas is refrigerated to −161°C (−260°F). The gas becomes a liquid, in the process shrinking to 1/600th of its volume in gaseous form. The liquefaction plant consists of so-called 'trains', processing modules, the size of which depends on the available compressors. In 2004, the largest trains could produce around 4 million tonnes per year (tpy). But, with improved compressor technology it is now possible to produce larger trains and further exploit the economies of scale. These costs may be further reduced by around 25% by replacing two 2-million-tonne trains with one 4-million-tonne train [6]. Today, Qatar has several single-train liquefaction plants with a capacity of 7.8 million tpy per train [31].

The liquefaction plant is usually the most expensive link in the LNG chain. This is because the liquefaction process demands a considerable amount of the gas delivered to the plant [32], but also because of the remote locations, strict design and safety standards and the large amounts of materials required [30].

Most LNG plants have their own fleet of LNG carriers, '... operating a "virtual" pipeline', according to Chandra [28]. This might change, however, with the increasing spot-trade market [28]. According to Jensen [6], a typical LNG carrier can transport 135,000 to 138,000 cubic meters of cargo: this capacity is currently increasing, due to better designs. By March 2011, the world fleet of LNG carriers had 44 active carriers with a capacity of over 200,000 cubic meters. The largest LNG carriers have a capacity of 266,000 cubic meters of LNG [33].

The final link in the LNG chain is the re-gasification terminal with vaporisers which warm the liquefied natural gas from −161°C to about +5°C, and into its normal gaseous form. Other main components of the re-gasification facilities are the offloading berths, LNG storage tanks and pipelines to the local gas grid [28].

Due to new technology and designs, there will be several changes or options coming in the near future that might improve the LNG chain. Floating LNG production, which will make the costly gas transport from the field to the onshore LNG plant unnecessary, is on its way. Vautrain and Holmes [34] claim that for a remote offshore field the cost of bringing the gas to an onshore plant might add as much as 40% to the total cost of the LNG plant.

Furthermore, the possibility of offloading the LNG offshore is currently under study, as is ship-to-ship transfer. This might lead to larger ships offloading some of the LNG onto smaller ships which could transport it directly into port, warm the LNG into gaseous form and offload it directly into the local pipe grid [28]. As this technology is not in widespread use, it is therefore outside the focus of this paper.

lng Capex

The costs of LNG projects are difficult to determine because the costs of the components, such as steel, nickel, wages and services may vary significantly over time. For example, in 2004 the cost of building a liquefaction plant had fallen to less than $300 tpy, due to the exploitation of economies of scale and the development of trains with larger capacity. Because of rapid increases in the price of materials and services, however, the cost of a liquefaction plant rose to $650 tpy in 2008 – more than double the 2004 price [35].

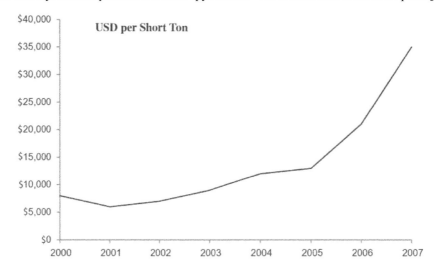

Figure 5 Nickel prices. *Source* of data: [35].

This corresponds well with the figures used in the report 'Natural Gas Pipeline Development in Northeast Asia' by Jung *et al.* [14], which will be used as a basis for the cost composition, but with revised figures. Jung *et al.* [14] break the total LNG costs into LNG liquefaction plant costs, LNG carrier costs and LNG re-gasification terminal costs.

The capital costs of the LNG liquefaction plant (P) are divided into a fixed cost for a greenfield plant with a capacity of 4 million tpy of LNG (5.5 bcmpa) and a variable cost per extra million tonne, if further expansion is needed. L is the amount of LNG, measured in million tonnes per year.

$$P = (\$5.5 \times 10^9) + (\$1 \times 10^9)(L - 4)$$

The cost of a single-train 4-million tpy onshore LNG plant is \$5.5, billion according to Vautrain and Holmes [34]. Train sizes of around 4 million tpy are the most common capacities, but this will probably change as the designs are further developed. Qatar already has several 7.8 million tpy trains [31]. Moreover, adding a train to an LNG plant in order to expand the capacity is far cheaper than a greenfield project. Adding a second train can reduce the unit costs per train by 20 to 30% [9], because many of the expensive facility components are already constructed and can be shared [30]. The Qatargas 4 project, where Qatargas added another train, with a capacity of 7.8 million tpy, to the existing Qatargas 2 and 3, will have a cost of around \$8 billion [36,37].

According to the US Energy Information Administration [30] around 50% of LNG liquefaction plant costs are construction and related costs, 30% are equipment costs and 20% are for bulk materials. These shares are only approximations and may change as the prices of the various components change.

The sizes of LNG carriers are also increasing due to better designs and technology. Today, a carrier might have a capacity of 266,000 cubic meters. There are 10 carriers of this size; these are also among the newest. Qatar Gas Transport Company's *Rasheeda* was delivered in August 2010. All the largest carriers have a speed of 19.5 knots, or about 36 km/h.

The cost of an LNG carrier with a capacity of 266,000 cubic meters is about \$290 million. The size of the fleet needed to transport the LNG depends on the distance (δ) from the market, the speed (λ) and the capacity (k) of the LNG carriers, and annual production at the liquefaction plant (N). λ is measured in kilometres per hour and k is measured in cubic meters of natural gas. The following equation is derived to find the number of carriers required and the capital cost of the LNG carriers (s). Here 266,000 cubic meter carriers will be used irrespective of the size of the field, because the aim of this paper is to analyse long-distance and large-scale transport.

$$S = \frac{\frac{(\$29 \times 10^7)N}{365}}{(\frac{\delta}{24\lambda}2) + 2}K$$

According to the US Energy Information Administration [30], 'the costs of building regasification or receiving terminals show wide variation and are very site-specific'. Therefore, it is also difficult to estimate the cost of a general LNG re-gasification terminal. The most expensive components are the storage tanks, which may account for one-third to one-half of the total construction costs, and the marine facilities [30].

The capital cost of a re-gasification terminal (R) is highly site-specific, but a rough estimate might be $1 billion for every 10 million tpy of LNG (L), or $100 million per million tpy LNG:

$$R = (\$1 \times 10^8)L$$

A US Energy Information Administration report from 2003 estimated that a new re-gasification terminal in the United States, with capacity between 3.8 and 7.7 million tpy, would cost $200 to $300 million. That estimate is probably too low today, because of the escalation of costs for materials and wages that started in 2004 and has not been reversed [36]. Furthermore, two LNG regasification terminals, the Gulf terminal in the United States and the Gate terminal in the Netherlands, which will both be operating from 2011, have announced their estimated total project costs to be $1.1 billion [38,39]. The Gulf terminal has a capacity of 5 million tpy; the Gate terminal has a capacity of 8.8 million tpy (12bcmpa), but this can be expanded to 16 bcmpa [31,39]. Jung *et al.* [14] use $500 million as an estimate for the cost of a 6-million-tpy re-gasification terminal.

lng Opex

Annual operating costs for the facilities needed to transport natural gas as LNG include maintenance costs, port charges, capital charges, taxes, fuel and boil-off. Boil-off is the small amount of LNG that evaporates from the storage tank during transport [40]. Fuel costs include liquefaction of the natural gas, fuel for the LNG carriers and re-gasification of the LNG [14,35] [35] [14]. Operating costs are first divided into different shares of the construction costs, mainly covering operational and maintenance costs. Thereafter the amount of the natural gas used as fuel deserves discussion (see below).

Annual operating costs for the transport of natural gas as LNG may be estimated as follows:

$$O_L = P\varsigma + Sv + R\sigma + N\omega p$$

Operating costs as a share of capital costs (ς,v,σ) are 3.5% for the LNG liquefaction plant (P), 3.6% for the LNG carriers (S) and 2.5% for the LNG re-gasification terminal (R) [14].

The variable *share used as fuel* (ω) depends on several parameters. These include the share of natural gas used in the liquefaction process (Θ), the share of natural gas used in the re-gasification process (Ω), boil-off per day (ξ) and shipping fuel per day (ϕ).

$$\omega = \Theta + \Omega + (1 - (1 - \xi)^{\frac{\delta}{24\lambda}}) + (1 - (1 - \varphi)^{\frac{\delta}{24\lambda^2}})$$

The liquefaction process whereby the natural gas is cooled down to $-161°C$ consumes a considerable share of the natural gas. Re-gasification and shipping consume a portion of the gas as fuel. The quantity of natural gas used for cooling, heating, boil-off and LNG carrier fuel depends on the design, efficiency and the size of the liquefaction plant, the LNG carrier and the re-gasification terminal [41].

According to the engineer Kandiyoti [42], a total of up to 20% of the natural gas is used in the process of liquefaction, shipping and re-gasification. This was supported by ship-owner Trygve Seglem in 2007, who stated that 20–25% of the natural gas is needed for the entire LNG transport chain [43]. Nevertheless, others have claimed that less natural gas fuel is necessary for LNG transport. An anonymised source in an international oil company [44] informed us by email that only 5–6% is needed specifically for the liquefaction process, 1–2% for transport by LNG carriers and 1% for re-gasification. According to a report from 2004 by the Norwegian Directorate for Watercourses and Energy [45], between 5 and 15% of the natural gas is used in the liquefaction process [46].

A share of only 5–6% for the liquefaction process, however, seems too low compared with figures given in the majority of the published sources available. Furthermore, the figure of 1–2% natural gas usage for shipping must refer to shorter distances only, where the return journey is not accounted for. Jung *et al.* [14] cite the following figures: 9% for liquefaction, 2.5% for re-gasification and 0.17% per day to boil-off. LNG carriers may also use some of the natural gas as fuel. These figures fit well with those indicated by Kandiyoti, who claims that the liquefaction process takes up to 9–10% of the natural gas, and that up to 6% is needed for a 20-day voyage. This seems to include both boil-off and fuel, but not fuel for the return voyage. This means that a little less than 0.14% per day is fuel only (not including boil-off). The re-gasification process claims 2–3% of the natural gas [47].

These shares may vary due to differences in design, efficiency and technology, among other factors. The natural gas that boils off during shipping may be used as fuel – or other fuels, such as bunker fuel or diesel, may be used instead [47]. This will probably reduce the share of the natural gas needed for the LNG chain. We assume that the boil-off is lost, and that the fuel for the LNG carriers is natural gas taken from the cargo.

COMPARISON OF LNG AND PIPELINE CAPEX

We will first discuss the break-even point between the two transport options by examining only the capital costs. The 'break-even point' refers to the position when the cost of constructing the pipeline infrastructure is equal to the cost of constructing the LNG chain needed to transport the natural gas. As mentioned, the literature assumes a break-even point somewhere between 3000 and 5000 km. Because the cost of pipeline construction starts from a low level and rises relatively steeply with distance (whereas LNG has a high threshold, but thereafter increases less), LNG construction costs will be lower after the break-even point has been reached. The costs of pipeline constructions will be lower for distances shorter than the break-even point.

Not only the distance, but also the quantity of natural gas transported affects the costs and the break-even point. According to our calculations, the economies of scale are more pronounced for pipelines than for LNG. Even though there are significant cost reductions for adding trains to an already-planned LNG greenfield plant, the cost reductions are higher for increasing the diameter of a pipeline (not yet constructed) to expand the capacity. Not only the pipeline diameter, but also the power of the compressor stations must be increased in order to expand the capacity of a pipeline [48].

That point is not accounted for in this analysis because we have used a fixed capacity per compressor station (110 MW). In any case, this seems to be a relatively high figure, as a 110 MW compressor station every 200 km will probably be able to pump relatively large amounts of natural gas through the pipeline. In addition, the LNG chain might gain something from economies of scale, because it is cheaper to increase the size of an existing plant than to build a greenfield plant. It is also cheaper to use a large LNG carrier than several carriers with smaller capacities. But, the transport of natural gas is not associated with economies of scale to the same degree as is pipeline transport.

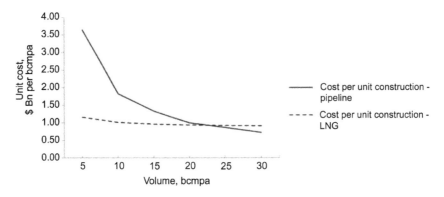

Figure 6. Capital cost per unit for 4000 km.

The break-even point for an annual transport of 30 bcm is about 5100 km, assuming a pipeline diameter of 1420 mm (56 inches). If, however, if the amount of natural gas is 20 bcmpa, and the pipeline has a diameter of 1220 mm (48 inches), the break-even point is around 3750 km. For 10 bcmpa, with a pipeline diameter of 1020 mm (40 inches), it is around 2200 km.

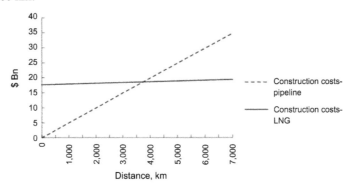

Figure 7. Break-even point for 20 bcmpa.

COMPARISON OF LNG AND PIPELINE OPEX

We have used the actual market price for natural gas sold by Russia to Germany in 2010 to price the natural gas throughout this comparison, $296 per 1000 cubic meter [49].

Even though construction costs might be lower for LNG when considering long distances or relatively small volumes of natural gas, this does not necessarily mean that LNG will be the cheapest transport option. The large amounts of natural gas needed during the LNG chain usually make annual operating costs higher for LNG than for pipelines.

The break-even point for constructing the transport facilities needed to transport 20 bcmpa is around 3750 km. Pipeline construction costs will be the lowest for shorter distances, whereas LNG construction costs will be lower for longer distances. But, if we include the operating costs and assume that the project will run for 20 years, the distance break-even point for 20 bcmpa will increase to around 4550 km; for 30 bcmpa it will increase from 5100 km to 5900 km when operating costs are included. The break-even point for 10 bcmpa will be 2800 km, increased from 2200 km.

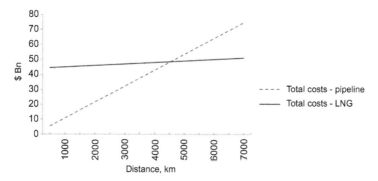

Figure 8. Break-even point for 20 bcmpa.

Operating costs will not always be higher for LNG than for pipeline transport. Our estimates show that for transporting 30 bcmpa over distances greater than 6550 km, annual operating costs for pipelines exceed those for LNG. One reason is that pipeline construction costs are higher, and we have developed operational and maintenance costs as a share of construction costs. Furthermore, for long distances the share of natural gas used as fuel for the compressor stations will approach the share of fuel used in the LNG chain. For particularly long distances, the fuel share will be higher for pipelines than for LNG transport. If the natural gas is transported more than 9100 km, pipeline transport will demand a greater share of the natural gas than LNG transport, regardless of transport volume. Nevertheless, LNG transport is more exposed to changes in the natural gas price than pipeline transport for reasonably long distances. This is shown in Figure 9, which is based on a distance of 4550 km from the field to the market, a volume of 20 bcmpa and a project life of 20 years. The costs of European Union Allowances (EUAs) are also included here.

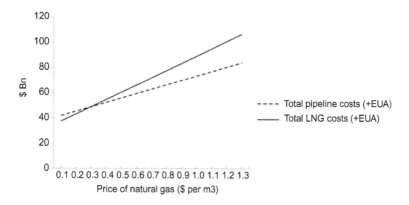

Figure 9. Total transport costs and gas price.

CO₂ EMISSIONS

Because of the relatively large amount of fuel required by the LNG process compared to pipelines, LNG causes greater CO_2 emissions than pipeline transport. CO_2 emission allowances will therefore be used in order to estimate the extra costs associated with the environmental damage brought on by LNG.

The extra operating costs can be calculated as follows:

$$E_p = \frac{36N\epsilon\left(1-(1\times(1-l)^{\frac{\delta}{n}})\right)}{10^6}A$$

$$E_L = \frac{36N\epsilon\left(\Theta+\Omega+(1-(1-\xi)^{\frac{\delta}{2\lambda}})+(1-(1-\varphi)^{\frac{\delta}{2\lambda^2}})\right)}{10^6}A$$

CO_2 emissions (ϵ) from natural gas are around 53.06 kg CO_2 per million Btu [50]. The price per ton CO_2 of emissions (A) is currently \$29.84 when buying from the European Union emission trading scheme, the European Union Allowance (EUA) [51]. As shown in Figure 10, LNG transport is more exposed to changes in the price of CO_2 emission allowances than pipeline transport. Figure 10 is based on a distance of 4550 km from field to market, a volume of 20 bcmpa and a project life of 20 years.

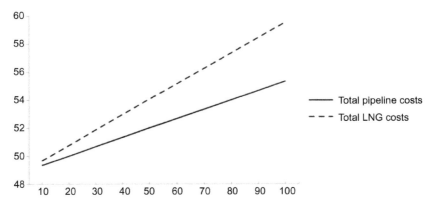

Figure 10. Transport costs and EUA prices.

The model

Combining all the equations results in a model that may help to answer the question about the relative cost-efficiency of pipelines and LNG. Let **f** be equal to total pipeline costs and let g equal total LNG costs, measured in dollars. (A full list of variables and parameters is provided at the end of the article.)

$$\frac{f\,(\delta,\mu,\alpha,c,\gamma,N,p,\tau,\xi,\eta,A,\epsilon)}{g(\gamma,N,L,p,A,\epsilon,\mathcal{Z},\nu,\sigma,\delta,\lambda,k,\Theta,\Omega,\xi,\phi)}$$

$$=\frac{(\$52{,}675\mu\delta+(\$3\times10^7)\alpha+\$3{,}091c)(1+\tau\gamma)+N\left(1-(1-l)^{\frac{\delta}{\eta}}\right)\left(p+\frac{36\epsilon}{10^6}A\right)\gamma}{((\$5.5\times10^9)+(\$1\times10^9)(L-4))(1+2\gamma)+\dfrac{\frac{(\$29\times10^7)N}{365}}{\left(-\frac{\delta}{24\lambda}-2\right)+2}k(1+\nu\gamma)+(\$1\times10^8)L(1+\sigma\gamma)+N\left(\Theta+\Omega+\left(1-(1-\xi)^{\frac{\delta}{24\lambda}}\right)\right)}$$

If the equation yields a figure higher than 1 for a given set of parameters, then LNG transport has the lowest costs. If the equation gives a figure smaller than 1, pipeline transport is economically preferable.

Such a large and complicated equation is not particularly elegant, and one may question whether it is necessary. But, according to our analysis, this equation captures the main factors that must be taken into account in choosing which type of infrastructure to build. Thus it mirrors the calculations that anyone choosing between LNG and pipelines must make, and the complexity of these decisions about crucial infrastructure. It is also possible to calculate the partial derivatives of **f** (total pipeline cost) and (g) (total LNG cost) with respect to the natural gas price (p) or with respect to the price of CO$_2$ emission allowances (A), where all other variables are held constant, in order to calculate how a one unit price increase affects total pipeline and LNG costs.

$$\frac{\partial f}{\partial p} = N\left(1 - (1 - \ell)\frac{\delta}{\eta}\right)\gamma$$

$$\frac{\partial g}{\partial p} = N\left(\Theta + \Omega + (1 - (1 - \xi)\frac{\delta}{24\lambda}) + (1 - (1 - \varphi)\frac{\delta}{24\lambda}2)\right)\gamma$$

$$\frac{\partial f}{\partial A} = N\left(1 - (1 - \ell)\frac{\delta}{\eta}\right)\frac{36_\varepsilon}{10^6}\gamma$$

$$\frac{\partial g}{\partial A} = N\left(\Theta + \Omega + (1 - (1 - \xi)\frac{\delta}{24\lambda}) + (1 - (1 - \varphi)\frac{\delta}{24\lambda}2)\right)\frac{36_\varepsilon}{10^6}\gamma$$

For example, the transport of 10 bcmpa over a distance of 3000 km during 20 years, and with the values of the other parameters as discussed above, gives:

$$\frac{\partial f}{\partial p} = 11,669,754,730 \qquad \frac{\partial g}{\partial p} = 27,114,448,860$$

This demonstrates how the costs of LNG transport (g) are more sensitive to changes in the price of natural gas than pipeline costs (f).

Similarly, the parameters give the following expressions for the partial derivatives with respect to A:

$$\frac{\partial f}{\partial A} = 22,291,099 \qquad \frac{\partial f}{\partial A} = 51,792,936$$

Again, LNG transport appears more exposed to price variations than transport by pipeline. A one unit increase in the price of greenhouse gas emission allowances results in a considerably larger cost increase for LNG than for pipelines, as shown below:

$$C = (\$52,675 \times 56 \; inches \times 1615km) + (\$3 \times 10^7)11 + (\$3091 \times 1,327,612 \; hp) = \$9,189,537,160$$

$$C = \$9,189,537,160 + \frac{\$10,750,000,000 + \$2,000,000,000}{2} = \$15,564,537,160$$

$$C = (\$52,675 \times 56 \; inches \times 1365 \; km) + (\$3 \times 10^7)10 + (\$3091 \times 1,206,920 \; hp) = \$8,050,272,517$$

$$P + S + R = (\$5.5 \times 10^9) + (\$1 \times 10^9)(20.3 - 4) + \frac{(\$29 \times 10^7)(28 \times 10^9)}{365} \, 152,950,000 \atop (\frac{3520}{24 \times 36}2) + 2$$
$$+ (\$1 \times 10^8)20.3 \approx \$25,280,000,000$$

$$O_p = (\$21,939,537,160 \times 3.5\%) + (28,000,000,000 - (28,000,000,000$$
$$\times (1 - 0.4\%)\frac{2839}{200}) \times \$0.296) = \$1,226,257,190$$

$$O_L = ((\$5.5 \; bn + (\$1.0 \; bn \times (20.3 - 4))) \times 3.5\%) + ((\$290 \; MM \times 5) \times 3.6\%)$$
$$+ ((\$100MM \times 20.3) \times 2.5\%) + (28,000,000,000 \times 13.8\% \times 0.296))$$

CONCLUSIONS

Many variables affect the cost of pipeline and LNG transport of natural gas. In this article we have developed a generic model for the comparison of pipelines and LNG that can be adapted to different projects by revising the prices for the various factors included in the model.

The exact break-even point between LNG and pipelines will depend on the volume of natural gas and the distance that it is transported. Pipeline transport is a better option for larger volumes and shorter distances. LNG transport has the lowest costs for smaller volumes (up to 15 bcmpa) and for longer distances.

A substantial amount of natural gas is required as fuel for internal use in the liquefaction process, and for compressor stations in the case of pipelines. This causes the costs of both transport options to vary with the price of natural gas and greenhouse gas emissions. For distances up to 9100 km, LNG transport is more exposed to fluctuations in the prices of natural gas and greenhouse gas emissions than pipeline transport. This is because the LNG process – liquefaction, shipping and re-gasification – requires a larger share of the natural gas than do pipeline compressor stations over such distances. At greater distances, pipelines will expend more gas than will LNG, making pipelines more sensitive to changes in the price of natural gas and greenhouse gas emissions. We have thus identified 9100 km as an important threshold for the comparison of LNG and pipelines. In addition to this threshold, the amount of gas transported also impacts significantly on the comparison. In general, an increase in the price of natural gas and/or greenhouse gas emissions will favour the choice of pipeline transport.

If the aim is to replace coal and oil with natural gas in order to reduce greenhouse gas emissions, account should also be taken of the emissions associated with the different transport options for natural gas. On the other hand, more effective technologies developed in the future may reduce the burning of natural gas in connection with its transport. This is particularly true in the case of LNG, where the technology is newer and far more complex than the technology involved in pipelines. Future innovations within LNG may improve the viability of LNG relative to pipeline transport, as well as relative to coal and oil.

Additional conditions must also be taken into account when considering the transport of natural gas. LNG transport avoids transit countries and the associated, possible legal and political risks, and provides flexibility to sell on the market where the price is highest. Price differences for natural gas on different regional markets can be so great as to cancel out the impact of the higher fuel consumption and greenhouse gas emissions involved in LNG.

This article has not taken into account greenhouse gas emissions from the production of steel for pipelines, or the materials for LNG facilities and tankers. We have shown the effect of variations in the prices of natural gas and greenhouse gas emissions on the relative cost-efficiency of LNG and pipelines, but with only a partial analysis of the full climate impacts. Full assessment of the full carbon footprint of these two transport options for natural gas would require expanding the model to cover also the production of steel for pipes. That would be a logical next step for further research.

List of Variables

N = natural gas (cubic meter per year)
L = LNG (million tonnes per year)
p = price of natural gas (US$ per cubic meter)

δ = distance (in km)
γ = number of operating years
C = pipeline capital costs (US$)
μ = pipeline diameter (inches)
α = number of compressor stations
c = total capacity of compressor stations (horsepower)
O_p = pipeline operating costs per year (US$)
τ = OPEX as a share of CAPEX – pipelines (%)
ℓ = loss per compressor station (%)
η = distance between compressor stations (in km)
P = capital cost of liquefaction plant
S = capital cost of LNG carriers
λ = speed of LNG carrier (km/h)
k = capacity per LNG carrier (cubic meter natural gas)
R = capital cost of re-gasification terminal
O_L = LNG operating costs per year (US$)
ꝛ = OPEX as a share of CAPEX – liquefaction plant (%)
v = OPEX as a share of CAPEX – LNG carriers (%)
σ = OPEX as a share of CAPEX – re-gasification terminal (%)
ω = share of natural gas used as fuel for the LNG chain (%)
Θ = liquefaction – share of natural gas used in the liquefaction process (%)
ξ = boil-off per day (% of natural gas)
f = shipping fuel per day (% of natural gas)
Ω = re-gasification – share of natural gas used in the re-gasification process (%)
E_P = pipeline CO_2 emission costs
E_L = LNG CO_2 emission costs
A = price of CO_2 emission allowance (US$ per ton CO_2)
Î = CO_2 emission (kg per million Btu of natural gas)

List of Parameters

p = $0.296 per m³ [49]
γ = 20 [45]
μ = 40", 48", 56"
c = 147,512 per compressor station
τ = 3.5% [14] ℓ = 0.4% [14] η = 200 km [24]
λ = 36.114 [33]
k = 152,950,000 [33]
ꝛ = 3.5% [14]
v = 3.6% [14]
σ = 2.5% [14]
Θ = 9.5% [14,47]
ξ = 0.17% per day [14]
f = 0.1389% per day [47]
Ω = 2.5% [14,47]
A = $29.84 per ton CO_2 [51]
Î = 53.06 kg per MMBtu [50]

REFERENCES

1. Stevens, P. 2009. *Transit Troubles: Pipelines as a Source of Conflict*, London: Royal Institute of International Affairs.

2. BP, 2011, Statistical review of world energy 2011: What's inside. Available online at: http://www.bp.com/liveassets/bp_internet/globalbp/globalbp_uk_english/reports_and_publications/statistical_energy_review_2011/STAGING/local_assets/pdf/natural_gas_section_2011.pdf (accessed 30 October 2011).

3. Jensen Associates, 2007, The outlook for the global trade in liquefied natural gas. Available online at: http://www.energy.ca.gov/2007publications/CEC-200-2007-017/CEC-200-2007-017.PDF (accessed 30 October 2011).

4. NTB, 2011, Finnmark fikk strøm fra snøhvit [Finnmark got electricity from Snow White]. Available online at: http://www.dn.no/energi/article2288190.ece (accessed 3 January 2012).

5. Yergin, D. and Stoppard, M. 2003. The next prize. *Foreign Affairs*, 82(6): 103–114.

6. Jensen, J. 2004. *The Development of a Global LNG Market. Is it Likely? If So, When?*, Oxford: Oxford Institute for Energy Studies.

7. Mazighi, A. 2003. An examination of the international natural gas trade. *OPEC Review*, 27(4): 313–329.

8. Tongia, R. and Arunachalam, V. 1999. Natural gas imports by South Asia. Pipelines or pipedreams?. *Economic and Political Weekly*, 34(18): 1054–1064.

9. Cornot-Gandolphe, S., Appert, O., Dickel, R., Chabrelie, M. and Rojey, A., 2003, The challenges of further cost reductions for new supply options (pipeline, LNG, GTL). Paper for the 22nd World Gas Conference, 1–5 June, Tokyo. Available online at: http://www.cedigaz.org/Fichiers/pdf_papers/challenge%20of%20further.pdf (accessed 16 February 2012).

10. Quintana, E., 2003, Pipelines vs. LNG: Competition in South America. Available online at: http://www.igu.org/html/wgc2003/WGC_pdffiles/Quintana_slide.pdf (accessed 15 February 2010).

11. Mäkinen, H. 2010. *The Future of Natural Gas as the European Union's Energy Source – Risks and Possibilities*, Turku: Pan-European Institute.

12. Menon, E. 2005. *Gas Pipeline Hydraulics*, Abingdon: Taylor & Francis Group.

13. Parker, N. 2004. *Using Natural Gas Transmission Pipeline Costs to Estimate Hydrogen Pipeline Costs*, Davis: Institute of Transportation Studies, University of California, Davis.

14. Jung, Y., Yokobori, K., Doi, N., Peng, H., Wang, Z. and Sinygin, O. 2000. *Natural Gas Pipeline Development in Northeast Asia*, Tokyo: Asia Pacific Energy Research Centre.

15. Kubota, S. 1996. *Natural Gas Trade in Asia and the Middle East*, Washington, DC: World Bank.

16. Canadian Energy Pipeline Association, Canadian Energy Pipeline Association. Available online at: http://www.cepa.com/pipeline101.aspx?page_guid=05817B59-0D2D-4388-9600-A915F34D1CE7 (accessed 23 March 2011).

17. Brown, D., Cabe, J. and Stout, T. 2011. National lab uses OGJ data to develop cost equations. *Oil & Gas Journal*, 109(1): 108–111.

18. Smith, C. 2010. Natural gas pipelines continue growth despite lower earnings; oil profits grow. *Oil & Gas Journal*, 108(41): 102–123.

19. *Penn World Table*, 2006, PWT 6.3. Available online at: http://www.pwt.econ.upenn.edu/php_site/pwt63/pwt63_form.php (accessed 18 April 2011).

20. Nabucco, Nabucco route 2008–2010. Available online at: http://www.nabuccopipeline.com/portal/page/portal/en/pipeline/route (accessed 21 April 2011).

21. Nabucco Consortium, Nabucco 2008–2010, Available online at: http://www.nabuccopipeline. com/portal/page/portal/en/pipeline/overview (accessed 21 April 2011).

22. Nabucco Consortium, Nabucco overview 2008–2010, Available online at: http://www. nabuccopipeline.com/portal/page/portal/en/commercial/overview (accessed 12 April 2011).

23. Webb, T., 2011, European gas pipeline costs double. Available online at: http://www.guardian. co.uk/business/2011/feb/20/european-gas-pipeline-nabucco-costsdouble (accessed 23 April 2011).

24. Whist, B. 2009. "Nordstream – a solution or a challenge for the EU?". In *The EU-Russia Gas Connection: Pipes, Politics and Problems*, Edited by: Liuhto, K. 166–203. Turku: Pan-European Institute.

25. Pankratov, S., 2010, European natural gas projects as guarantee of energy security. Available online at: http://www.unece.org/energy/se/pp/EnComm19_Nov10/24Nov/3_Pankratov.pdf (accessed 9 March 2011).

26. Gazprom, 2011, Yamal–Europe. Available online at: http://www.gazprom.com/production/ projects/pipelines/yamal-evropa/ (accessed 22 March 2011).

27. Meps, 2011, Meps. Available online at: http://www.meps.co.uk/ (accessed 23 March 2011).

28. Chandra, V., 2006, Liquefied natural gas chain. Available online at: http://www.natgas.info/ html/gaspipelines.html (accessed 25 March 2011).

29. Jensen, J. 2003. The LNG revolution. *The Energy Journal of the International Association for Energy Economics*, 24(2): 1–46.

30. US Energy Information Administration, 2003, The global liquefied natural gas market: Status and outlook. Available online at: http://www.eia.doe.gov/oiaf/analysispaper/global/ lngindustry.html (accessed 29 March 2011).

31. True, W. 2011. LNG world trade. *Oil & Gas Journal*, 109: 138

32. Chandra, V., 2006, Gas pipelines. Available online at: http://www.natgas.info/html/ gaspipelines.html (accessed 7 April 2011).

33. Ship-Building History, 2011, The world fleet of LNG carriers. Available online at: http://www. shipbuildinghistory.com/today/highvalueships/lngactivefleet.htm (accessed 24 April 2011).

34. Vautrain, J. and Holmes, C. 2011. Conditions improving for floating LNG production. *Oil & Gas Journal*, 109(10): 114–117.

35. Jordan Cove Energy Project, 2008, Gas supply potential and development costs of Rocky Mountain gas and LNG delivered to the Pacific NW. Available online at: http://www. jordancoveenergy.com/pdf/JCEP%20Task%203%20Rockies%20Gas%20and%20LNG%20 June%2013.pdf (accessed 15 February 2012).

36. True, W. 2007. LNG construction projects: plans move ahead, buck cost pressures. *Oil & Gas Journal*, 105(37): 20–25.

37. Qatargas, 2010, Qatargas 4 project. Available online at: http://www.qatargas.com.qa/Projects. aspx?id=78 (accessed 15 February 2010).

38. Gulf LNG Energy, 2008, Project details. Available online at: http://www.elpaso.com/gulflng/ docs/GulfLNGSummary.pdf (accessed 30 March 2011).

39. Gate Terminal, 2008, Facts and figures. Available online at: http://www.gate.nl/pagina. php?parent_id=2&pagina_id=8&fotoalbum_id=&taal_id= (accessed 30 March 2011).

40. California Energy Commission, 2011, Glossary of LNG-related terms and definitions. Available online at: http://www.energy.ca.gov/lng/glossary.html#boil_off (accessed 25 April 2011).

41. Faeraas, K., 2006, Email correspondence with authors, 6 December.

42. Kandiyoti, R. 2008. *Pipelines: Flowing Oil and Crude Politics*, London: I.B. Tauris.

43. Bjørndal, B., 2007, Er på de jævligste steder [Is in the most awful places]. Available online at: http://www.dn.no/energi/article1013053.ece?WT.svl=article_title (accessed 31 March 2011).

44. Anonymous source in international oil company, 2006, email correspondence with authors, 27 November.

45. Bergesen, B., Svendsen, P. and Selfors, A. 2004. *Gass i Norge [Natural Gas in Norway]*, Oslo: Norwegian Directorate of Hydropower and Energy.

46. Selfors, A., Thorsen, K., Hofstad, K., Fagerlund, K. and Wiggen, T. 2004. *Naturgass: En generell innføring [Natural Gas: A General Introduction]*, Oslo: Norwegian Directorate of Hydropower and Energy.

47. Kandiyoti, R., 2011, Email correspondence with authors, 21 April.

48. US Energy Information Administration, 2007, Natural gas compressor stations on the interstate pipeline network: developments since 1996. Available online at: http://www.eia.doe.gov/pub/oil_gas/natural_gas/analysis_publications/ngcompressor/ngcompressor.pdf (accessed 11 March 2011).

49. International Monetary Fund, 2011, Table 3. Actual market prices for non-fuel and fuel commodities, 2007–2011. Available online at: http://www.imf.org/external/np/res/commod/Table3.pdf (accessed 1 April 2011).

50. US Energy Information Administration, 2011, Voluntary reporting of greenhouse gases program fuel emission coefficients. Available online at: http://www.eia.doe.gov/oiaf/1605/coefficients.html (accessed 8 April 2011).

51. Klima- og forurensningsdirektoratet, 2011, Kjøp et bestemt antall kvoter [Buy a specific quota]. Available online at: http://co2.klif.no/en/-HANDEL-/Kjop-et-bestemt-antall-kvoter/ (accessed 7 April 2011).

Compressed Natural Gas Direct Injection: Comparison Between Homogeneous and Stratified Combustion

Shahrir Abdullah[1,2], Wan Mohd Faizal Wan Mahmood[1,2], Saad Aljamali[1] and Azhari Shamsudeen[2]

[1]Department of Mechanical and Materials Engineering, Faculty of Engineering and Built Environment, Universiti Kebangsaan Malaysia, UKM Bangi, Selangor, Malaysia
[2]Centre for Automotive Research, Faculty of Engineering and Built Environment, Universiti Kebangsaan Malaysia, UKM Bangi, Selangor, Malaysia

ABSTRACT

Due to abundance of natural gas, the use of natural gas for automotive use, particularly for internal combustion engine (ICE), is more practical and cheaper than their future successors. Even though natural gas is a cleaner fuel than other fossil fuels and has a higher octane number and can lead to higher thermal efficiency, its low carbon number makes it less attractive as compared to gasoline and diesel. Based on its potential, an engine referred to as compressed natural gas direct injection engine (CNGDI) was designed, developed and tested to operate on compressed natural gas (CNG) as monofuel directly and centrally injected into the engine. Computational and experimental works have been performed to investigate the viability of the design. Computational fluid dynamics (CFD) simulations and experimental works with homogenous combustion showed that the results were in good agreement. From experimental works, it is found that combustion characteristics could be improved by using a stratified charge piston configuration with some drawback on performance. In terms of exhaust emissions, stratified configuration causes slight increase in the emission of CO, CO_2 and NOx, which highlight a need for further study on this issue.

Keywords: CNGDI, Internal combustion, Performance, Emissions, Homogenous mixture, Stratified mixture

INTRODUCTION

In development of any engine, it is desirable to optimise the engine parameter and configuration in order to maximise its performance while keeping the emission within stipulated limits. Due to abundance of natural gas, the use of natural gas for internal combustion engine (ICE) is more practical and cheaper than their future successors, such as electric and fuel cell cars. Several advantages related to natural gas utilisation in ICEs are its higher thermal efficiency and relatively lower exhaust emissions due to the higher octane level and lower ratio of carbon and hydrogen ratio, respectively [1].

It is understood that configuring conventional ICEs to improve efficiency while reducing exhaust emissions is difficult where strategies to improve engine efficiency will eventually increase harmful emissions, such as carbon monoxide (CO) and nitrogen oxides (NO_x) [2]. The significant advantage that compressed natural gas (CNG) has in antiknock quality is related to the higher auto-ignition temperature and higher octane number compared to that of gasoline. As the air-fuel ratio for natural gas is 17.23, which requires less fuel required that is less compared to other fuels such as gasoline and diesel, it is possible to obtain the maximum cylinder pressure and rate of heat release at the shorter combustion duration through a right combination of fuel injection, valve and ignition timings while keeping a low level of HC and CO emissions [3].

The use of alternative fuels, including CNG, has attracted popularity along with the importance of emergent alternative fuel technology because the progressively strict regulatory limits on emission levels [4]. Direct injection (DI) in the spark ignition engine considerably raises the engine volumetric efficiency and declines the requirement to use the throttle valve for regulatory purposes [5].

Hence, this chapter presents aspects of the design and development of a compressed natural gas direct injection engine (CNGDI), which can be optimised to yield maximum performance while keeping the emission low. In order to accomplish this study, two types of mixture will be analysed, namely, homogenous and stratified mixtures.

DEVELOPMENT OF THE CNGDI ENGINE

In this work, a monofuel CNGDI engine was designed and developed based on a gasoline port injection (PI) engine as shown in Figure 1. This new engine design was designed with a specific purpose to enhance the natural gas engine performance as well as to minimise the exhaust emissions. It was also designed using two types of piston crown designs, which are a homogenous piston crown for optimum performance, and stratified piston crown for reduction of exhaust emission.

(a)

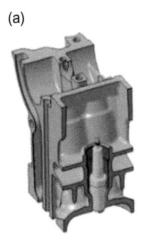

(b)

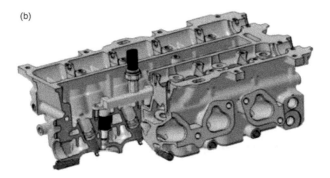

Figure 1. CNGDI engine head showing the location of spark plug and fuel injector: (a) cylinder head for referral gasoline engine and (b) cylinder head for CNGDI engine.

In general, the design and development process of the main components in an automotive engine are not straightforward. One of the main engine components is its cylinder head, where careful design is required for optimum performance and emission of a vehicle.

The cylinder head is also the platform that is heavily loaded with mechanisms for internal combustion process such as valve train and fuel rail [6]. Hence, the cylinder head of a direct injection engine is highly influenced by the geometry of the injector location at the combustion chamber and has to withstand a very high combustion pressure and temperature. In fact, small changes in the cylinder head geometry can lead to considerable changes in the air-fuel mixture distribution and performance of the engine [7].

The cylinder head could also fail during operation due to thermal fatigue cracking especially in the water jacket cooling area because of narrow path between the valves and the exhaust valve seat [8], as shown in Figure 2. For its structural strength, the finite element analysis can be used to obtain the stress and strain profiles of the cylinder structure, which could be analysed further to ensure that the maximum stress does not exceed the allowable yield strength limit [9]. Furthermore, the stress-strain and displacement distributions at various loads and pressure can be simulated. Besides, other researchers also had conducted similar analyses under combustion loading and critical assembly parts in the cylinder head [10]. In this work, the effect of gas pressure during combustion process was examined through the stress and displacement distributions, as shown in Figure 3.

Figure 2. Water jacket design in CNGDI cylinder head.

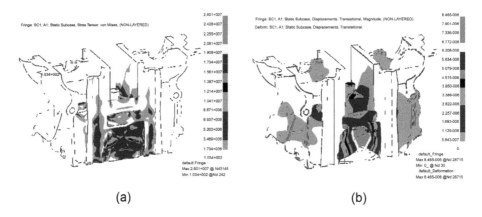

(a)   (b)

Figure 3. Finite element analysis of the cylinder head: (a) stress and (b) displacement.

Designs of the cylinder head intake and exhaust were guided by a computational fluid dynamics (CFD) simulation in order to ensure the smooth flows of air-fuel mixture and combustion products into and away from the combustion chamber, respectively. With optimal shape design, the inflow and outflow can increase the efficiency of combustion engines and influence the engine performance and exhaust emissions.

During the design of the cylinder head, the intake and exhaust valves were orientated a few degrees from the central axis of the cylinder bore in order to accommodate the spark plug and the fuel injector vertically close to the central axis. The combined valve train and cam system was analysed for kinematic and dynamic responses in order to optimise the angle of valve orientation and some other characteristic parameter for the cam system. By combining the finite element analysis on the stress-strain profile of the cylinder head, the CFD analysis of the cooling system and the dynamic response analysis of the valve train and cam system, the improved design for cylinder head can be produced. Then, prototypes of the CNGDI single-cylinder engine and the CNGDI multi-cylinder head were fabricated by casting as shown in Figure 4. These prototypes were installed and single- and multi-cylinder engine test beds for further internal combustion experiments.

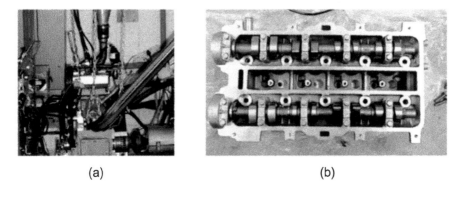

(a)   (b)

Figure 4. Cylinder head prototypes: (a) single-cylinder engine and (b) multi-cylinder head.

METHODOLOGY

For the internal combustion study, the analysis started with a CFD simulation of combustion process, which was used to derive the optimum shape of critical engine components that form the combustion chamber as well as the characteristic parameters such as injection and ignition timings. Based on the optimal CFD results, the experiment was performed to further explore the performance and emissions of the newly designed engine.

Engine Specifications and Fuel Properties

A four-cylinder spark ignition engine direct injection connected to CNG tanks as the source of fuel was used in this work. The engine specifications are given in Table 1.

Table 1. Engine specifications

Parameter	Value	Unit
Number of cylinders	4	-
Type	Inline	-
Capacity	1596	cm³
Bore	76	mm
Stroke	88	mm
Connecting rod length	131	mm
Crank radius	44	mm
Compression ratio	14	-
Intake valve opening	12	° before TDC
Intake valve closing	48	° after BDC
Exhaust valve opening	45	° before BDC
Exhaust valve closing	10	° after TDC
Maximum intake valve lift	8.1	mm
Maximum exhaust valve lift	7.5	mm

In addition, Table 2 lists key properties of CNG for internal combustion as compared to gasoline. Based on the table, it can be deduced that there are several properties in which CNG has advantages, such as a better antiknock quality, that is related to higher auto-ignition temperature and higher octane number, as well as higher air-fuel ratio and heating value. In Malaysia, the typical composition of commercially available CNG is 94.42% methane, 2.29% ethane, 0.03% propane, 0.25% butane, 0.57% carbon dioxide, 0.44% nitrogen and 2% other compounds.

Table 2. Combustion-related properties of gasoline and CNG

Properties	Gasoline	CNG
Motor octane number	80–90	120
Molar mass (g/mol)	110	16.04
Carbon weight fraction (mass %)	87	75

Air-fuel ratio	14.7	17.23
Stoichiometric mixture density (kg/m³)	1.38	1.24
Heating value (MJ/kg)	43.6	47.4
Heating value of stoichiometric mixture (MJ/kg)	2.83	2.72
Flammability limits (vol. % in air)	1.3–7.1	5–15
Spontaneous ignition temperature (°C)	480–550	645

Model for CFD Simulation

In internal combustion engine spark ignition, a complete combustion can produce better engine performance by controlling of engine combustion parameters. Therefore, a numerical study and optimisation of combustion parameters in a CNGDI engine were performed using a computational fluid dynamics (CFD) simulation with single cylinder moving mesh modelling with a source code developed and incorporated as user subroutine to the base CFD code. In developing the moving mesh and boundary algorithms, every event is made as a function of crank angle and represents different configurations of mesh and boundary geometries for an engine cycle [11], as shown in Figure 5.

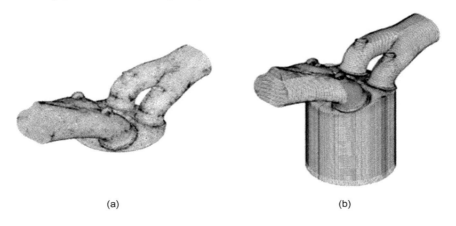

(a)   (b)

Figure 5. Mesh formation using CFD software: (a) surface mesh and (b) volume mesh.

The combustion process was simulated using the Eddy break-up model with the three global reaction schemes. The injection and ignition events were implemented to the engine computational mesh to control the combustion parameters. The CFD analysis used moving mesh simulation, which has been programmed to follow the motion of the intake valves, the exhaust valves and the piston. As the piston moves from bottom dead centre (BDC) to top dead centre (TDC), the height of the cylinder and valve position varies depending on the specific time step used and certain designated events.

During CFD simulation, several engine speeds were simulated in order to investigate the effect of the three engine parameters, namely, timings for the start of injection (SOI), the end of injection (EOI) and the spark ignition (SI), which will affect the engine performance and emission levels of CO, HC and NO. With a correct combined set of timings of SOI, EOI and SI, the indicated power can be optimised while maintaining a sound CO and NO levels. Then, the optimisation work was done by the combined CFD, the Gaussian process and genetic algorithm (GA) methods at every engine speed. The development of single-cylinder model was developed based on the following five stages:

- The construction and generation of moving mesh for the combustion chamber model to provide an approximation of the actual piston motion
- Modelling of the combustion process using a CFD code (STAR-CD) at speeds of 1000, 2000, 3000 and 4000 rpm
- Validation of CFD simulations with the experimental data from the single-cylinder test bed for the above speeds
- A parametric analysis using a coupled neural network and the Gaussian process at speeds of 1500, 2500 and 3500 rpm
- Optimisation using multi-objective GA (MOGA) for all the seven speeds, i.e. 1000, 1500, 2000, 2500, 3000, 3500 and 4000 rpm

Experimental Configuration

Using the CNGDI engine installed on a test bed, experimental investigations can be performed in order to study the performance and exhaust emissions of homogenous mixture and stratified mixture [12].

The engine test bed used in this experiment is depicted in Figure 6. Furthermore, investigation of optimum injection timings and the in-cylinder combustion pressure measurement of both homogeneous and stratified combustions were carried out, analysed and compared. The test was performed at engine speeds of 1500–4000 rpm. Some of the results were compared with the CFD analysis mentioned earlier. An engine control system and portable exhaust gas analyser were used for controlling engine operations and recording engine performance and emission data. The software used for the test bench shown above is Kronos 4. Fuel system had the pressure regulator to keep fuel pressure around 20 bar, which was maintained at the fuel entry into the combustion chamber. An air mass flow sensor was installed before the throttle valve to record air mass flow, a dynamometer typed FR250 with maximum load of 800 Nm was connected and the torque measured was calibrated using the control levers and weights.

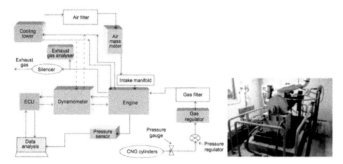

Figure 6. Experimental setup.

The results were recorded in a steady-state condition and at ambient pressure, temperature and humidity. All readings were recorded in order to estimate the optimal air inlet density. The portable Kane-May exhaust gas analyser was used and calibrated for each test to ensure correct results. The pressure was measured by a pressure sensor of type

6125B-Kistler in the first cylinder to record in-cylinder pressure with specified accuracy. The setting of the electronic control unit (ECU) is modified using the MoTeC software.

The engine was run under the full load wide-open throttle conditions, and the experiments were run using two types of piston configuration, as follows:

- The homogenous piston configuration is used as shown in Figure 7 in the first test.
- The stratified piston configuration is used as shown in Figure 8 in the second test.

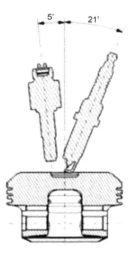

Figure 7. Homogenous piston configuration.

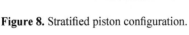
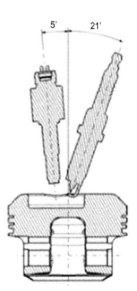

Figure 8. Stratified piston configuration.

RESULTS AND DISCUSSION

This section displays some results from the CFD simulation, which has been used as the basis for design optimisation of the cylinder head before it was fabricated. Then, the cylinder head together with the valve train, the cam system and the fuel rail was installed on the current based engine on the test bed before it was tested for various engine speeds.

CFD Simulation of Combustion Process

The CFD simulation results of the same work have been presented and discussed in Refs. [1, 2, 11]. The simulation was performed on a combustion chamber of the engine cylinder specified in Table 1 for a stoichiometric air-fuel mixture. The simulation results for 3000 rpm were given in Figure 9 for different crank angles, where the fuel is considered as 100% methane [13].

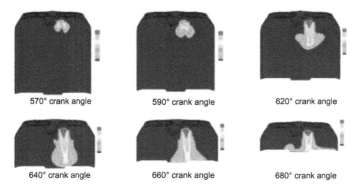

Figure 9. Simulated air-fuel mixture contour during compression stroke.

The simulation depicts the progression of air-methane profile in a shrinking cavity of combustion chamber at pre-ignition stage during the compression stroke. The post-ignition stage resulted in rapid increase of in-cylinder pressure, which produced torque and power output as depicted in Figure 10 in the graph of pressure with the engine displacement. The CFD results were compared with the experimental results as explained in the next section.

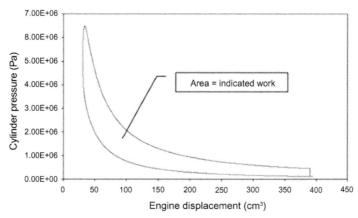

Figure 10. Simulated pressure and engine displacement in a p-v diagram.

Comparison between Homogenous and Stratified Combustions

The next subsections show the results obtained from experiment using both types of piston configuration, where the results are plotted in the same graphs. The results for power and torque were also compared with the CFD results for homogenous piston configuration. Together with the CFD simulation, the experiment was limited to a speed of 4000 rpm.

Power and Torque

Figure 11 shows the brake power and brake torque with the engine speed. The results were recorded from 1500 to 4000 rpm for both homogenous and stratified combustions. From the results, higher power and torque were obtained in stratified combustion with improvement observed at low speeds between 1500 and 2500 rpm. The maximum power recorded with stratified combustion was 54.75 kW at 4000 rpm, which is 3% higher than that of homogenous combustion. This finding is consistent with the study carried out by Sendyka and Cygnar [14] on gasoline direct injection engine.

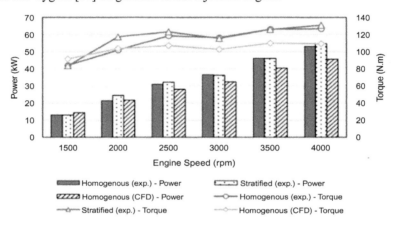

Figure 11. Power and torque of homogeneous and stratified combustions at different engine speeds.

In both combustion modes, the torque curves exhibit dual-peak profile, which is the typical characteristic of a double overhead cam (DOHC) engine with unmodified cam profile as used in the present investigation. Higher power obtained is the results of higher pressure and higher heat release rate. In addition, a late injection timing with high pressure and suitable combustion duration increases the engine performance, and good propagation flame is obtained [15]. Furthermore, high heat released with the lean mixture produced high indicated power.

As comparison, in another study by Kalam and Masjuki [16], the average brake power over the test cycle obtained was 47.39, 36.90 and 45.37 kW the gasoline port injection, CNG bi-fuel and CNG direct injection engines, respectively, using homogenous piston. The main factor affecting the brake torque is the lack of chemical energy conversion to mechanical energy, which is strongly related to volumetric efficiency, fuel mixing, net heat release rate and cylinder pressure [12].

Brake Mean Effective Pressure

Generally, the brake mean effective pressure (BMEP) is affected by heat release rate, good mixture and sufficient combustion time. Figure 12 depicts the BMEP with the engine speeds. The results show that BMEP increases with the engine speed and higher BMEP was obtained with the stratified combustion, especially at several low speeds as shown. The maximum value recorded for the stratified combustion is 10.3 bar at 4000 rpm.

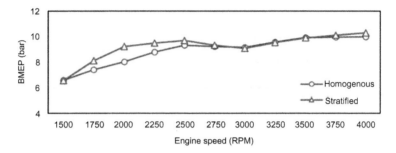

Figure 12. BMEP of homogeneous and stratified combustions at different engine speeds.

Brake-Specific Fuel Consumption

Figure 13 shows brake-specific fuel consumption (BSFC) versus engine speed. The results show a lower BSFC obtained with stratified combustion in comparison with homogenous combustion for all engine speeds.

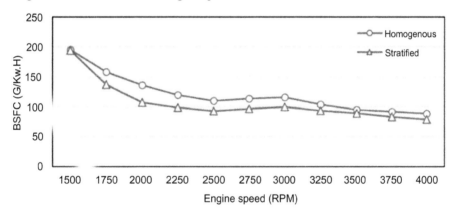

Figure 13. BSFC of homogeneous and stratified combustions at different engine speeds.

The main reason is that stratified combustion has lower fuel consumption where the fuel surrounding the spark plug is richer. This leads to ignition and initiation of combustion at this area that produces sufficient energy to propagate the flame and sustain the combustion smoothly through the leaner layers of air-fuel mixture, resulting in a more efficient combustion. This is consistent with the experiment by Baeta et al. on their torch ignition engine [17].

Lambda and Volumetric Efficiency

Figure 14 depicts the lambda and volumetric efficiency versus engine speed. The recorded lambda was more than one ($\lambda \geq 1$) accounting for a lean combustion which in turn decreases the fuel consumption. The lambda is more at the stratified combustion than the homogenous combustion. Consequently, for the stratified combustion, the volumetric efficiency is higher. From these results, there were two critical points at engine speeds, i.e. at 2000 and 3000 rpm as shown by the volumetric efficiency values in the graph.

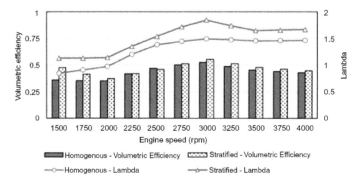

Figure 14. Lambda and volumetric efficiency of homogeneous and stratified combustions at different engine speeds.

Combustion Pressure

Based on the same experimental data, the in-cylinder pressure generated from the combustion process is plotted against engine displacement or piston swept volume. Figure 15 shows the cylinder pressure of the homogenous combustion versus cylinder volume and crank angle. The maximum recorded pressure was 186 bar at 4000 rpm just after the top dead centre.

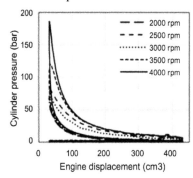
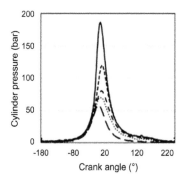

Figure 15. Cylinder pressure in homogenous combustion.

From the *p-v* diagram, the indicated work and heat release can be calculated. Other factors affecting the *p-v* cycles include the air-fuel ratio and ignition timing. At 2500 rpm, the BMEP and torque produced higher than that of 3000 rpm, which explains the double-peak phenomenon for the DOHC engine with fixed cam profiles. The work then increased at 3500 rpm and eventually at 4000 rpm. The combustion pressure influences the brake mean effective pressure as shown, which in turn affects the power and torque produced in Figure 11. All the peak pressure occurred just after TDC.

As comparison, Figure 16 shows the cylinder pressure of a stratified combustion versus engine displacement and crank angle. A high combustion pressure of 145 bar was observed at 4000 rpm at 7° after TDC. However, all the peak values of pressure are about 20% lower than the ones produced by the homogenous combustion.

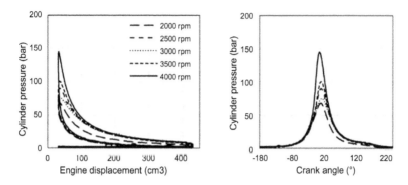

Figure 16. Cylinder pressure in stratified combustion.

Similarly, the indicated work at 3000 rpm is lower than at 2500 rpm and subsequently at 3500 and 4000 rpm. Consequently, the BMEP is more at 2500 rpm than at 3000 rpm with values of 9.69 and 9.08 bar, respectively, as shown in the figure. The most likely reasons that lead to this kind of pressure degree variation are the same with that for the homogenous combustion.

Emissions

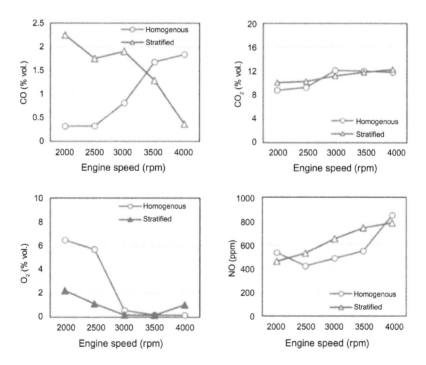

Figure 17. Emissions for homogeneous and stratified combustion at different engine speeds.

For the final sets of result, various emissions are plotted versus the engine speeds as shown in Figure 17. The results demonstrate a high CO at stratified combustion at a low engine speed, but CO decreases at high speed compared to homogenous combustion. Meanwhile, CO_2 is also lower for stratified combustion in high speed, whereas the value of CO_2 increases with the engine speed increase for both combustion modes.

Moreover, NO is recorded lower with stratified combustion mode only at 2000 and 4000 rpm, while slightly higher than homogeneous combustion at other speeds. However, the study of Baeta et al. [17], which employed the side injection strategy as opposed to the central injection strategy used in this work, reported reductions of NO_x, CO and CO_2 with stratified combustion in gasoline engine. This highlights the need for further studies, which are underway to look into the emission issue for the central injection strategy, particularly on NO.

CONCLUSIONS

A CNGDI engine that operates on monofuel, namely, natural gas, has been designed, developed and tested. Computational and experimental works have been performed to investigate the viability of the new design. Baseline computational and experimental works with homogenous combustion showed that the results were comparable. From computational work, detailed CNGDI homogeneous combustion characteristics were obtained via CFD simulation and studied. Combustion characteristics could be improved by using a stratified charge piston configuration. Experimental work on stratified piston configuration has shown that it improves the engine torque and power especially at low speeds as compared to the homogeneous piston. In terms of exhaust emissions, stratified CNGDI design causes slight increase in the emission of CO, CO_2 and NO_x. This highlights the need for further studies, which are underway to look into this emission issue.

REFERENCES

1. W.H. Kurniawan and S. Abdullah. Numerical analysis of the combustion process in a four-stroke compressed natural gas engine with direct injection system. Journal of Mechanical Science and Technology. 2008;22(10):1937-1944. DOI: 10.1007/s12206-008-0737-6

2. S. Abdullah, W.H. Kurniawan, M. Khamas and Y. Ali. Emissions analysis of a compressed natural gas direct injection engine with a homogenous mixture. International Journal of Automotive Technology. 2011;12(1):29-38. DOI: 10.1007/s12239-011-0004-1

3. K. Zeng, Z. Huang, B. Liu, L. Liu, D. Jiang, Y. Ren and J. Wang. Combustion characteristics of a direct-injection natural gas engine under various fuel injection timings. Applied Thermal Engineering. 2006;26(8-9):806-813. DOI: 10.1016/j.applthermaleng.2005.10.011

4. A.R.A. Aziz, Firmansyah and R. Shahzad. Combustion analysis of a CNG direct injection spark ignition engine. International Journal of Automotive and Mechanical Engineering. 2010;2(Jul-Dec):157-170. DOI: 10.15282/ijame.2.2010.5.0013

5. T. Yusaf, P. Baker, I. Hamawand and M.M. Noor. Effect of compressed natural gas mixing on the engine performance and emissions. International Journal of Automotive and Mechanical Engineering. 2013;8(Jul-Dec):1416-1429. DOI: 10.15282/ijame.8.2013.29.0117

6. F. Zhao, M.C. Lai and D.L. Harrington. Automotive spark-ignited direct-injection gasoline engines. Progress in Energy and Combustion Science. 1999;25(5):437-562. DOI: 10.1016/S0360-1285(99)00004-0

7. B. Yadollahi and M. Boroomand. The effect of combustion chamber geometry on injection and mixture preparation in a CNG direct injection SI engine. Fuel. 2013;107(May):52-62. DOI: 10.1016/j.fuel.2013.01.004

8. C.C. Lee, K.N. Chiang, W.K. Chen and R.S. Chen. Design and analysis of gasket sealing of cylinder head under engine operation conditions. Finite Element in Analysis and Design. 2005;41(11-12):1160-1174. DOI: 10.1016/j.finel.2004.12.007

9.   S.W. Chyuan. Finite element simulation of a twin-cam 16-valve cylinder structure. Finite Elements in Analysis and Design. 2000;35(3):199-212. DOI: 10.1016/S0168-874X(00)00002-0

10.   E. Danielson, D. Turner, J. Elwart and W. Bryzik. Thermomechanical stress analysis of novel low heat rejection cylinder head designs. SAE Technical Paper. 1993;03(01):930985. DOI: 10.4271/930985

11.   S. Abdullah, W.H. Kurniawan and A. Shamsudeen. Numerical analysis of the combustion process in a compressed natural gas direct injection engine. Journal of Applied Fluid Mechanics. 2008;1(2):65-86.

12.   S. Aljamali, S. Abdullah, W.M.F. Wan Mahmood and Y. Ali. The effect of injection timings on performance and emissions of compressed natural-gas direct injection engine. Journal of Combustion. 2016;2016:6501462 (7 pages). DOI: 10.1155/2016/6501462

13.   W.H. Kurniawan. Optimisation of Combustion Processes in Four Stroke Direct Injection Engine Using Compressed Natural Gas [thesis]. UKM Bangi: Universiti Kebangsaan Malaysia; 2007. 226 p.

14.   B. Sendyka and M. Cygnar. Stratified charge combustion in a spark-ignition engine with direct injection system. In: K.N. Hoon, editor. Advances in Internal Combustion Engines and Fuel Technologies. InTech; 2013. DOI: 10.5772/53971

15.   S. Aljamali, S. Abdullah, W.M.F. Wan Mahmood and Y. Ali. Effect of fuel injection timings on performance and emissions of stratified combustion CNGDI engine. Applied Thermal Engineering. 2016;109(2016):619-629. DOI: 10.1016/j.applthermaleng.2016.08.127

16.   M.A. Kalam and H.H. Masjuki. An experimental investigation of high performance natural gas engine with direct injection. Energy. 2011;36(5):3563-3571. DOI: 10.1016/j.energy.2011.03.066

17.   J.G.C. Baeta, F.A. Rodrigues Filho, M. Pontoppidan, R.M. Valle and T.R.V. da Silva. Exploring the performance limits of a stratified torch ignition engine using numerical simulation and detailed experimental approaches. Energy Conversion and Management. 2016;126:1093-1105. DOI: 10.1016/j.enconman.2016.08.073

4

Failure Analysis of a High-Pressure Natural Gas Heat Exchanger and its Modified Design

Lei-Yong Jiang, Yinghua Han, Michele Capurro and Mike Benner

Aerospace, National Research Council of Canada, Ottawa, Ontario, Canada

ABSTRACT

The beauty of numerical simulations is its ability to reveal the physics or nature of practical engineering problems in detail, and then, to identify adequate solutions. In this chapter, an excellent example is demonstrated. The rupture of a heavy-duty, high-pressure natural gas heat exchanger is numerically investigated, and the importance of gravity effect is identified, which is often considered as a trivial factor. For the original design, the natural convection in the flow field of the heat exchanger is comparable with the forced convection at the designed operating conditions. These two convections are perpendicular and compete with each other, the flow field is highly unsteady, and high-temperature natural gas is trapped in the upper portion of the vessel, which causes the damage of the exchanger. By vertically mounting the exchanger assembly and locating the outlet pipe on top of the exchanger, the flow parameters become rather uniform at each vertical cross section and the wall temperature of the heat exchanger remains more or less the same as the heated natural gas. The proposed design has been successfully used up to now.

Keywords*: Forced convection, Natural convection, Heat transfer, Heat exchanger, Turbulent diffusion*

INTRODUCTION

The beauty of numerical simulations is its ability to reveal the detailed phenomena or nature of complicated practical engineering problems, which are difficult and sometimes impossible from experimental studies. Based on the obtained numerical results, adequate solutions can easily be identified.

This chapter gives an excellent example for this type of approaches. To identify the reasons for the rupture of a heavy-duty, high-pressure natural gas heat exchanger, as shown in Figure 1, the flow field of the heat exchanger was numerically examined. Based on the findings, a new configuration was suggested and the corresponding flow field was studied.

The installed modified heat exchanger has been trouble-free used to date. In the following sections, the computational domain, mesh, numerical methods, flow features of the two designs, and the cause of the heat exchanger damage are presented and discussed.

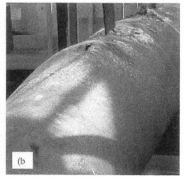

Figure 1. The natural gas heat exchanger: (a) the damaged heat exchanger; and (b) a close view of the cracks on the top surface of the vessel.

NUMERICAL SIMULATIONS

Computational Domain and Mesh of the Original Design

The natural gas heat exchanger has a nominal power of 390 KW, and the effective length of its heavy-duty vessel is 3785 mm with an outside diameter of 457.2 mm. As a sketch shown in Figure 2, it accommodates 138 (276 rods) heating elements. The diameter of these elements is 10.9 mm, and the length is 3277 mm for 64 long elements and 3252 mm for 74 short elements. Five keepers are inserted inside the vessel to maintain the proper radial positions of these elements. The nominal diameter of the inlet and exit pipes is 80 mm. The computational domain covers the whole flow field of the heater from the inlet to the exit, including heat elements and five keepers. It is important to mention that the whole natural gas heat exchanger assembly was mounted horizontally.

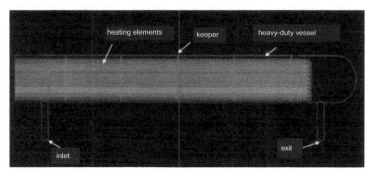

Figure 2. The computational domain of the original design.

The mesh for one section of the heat exchanger vessel is shown in Figure 3(a), and the mesh at a cross section cutting through heating elements is illustrated in Figure 3(b). In these two plots, the meshed areas are where the natural gas flows, and the unmeshed hollow regions or circles are where the heating elements are located. Figure 3(c) is the mesh cutting through one keeper. As shown in Figure 3(c), there are hundreds of small holes (11.5 mm in diameter) on the perforated plate of the keeper, 276 holes are considered blocked by the heating elements, and the rest meshed are flow passages. A narrow annular flow channel surrounding the keeper is used to keep the heating elements away from the vessel inner surfaces. Adjacent to the annular flow channel, parts of full circles are cut out by a flat bar of the keeper. The mesh size is ~4.0 million in the number of cells.

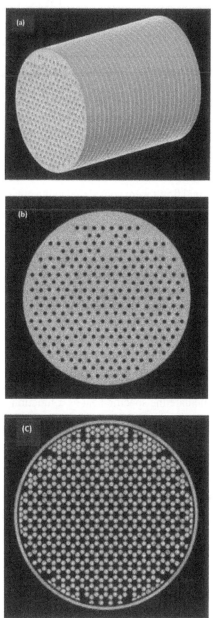

Figure 3. Meshes: (a) mesh for one section of the heat exchanger; (b) mesh at the section across heating elements; and (c) mesh across one heating-element keeper.

Boundary Conditions

The inlet boundary conditions for the numerical simulations are listed in Table 1.

Table 1. The inlet boundary conditions

Mass flow rate	0.237 kg/s
Temperature	295.3 K
Absolute pressure	30.4 bar

The heavy-duty vessel was wrapped with insulation material, and so it was reasonable to assume adiabatic boundary condition for its external wall boundaries. A heat flux of 4.48 KW/m^2 was specified at the heating-element surfaces starting from the middle cross section of the inlet pipe to the end of the heater elements. An increase in natural gas temperature by ~200 K, from the room temperature, was expected. In the investigation, the natural gas was considered as pure methane.

Numerical Methods

Steady, turbulent, thermal flows were considered in the present work, and a commercial software package, Fluent, was used for all simulations. The governing Favre-averaged conservation equations of mass, momentum, and enthalpy are not reproduced here, but can be readily found in [1, 2].

For closure of these partial differential equations, the realizable k-ε turbulence model was applied to model turbulent momentum transfer. A benchmark study on turbulence models indicated that this model was superior to other four popular two-equation models and could provide similar results as those from the Reynolds stress model, a second-momentum closure [3]. The Reynolds analogy [4] was used to account for turbulent enthalpy transfer, and for this type of pipe flows, the turbulence Prandtl number of 0.7 was used [5, 6]. The gravity of 9.8 m/s^2 was assigned in the direction consistent with the heat exchanger mounting orientation.

For the thermal properties of methane, polynomials derived from the NIST JANAF tables [7] were used to calculate the specific heat as a function of temperature. Data from NIST [8] were used to obtain polynomials to determine the molecular viscosity and thermal conductivity of methane as functions of temperature.

A segregated solver with a second-order accuracy scheme was chosen to resolve the flow fields. At convergence, the imbalance of mass flow rate between the inlet and exit was less than 0.34% for the original design and 0.007% for the modified configuration, while for the energy imbalance it was 0.38% for the former and 0.007% for the later. Due to the unsteady nature of the thermal flow field of the original design, the convergence could not reach the level for the modified case. Sixteen cores of a 64-bit LINUX cluster with 4 GB RAM for each core were used to perform all simulations.

RESULTS AND DISCUSSION

Results of the Original Design

Figure 4 shows the temperature contours along the longitudinal symmetric plane of the heat exchanger. Significantly, variation of temperature inside the heater is observed. High-temperature region exists in the upper portion of the vessel, while the low-temperature regions occur in the lower portion. The temperature profiles along the top and bottom walls are displayed in Figure 5. It is obvious that the top wall temperature reaching ~1700 K is considerably higher than the allowed service temperature of steel pipes, SA-106 GR.B [9]. Certainly, the heavy-duty vessel could not survive at such high-temperature and high-pressure operating conditions. Another important feature in Figure 4 is the unsteady nature of the thermal flow field. Large eddies or fluid pockets randomly occur in the regions along and above the central axis of the vessel.

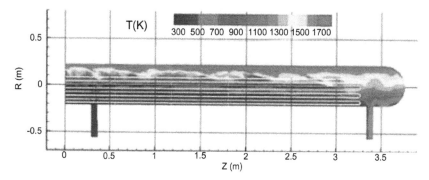

Figure 4. Temperature contours at the longitudinal symmetric plane.

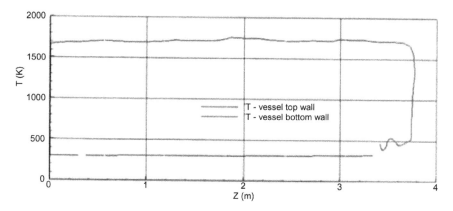

Figure 5. Temperature profiles along the vessel top and bottom walls.

Why is the vessel wall temperature so high when the natural gas is set to be heated by only ~200 K? And why is the thermal flow field so unsteady in nature? These questions can be answered by analyzing the flow features or characteristics inside the heat exchanger vessel.

The first or primary cause for the heat exchanger damage is that the forced convection in the flow field is weak, the natural convection is strong and comparable with the former, and these two actions are perpendicular and compete with each other. Figure 6 is the velocity magnitude contour plot across the symmetric plane. As observed, the velocity inside the heater vessel is low, the mean velocity magnitude over the whole domain is only 0.174 m/s, and the mean Reynolds number is ~2800. This means that the forced convection mainly in the longitudinal direction is weak. The absolute pressure distribution in the vessel is shown in Figure 7, and it varies a little around 3.04×10^6 Pa.

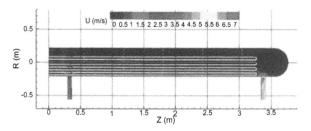

Figure 6. Velocity contours at the longitudinal symmetric plane.

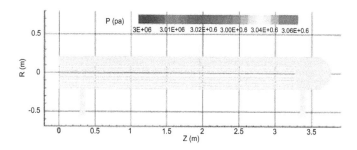

Figure 7. Absolute pressure contours at the longitudinal symmetric plane.

The methane density contours at the symmetric plane are shown in Figure 8. The density changes dramatically inside the heat exchanger vessel. High-density regions appear in the inlet pipe and lower portion of the vessel, and the maximum value reaches 20 kg/m³, while the low-density regions happen in the upper portion of the vessel with a minimum of 3.0 kg/m³. Due to the gravity, large differences in density induce strong natural convection inside the vessel.

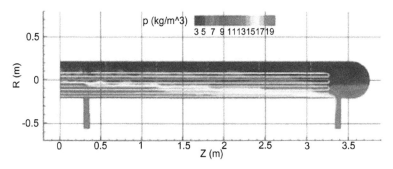

Figure 8. Density contours at the longitudinal symmetric plane.

As shown in Figure 4, the unsteady flow feature, randomly distributed flow pockets, is also observed in Figure 8. Velocity vectors at the portion of the symmetric plane are illustrated in Figure 9, where the vessel and keeper walls are indicated by blue lines, the length of vectors represents the magnitude of local velocities, and for comparison a reference vector of 0.2 m/s is provided. As shown in Figure 9, large counterclockwise recirculation regions are formed in the upper half of the vessel, which are induced by the relatively high horizontal velocities in the lower half of the vessel. The vertical velocity component corresponding to the natural convection is comparable with the horizontal component related to the forced convection. As a result of the competition between the two convections, the flow field inside the vessel becomes unstable in nature. The gas temperature at one point in the high-temperature region can vary by ±80 K.

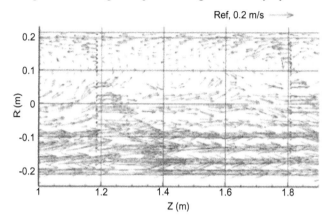

Figure 9. Velocity vectors at part of the longitudinal symmetric plane.

These observations are consistent with a first-order analytical assessment in Ref. [10]. As stated in the book, when the ratio of $R = Gr/(Re)^2 \approx 1$, the combined forced and natural convections must be considered in heat transfer analysis. Here, Gr is the Grashof number and Re stands for Reynolds number. Based on the averaged values of flow parameters, this ratio equals to 0.6 for this case.

Figures 10–13 provide detailed distributions of temperature and velocity magnitude at the inlet, outlet, and four middle cross sections, and at the five keeper cross sections, respectively. These plots further confirm the above observed flow features. The high-temperature region occupies about one-third of the cross-sectional areas, and the low-temperature region gradually decreases from half of the area at the inlet section, to about one-third of the area at the last keeper section, and eventually a fraction at the outlet section (Figures 10 and 12). As observed in Figures 11 and 13, the velocity magnitude in the lower halves at these cross sections is higher than that in the upper halves.

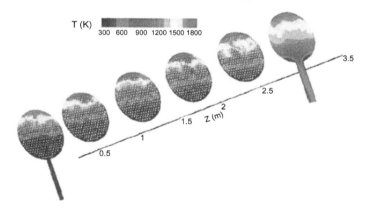

Figure 10. Temperature contours at the inlet, outlet, and four middle cross sections.

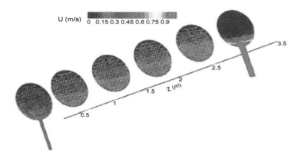

Figure 11. Velocity magnitude contours at the inlet, outlet, and four middle cross sections.

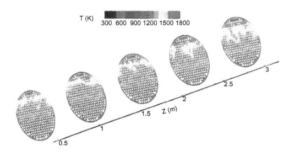

Figure 12. Temperature contours at the five keeper cross sections.

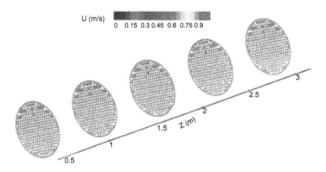

Figure 13. Velocity magnitude contours at the five keeper cross sections.

The second reason for the heat exchanger damage is that the flow exit is located at the lowest position of the whole flow domain (Figure 2). Consequently, the high-temperature or low-density fluid is trapped in the upper portion of the vessel, does not flow out of the vessel, and keeps recirculating, as shown in Figures 9 and 14.

Notice that the fluid in the upper high-temperature regions is continuously heated by the heating elements that are more or less uniformly distributed over the vessel cross sections. The only way, for the fluid in these swirling regions to release some of the heat, is through diffusion (molecular and week turbulent), which is significantly less effective than convection. When the flow reaches quasi-steady, the gas temperature can be as high as ~1700 K (Figure 4). This is why although the mean methane temperature at the exchanger exit is increased by only ~200 K, the temperature at the top wall of the vessel can reach ~1700 K.

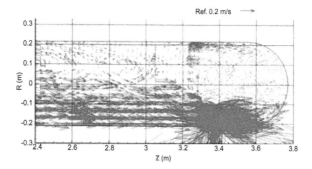

Figure 14. Velocity vectors at the downstream part of the longitudinal symmetric plane.

The above results and discussion suggest that to avoid the competition between the forced and natural convections in a perpendicular manner, the heat exchanger assembly should be mounted vertically, and to avoid fluid trapping, the flow exit pipe should be located on top of the vessel. With these arrangements, it is expected that the gravity effect or natural convection effect would be more or less uniform at each horizontal cross section, and no local high-temperature region would occur inside the heat exchanger.

Results of the Modified Natural Gas Heat Exchanger

The modified heat exchanger configuration is shown in Figure 15, where the whole assembly is mounted vertically and the outlet pipe is moved to the vessel top, and other parts remain the same as the original design. Similar mesh was generated for the new design, and the boundary conditions and numerical methods were unchanged.

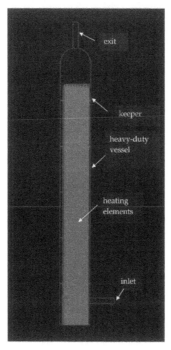

Figure 15. Modified heat exchanger configuration.

The temperature contours along the longitudinal symmetric plane are shown in Figure 16. The flow temperature gradually increases from 295 K at the inlet to 495 K at the exit with an increase of 200 K. The maximum temperature is 564 K at the top surfaces of the heating elements (also see Figure 21 later), and the temperature difference between the element walls and surrounding fluid is the driving force for heat transfer from the heat elements to the fluid. The temperature profiles at the right- and left-side walls are displayed in Figure 17. The wall temperature gradually increases along the vertical direction from 295 K to 495 K, and the maximum wall temperature is equal to the exit gas temperature.

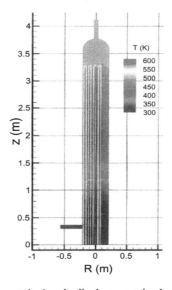

Figure 16. Temperature contours at the longitudinal symmetric plane.

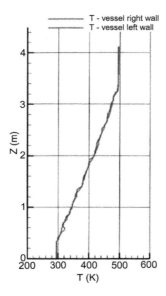

Figure 17. Temperature profiles along the vessel right and left walls.

Similar to the original design, the velocity magnitude shown in Figure 18 is low inside the vessel, and its averaged value is 0.18 m/s with a maximum of 5.3 m/s at the center of the exit. The absolute pressure distribution inside the vessel also varies a little around 3.04×10^6 Pa, as indicated in Figure 19. Figure 20 presents the density contours at the symmetric plane. It gradually decreases from 20 kg/m³ at the inlet to 11.8 kg/m³ at the exit and is more or less uniform at vertical cross sections.

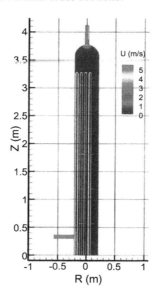

Figure 18. Velocity magnitude contours at the longitudinal symmetric plane.

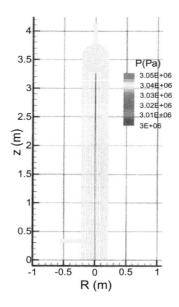

Figure 19. Absolute pressure contours at the longitudinal symmetric plane.

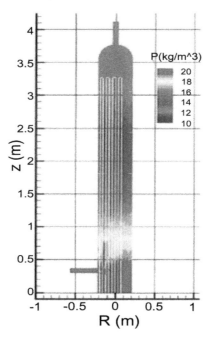

Figure 20. Density contours at the longitudinal symmetric plane.

Detailed distributions of temperature and velocity magnitude at the inlet, five middle and exit cross sections are provided in Figures 21 and 22. The same parameter plots across the five keepers are given in Figures 23 and 24. These figures clearly indicate that the flow parameters are rather uniform at each cross section, particularly at the five keeper cross sections. The temperature gradually increases from the upstream to downstream sections, as illustrated in Figures 21 and 23, and the maximum temperature is about 560 K. As shown in Figure 22, the flow velocity gradually increases from the inlet to the exit, except for small local regions at the inlet and first middle sections.

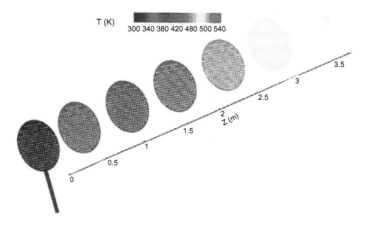

Figure 21. Temperature contours at the inlet, outlet, and five middle cross sections.

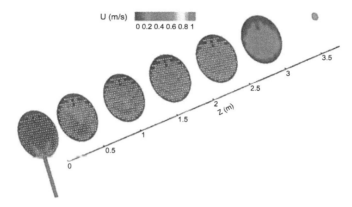

Figure 22. Velocity magnitude contours at the inlet, outlet, and five middle cross sections.

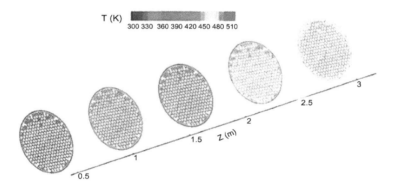

Figure 23. Temperature contours at the five keeper cross sections.

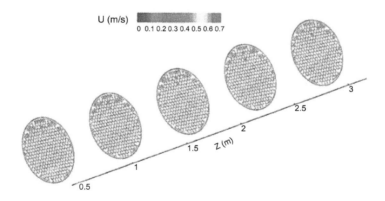

Figure 24. Velocity magnitude contours at the five keeper cross sections.

In summary, the flow features of the modified design are remarkably different from those for the original design, except that the velocity magnitude is low and the absolute pressure is about 3.4×10^6 Pa for both cases. For the modified design, both the natural and forced convections are aligned in the vertical direction; therefore, the flow parameters are more or less uniform at each vertical cross section and the flow field is stable without randomly located large recirculation regions. Moreover, the gas flows out of the exit at the required temperature and the vessel wall temperature remains the same as the surrounding gas. This proposed design has been successfully used to date.

CONCLUSIONS

To investigate the damage of a natural gas heat exchanger, the numerical simulations of the flow fields of the original and modified designs are performed. It is found that there are two reasons for the damage. First, at the required operating conditions, the forced convection is weak, and the natural convection is strong and comparable with the forced convection. These two actions are perpendicular and compete to each other. As a result, strong unsteadiness in the flow field is induced. Second, the whole assembly is mounted horizontally and the flow exit pipe is located at the lowest position. Consequently, the high-temperature or low-density fluid is trapped in the upper portion of the vessel. The trapped fluid is continuously heated by the heating elements located in the upper region of the vessel and eventually exceeds the allowed service temperature of the steel pipe.

The numerical results and analysis suggest that the heat exchanger assembly should be mounted vertically and the exhaust pipe should be located at the top of the exchanger. With these modifications, the flow parameters become more or less uniform at each vertical cross section, the flow field becomes stable, the methane temperature at the exit reaches the designed value, and the vessel wall temperature remains the same as the surrounding gas. This new design has been trouble-free used up to now.

REFERENCES

1. Poinsot T, Veynante D. Theoretical and Numerical Combustion. Philadelphia, PA: R. T. Edwards Inc.; 2005

2. ANSYS Inc., Fluent 18.0 Documentation. Lebanon, NH, USA; 2016

3. Jiang LY. A critical evaluation of turbulence modelling in a model combustor. ASME Journal of Thermal Science and Engineering Applications. 2013;5(3):031002

4. Jiang LY, Campbell I. Reynolds analogy in combustor Modelling. International Journal of Heat and Mass Transfer. 2008;51(5-6):1251-1263

5. Hinze JO. Turbulence. New York: The McGraw-Hill Book Company Inc.; 1987. p. 372-753

6. White FM. Heat and Mass Transfer. New York: Addison-Wesley Publishing Company; 1988. p. 320-641

7. Chase MW. National Institute of Standards and Technology (U.S.), NIST-JANAF Thermochemical Tables, 4th edition, Washington, DC, 1998

8. Lemmon EW, McLinden MO, Huber ML. REFPROP, Reference Fluid Thermodynamic and Transport Properties, NIST Standard Reference Database 23, Version 7.0, 2002

9. OneSteel Piping Systems. 2012. Available from: http://www.onesteelbuildingservices.com/pdffiles/OneSteel_%20Pipe_Catalogue_web.pdf

10. Incropera FP, DeWitt DP. Fundamentals of Heat and Mass Transfer. USA: John Wiley & Sons Inc.; 2002

5

Concepts for Regasification of LNG in Industrial Parks

Tatiana Morosuk, Stefanie Tesch and George Tsatsaronis

Exergy-Based Methods for Refrigeration Systems, Institute for Energy Engineering, Technische Universität Berlin, Germany

ABSTRACT

The exponentially growing markets of liquefied natural gas (LNG) require efficient processes for LNG regasification within import terminals. Usually, the regasification of LNG is accomplished by direct or indirect heating. However, integrating LNG regasification into different processes within industrial parks (mainly processes involving low temperatures) is an efficient approach because of the utilization of the low-temperature energy. In some LNG import terminals, integration technologies are already being used. Previous publications showed an increase in the thermodynamic efficiency for systems combining air separation (as an example) and LNG regasification. In addition, the variation in the efficiency as well as the capital investment depends on the schematic and operation conditions. This fact creates great potential for improving the systems. In this chapter, different schematics are evaluated using exergy-based methods in order to improve the effectiveness of complex industrial processes that can involve LNG regasification.

Keywords: LNG, Regasification, Refrigeration process, Cryogenic process, Exergy-based methods

INTRODUCTION

Natural gas became a very important primary energy carrier in the last decades. The world fuel share of natural gas increased from 16% (in the year 1973) to 21% at present. Approximately 50% of the natural gas is supplied as liquefied natural gas (LNG) (Figure 1). In the year 2015, 19 countries exported LNG, with Qatar, Australia, Malaysia, and Nigeria being the main exporting countries. The number of importing countries increased to 34 in the year 2015 [1–4].

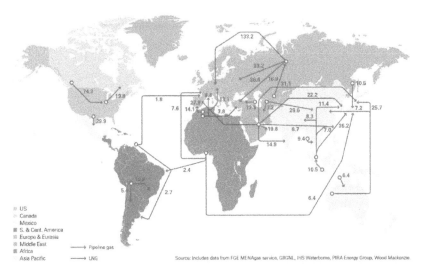

Figure 1. Major trade movements 2015 (in billion cubic meters) [3].

The total chain of LNG consists of the following four steps: exploration and pretreatment, liquefaction and storage, transportation by ship as well as regasification, storage, and distribution.

Figure 2 shows the options of different technologies for the regasification of LNG. Thermal energy coming from the combustion of natural gas, seawater or cooling water, air, and process integration technologies can be used for the regasification of LNG.

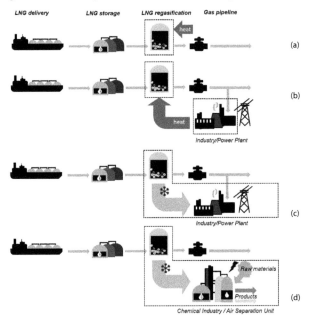

Figure 2. Options for the regasification of LNG: (a) direct or indirect heat transfer process, for example, ORV, STV, and SCV; (b) heat utilization of an industrial process; (c) LNG-based cogeneration for electricity generation; and (d) LNG-based cogeneration for chemical products.

A heat transfer process (direct or indirect) between LNG and other working fluid(s) is the basic principle used for the regasification of LNG (Figure 2a) in almost all import terminals overall the world. At present, five regasification technologies are used [5]: open rack vaporizers (ORV), shell-and-tube vaporizers (STV), submerged combustion vaporizers (SCV), and combined heat and power units with submerged combustion units (CHP-SCV). Other types of vaporizers, the so-called atmospheric evaporators, are used only for the regasification of very small amounts of LNG and operate periodically. Heat from industrial processes can also be used for the regasification of LNG (Figure 2b), and this, however, will not affect the improvement of the industrial process, because the block "regasification of LNG" and block "Industry/Power Plant" have separate system boundaries. Techno-economic evaluation of these options is discussed in Refs. [6, 7]. Within these technologies (Figure 2a and b), the low-temperature exergy of the LNG is destroyed without any use.

However, low-temperature exergy of the LNG is a valuable "fuel" for many industrial processes such as chemical, power generation, and so on. Therefore, researchers are working on the development of different options for using the low-temperature exergy of LNG (Figure 2c and d). These options can be classified as "industrial parks" because the vaporization of LNG becomes an integral part of complex processes generating electricity or chemical products (common boundary conditions). There are two options for the realization of the concepts (Figure 2c and d):

- The regasification of LNG could be integrated into a system for the generation of electricity. One of the first publications, where this idea has been described, was Ref. [8]. An extended review of such technologies as well as novel concepts was reported, for example, in Refs. [9, 10].
- The low-temperature exergy of LNG could be used within: (a) desalination processes as reported in Refs. [11, 12] and (b) agro-industrial processes for freezing purposes as discussed in Refs. [13–15].

The implementation of the regasification of LNG into chemical industries (Figure 2d) is well known from the industrial project developed by Osaka Gas in Japan [16]. Here, the LNG import terminal is integrated within an industrial complex with refinery and petrochemical plants. LNG is regasified in four steps, which is related to the temperature levels of the refinery and the petrochemical plant. These steps are as follows: (a) separation of light hydrocarbons produced as a by-product in the oil refining process (the temperature level is around $-100°C$; an energy source to separate olefin used as a raw material of polymer products at the petrochemical plant), (b) liquefaction of carbon dioxide, a by-product in the production of hydrogen (the temperature level is around $-55°C$), (c) low-temperature storage of butane ($-8°C$), and (d) cooling of water used to cool the intake air for gas turbines ($10°C$).

Since this chapter focuses on the regasification of LNG in conjunction with air separation processes (concept of industrial parks shown in Figure 2d), the state-of-art of such a technology will be given.

A concept for the regasification of LNG integrated into an air separation unit was reported in Ref. [17]. A recycle nitrogen stream is used to evaporate the LNG stream. This integration leads to a decrease in the total specific power consumption from 1.3 kWh/m^3 (related to the sum of oxygen and nitrogen steams) to 0.8 kWh/m^3. In addition to that the installation costs are reduced by 10%.

In Ref. [18] was proposed a high-performance energy-supply system with cryogenic air separation using the cold of LNG and a power generation system with gas and steam turbines, where the required electrical power is reduced from 1.2 kWh/m³ (per oxygen steam) to 0.57 kWh/m³. In this paper, two different options of a double-column distillation process are discussed.

The integration of the regasification of LNG into a one-column air separation system was proposed and evaluated in Ref. [19]. The reported power consumption is decreased by 39%. Another configuration of a one-column air separation system with an oxy-fuel power generation cycle and regasification of LNG was evaluated in Ref. [20]. The achieved reduction in the power consumption is 38.5%. Later, a novel system has been developed [21], where the cold of LNG is used to precool the air. The power consumption is decreased in this case by 56%.

There are also several patents related to the integration of LNG into an air separation unit, e.g., Refs. [22–26]. The data related to energy consumption or/and efficiency are not mentioned.

The authors developed several concepts for the integration of LNG regasification into air separation systems. Conventional and advanced exergy analyses as well as economic analyses have been applied to evaluate the performance of these industrial parks. Detailed information can be found in Refs. [27, 28].

PROCESS DESCRIPTION

Before the authors' concepts for integrating LNG regasification into air separation systems are discussed, a conventional air separation process is evaluated. In this chapter, only generalized information based on Refs. [27, 28] have been reported.

Case A—air Separation Unit

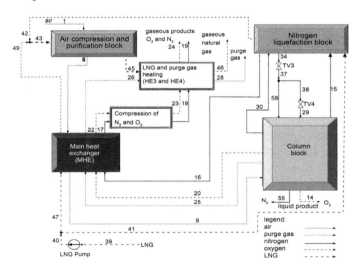

Figure 3. Conceptual schematic of Case A (air separation unit).

Main products of an air separation unit are oxygen and nitrogen, which could be in liquid and in gaseous form. In some air separations plants, noble gases (argon, for example) are gained. The typical air separation unit is composed of three to four blocks:

- Air compression and purification block
- Air liquefaction block (main heat exchanger (MHE))

- Column block (CB)
- Nitrogen liquefaction block (NLB) (is not mandatory).

The nitrogen liquefaction block is necessary in order to produce higher amounts of liquid products and to achieve a higher purity of the products. This block consists of a large number of components. It affects the thermodynamic efficiency and the investment costs. The conceptual design of the single air separation unit (Case A) is shown in Figure 3.

Air Compression and Purification Block

The air compression block consists of two air compressors with interstage cooler. The dustless air is compressed to 5.6 bar [29]. Within the purification block, impurities which will freeze at low temperatures are removed using adsorption technology. The considered impurities in the compressed air stream are water vapor and carbon dioxide. The concentration must be lower than 0.1 ppm for water vapor and 1.0 ppm for carbon dioxide [30].

Main Heat Exchanger

The compressed air leaving the air compression and purification block is cooled to -173 °C within the MHE. The air leaves the MHE partially in liquid form. The streams leaving the column block are used to cool down the air. The MHE is a multi-stream (four cold and one hot stream) counterflow heat exchanger and is together with the column block embedded in a so-called cold box in order to decrease the heat sink from the environment.

Column Block

After the MHE, the cold air is fed to the column block. The column block consists of two separate columns, which are thermally coupled by the condenser/reboiler. The lower column is the high-pressure column (HPC), with a pressure of 5.6 bar, and the upper column is the low-pressure column (LPC) with a pressure of 1.3 bar. Both columns are simulated as sieve tray columns. Several side streams leaving the HPC are fed to the LPC. The top-products of the HPC are gaseous and liquid nitrogen streams. The liquid nitrogen stream is removed from the system as a product stream, and the gaseous stream is fed to the MHE. The top product of the LPC is also gaseous nitrogen, which is fed to the MHE. At the bottom, liquid and gaseous oxygen are gained. While the liquid stream is also removed from the system, the gaseous stream is fed to the MHE. In addition, a side stream from the LPC is fed to the MHE which contains mainly nitrogen and is called purge gas stream.

Nitrogen Liquefaction Block

The NLB consists of four compressors, two expanders, two heat exchangers, and several mixing and splitting devices [27]. One of the two gaseous nitrogen streams (stream 31) within the MHE is fed to the nitrogen liquefaction block. Here, stream 31 is mixed with streams 44 and 47, which are already in the nitrogen liquefaction block. The resulting stream (stream 32) is then heated in HE1 and compressed within a three-stage compression process with interstage cooling to 38 bar. The stream is split into streams 45 and 39. Stream 39 is fed to NC4, compressed to 46 bar, and fed together with stream 45 to HE1, where both streams are cooled. The stream with a pressure of 38 bar (stream 46) is afterwards fed to EXP1 and mixed with the incoming stream. The second stream leaving the HE1 is again split into two streams: stream 42 and stream 21. Stream 42 is fed to EXP2, and after this, it is used in the HE2 to cool stream 21. This stream leaves the nitrogen liquefaction block (stream 48) and is split into two parts (streams 58 and 59), which are fed to both columns as a reflux.

Product Compression

The nitrogen and oxygen streams leaving the MHE are fed to the NC5 and OC and are compressed to 20 bar, but this pressure depends on the consumer. After compression, the nitrogen stream is used to heat the purge gas stream, which also leaves the MHE. The required temperature for the purge gas is 170°C [31], because the purge gas stream is used to desorb the impurities in the purification block.

Case A Design 1

Case A Design 1 (Case AD 1) (Figure 4 [27]) is the concept of the industrial park where the LNG stream is regasified within the MHE after having been pressurized in an LNG pump.

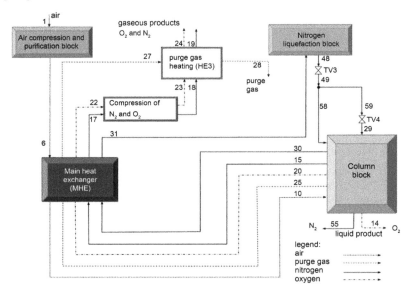

Figure 4. Conceptual schematic of Case AD1.

The air compression and purification block is identical with the same block in Case A.

Main Heat Exchanger

In comparison to Case A, the main heat exchanger is adjusted by the LNG stream. It also includes four cold streams, which are now oxygen, purge gas, nitrogen, and LNG (the second nitrogen stream is not used within the MHE anymore). The hot stream is air, which is cooled to −173 °C.

Column B lock

The column block is almost identical to the column block in Case A. The only difference is that the top product (nitrogen stream, stream 30) is directly fed to the nitrogen liquefaction block, instead of passing by the MHE.

Nitrogen Liquefaction Block

The implementation of LNG within MHE has affected the nitrogen liquefaction block. Here, the nitrogen liquefaction block consists of three compressors, one expander, as well as one mixing and one splitting device. The top product of the HPC (stream 30) is fed to the NLB, heated in the HE2, and afterwards mixed with stream 44, which is also heated in the HE2 (stream 42). They form stream 32, which is heated in the HE1 and is then compressed in a three-stage compression process. Between the first and the second stages, the stream is cooled in HE3, which is located in the product compression block. After the compression process, the stream is cooled in HE1 and split into streams 42 and 41. Stream 42 is fed to EXP2, heated within HE2, and mixed with the incoming stream 30, whereas stream 41 is cooled within the HE2 and fed to the column block as a reflux.

Product Compression

Also in this system, the product streams are compressed to 20 bar. One more heat exchanger is required here in comparison with Case A. Here, the nitrogen stream from the NLB is used to heat the purge gas stream to the required temperature (HE3). This nitrogen stream and the nitrogen stream leaving the NC5 are fed to the HE4 in order to heat the LNG stream to ambient temperature.

Case A Design 2

Case A Design 2 (Case AD2) (Figure 5 [27]) is the concept where LNG being pressurized in an LNG pump is further regasified within MHE, the air compression and purification block, and the nitrogen liquefaction block. The concept is shown in Figure 5.

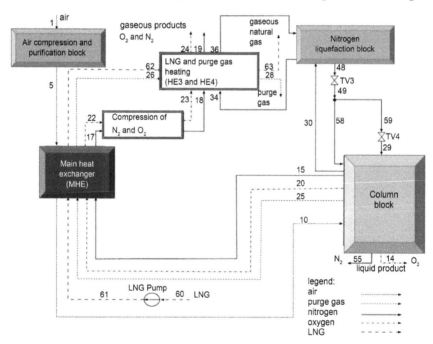

Figure 5. Conceptual schematic of Case AD2.

Air Compression and Purification Block

The structure of the air compression and purification block differs from the structure of the two systems discussed above. In Case AD2, air is compressed within a three-stage compression processes to 5.6 bar, which requires an additional interstage cooler. The cooling medium in the interstage coolers is the LNG stream. Thus, after the water has been removed from the air, the air could be cooled to a lower temperature while heating the LNG stream. This leads to a decrease in the power consumption in the following air compressors. Consequently, the air enters the MHE with a slightly lower temperature compared to Cases A and AD1.

Main Heat Exchanger

The main heat exchanger has the same structure as in Case AD1. The cold streams are gaseous oxygen, nitrogen, purge gas, and the LNG, whereas the hot stream is air. Hence, in Case AD2, the LNG stream is divided into two parts: one is fed to the MHE, and the second one to the nitrogen liquefaction block.

Column Block

The column block is identical to the Case AD1. In addition, here the top-product of the LPC is directly fed to the nitrogen liquefaction block.

Nitrogen Liquefaction Block

The structure of the nitrogen liquefaction is different from the Cases A and AD1. It now consists of only one heat exchanger and two compressors. The top product of the HPC (stream 30) and one part of the total LNG stream are heated in the HE2. The nitrogen stream is compressed within a two-stage compression process. Afterwards, it is cooled in the HE2 and fed to both columns as a reflux.

Product Compression

The gaseous oxygen and nitrogen streams leaving the MHE are also compressed to 20 bar. The nitrogen stream is then used to heat the purge gas. Finally, the LNG stream is heated to ambient temperature within HE4 using the compressed nitrogen and oxygen streams and the heated pure gas stream.

METHODOLOGY

The exergy-based methods are meaningful tools to analyze, understand, and improve energy conversion systems [32]. These methods consist of several analyses [33, 34]:

- Conventional exergy analysis
- Exergoeconomic analysis
- Exergoenvironmental analysis
- Advanced exergy analysis
- Advanced exergoeconomic analysis
- Advanced exergoenvironmental analysis.

In this chapter, the conventional and advanced exergetic analyses are applied for evaluation of the three proposed cases. Additionally, the results from an economic analysis are reported.

Conventional Exergetic Analysis

A conventional exergetic analysis identifies the sources of the thermodynamic inefficiencies within components and the overall system. The approaches "exergy of fuel" and "exergy of product" are applied [32]. The exergy destruction within each component

(Eq. (1), the subscript k refers to the component being evaluated) and within the overall system (Eq. (2), subscript *tot*) is calculated from

$$\dot{E}_{F,k} = \dot{E}_{P,k} + \dot{E}_{D,k} \tag{1}$$

$$\dot{E}_{F,tot} = \dot{E}_{P,tot} + \dot{E}_{D,tot} + \dot{E}_{L,tot} \tag{2}$$

The exergetic efficiencies of component k (Eq. (3a)) and the overall system (Eq. (3b)) are defined as

$$\varepsilon_k = \frac{\dot{E}_{P,k}}{\dot{E}_{F,k}} \tag{3a}$$

$$\varepsilon_{tot} = \frac{\dot{E}_{P,tot}}{\dot{E}_{F,tot}} \tag{3b}$$

Advanced Exergetic Analysis

The advanced exergetic analysis is an extension of the conventional exergy analysis and helps to identify the interrelations among the exergy destructions within the components and the real potential for improving the energy conversion system (the methodology could be found in Refs. [33, 34]. In the advanced exergetic analysis, the exergy destruction could be spilt into avoidable and unavoidable or/and endogenous and exogenous parts. Furthermore, these parts could be combined to determine the
- unavoidable endogenous exergy destruction,
- unavoidable exogenous exergy destruction,
- avoidable endogenous exergy destruction, and
- avoidable exogenous exergy destruction.

The unavoidable exergy destruction represents the part which could not be reduced due to technological limitations associated with the component being considered. Thus, the avoidable exergy destruction is the part which could be reduced by thermodynamically improving the component. The endogenous exergy destruction represents the part which is caused by the irreversibilities within the component itself, while the exogenous exergy destruction is the part which occurs within this component due to the exergy destructions within the remaining components of the overall system.

In this chapter, the exergy destruction is split into unavoidable and avoidable parts. More information about other options to split the exergy destruction has already been reported in Ref. [27].

Splitting the exergy destruction into the unavoidable and avoidable parts requires identifying the technological limitations of the different types of components. The following assumptions are used: minimum temperature difference of 0.5 K for all heat exchangers; maximum isentropic efficiency of 80% for the LNG pump, and maximum isentropic efficiency of 90% for the compressors and expanders. The splitting of the exergy destruction was not applied to the column block, throttling valves, splitting devices, and dissipative components.

Economic Analysis

The economic analysis estimates the cost of components as well as the fixed and total capital investment. In this chapter, the economic analysis is conducted based on Ref. [32]. Additional details are given in Ref. [28].

Purchased Equipment Costs

The cost of all components (purchased equipment costs (PEC)) is estimated using cost data available in the literature and are adjusted according to the operation conditions using temperature, pressure, and material factors. The factors are obtained from Ref [38], whereby the temperature factor has to be adjusted for temperatures below 0°C. All components which work at temperatures higher than −29°C are made of carbon steel [35]. For lower temperatures, materials like stainless steel, aluminum, cooper, or monel could also be used.

Cost of the Heat Exchangers

For the heat exchangers, two different kinds of heat exchangers are assumed: shell-and-tube and plate heat exchangers.

The interstage coolers in the air compression and purification block and in the nitrogen liquefaction block are shell-and-tube heat exchangers. The remaining heat exchangers (HE1, HE2, HE3, HE4, and MHE) are plate heat exchangers. To estimate the costs, the heat duty and the temperature differences are obtained from AspenPlus [36]. The overall heat transfer coefficients are selected according to the available data. The costs are estimated based on data from Ref. [37].

Cost of the Turbomachinery

This set of components includes the compressor, expanders, and the LNG pump. The compressors are centrifugal compressors and the expanders are axial expanders. For all turbomachinery, the required or generated power is the determined factor for the cost estimation. The costs are taken from Refs. [37–39], for the compressors, expanders, and the pump, respectively.

In general, the cost of compressors includes the cost for the electrical motor. However, in Case A, there is one exception. The cost of NC3 and NC4 is estimated without motor, because they are connected to EXP1 and EXP2, respectively.

Cost of the Column Block

The estimation of the costs of the column block is divided into two parts: empty shell and trays [29]. The low-pressure and high-pressure columns are simulated as sieve tray columns with 96 and 54 stages, respectively. To estimate the costs of the two empty shells, the diameter and the height must be known. According to Ref. [40], the diameter must be lower than 4–5 m, because, otherwise, it will be difficult and costly to construct a sieve tray column. Here, a diameter of 3 m for both columns is assumed. For the calculation of the height of each column, the distance between each tray must be known. In Refs. [41–43], values of 80 mm to 300 mm, 300 mm to 600 mm, and around 610 mm are mentioned, respectively. We assumed a value of 400 mm, which results in a height of 21.6 m and 38.4 m for the HPC and LPC, respectively. Both columns on top of each other have a total height of 60 m, which is in the range of the size for the cold box of an air separation unit [41]. The estimation of the costs of the trays depends on the diameter of the columns and on the number of trays. The costs for the empty shell and the trays are obtained from data reported in Ref. [39].

Estimation of the Costs of the Purification System

The estimation of the costs of the purification systems is based on the results of the above-mentioned groups of components. The percentage distribution of the costs of the different types of components is given by Ref. [45]. The purification system accounts for 13% of the total cost of the components.

Fixed and Total Capital Investment Costs

After estimation of the purchased equipment costs, the fixed capital investment (FCI) is calculated. The fixed capital investment is the sum of the direct and indirect costs. The direct costs could be further divided into onsite and offsite costs. Here, the offsite costs are here neglected. The onsite costs contain the purchased equipment costs and additional costs such as installation, piping, electrical equipment and instrumentation and controls. In the literature [32, 39], these additional costs are calculated as a share of the purchased equipment costs. Another possibility to consider the additional costs of each component is the modular method, which considers the module factor according to Ref. [44]. Therefore, the purchased equipment cost of each component is multiplied by a specified module factor which is individual for each component type.

The indirect costs consist of engineering, supervision, construction costs, contractor's profit, and contingencies. All these costs are calculated as a given percentage of the direct costs. For the total capital investment (TCI), the different time points of the investments are considered and the related required payments of interest.

Safety Aspects

LNG has an outstanding safety history. Commercial LNG transportation started in the 1960s without serious accidents. Only six incidents which are mainly related to collisions with other ships or run a ground have been reported in Ref. [46], but in all these cases no LNG was released. The good safety history is attributed to the well-developed technology for LNG tankers and the strict safety regulations. Nowadays, two types of LNG carriers exist: spherical type and membrane type. Both tanks are of double-hulled construction, which increases the safety of LNG carriers. Especially since 1980, the number of annual incidents related to the transport of oil, LNG, and LPG decreased due to a wide range of safety regulations, design, crew competence, and ship management improvements [47].

In general, the main hazards related to LNG are fires, explosion, cryogenic freeze burns, embrittlement of metal, and confined spaces [5]. The main sources of LNG hazards are, for example, liquid leaks under pressure, liquid leaks from storage tanks, rollover of an LNG storage tank, and liquid pools evaporating to form a flammable vapor plume [46]. Not all of the above-mentioned sources of LNG hazards occur in each step of the LNG chain. Thus, leaks under pressure occur in liquefaction and regasification process and during the transfer of LNG from storage and vice versa. The risk assessment of the LNG technology is widely spread in the literature. Ramsden et al. [49] published a study including the main important safety regulations for the transport of LNG. A detailed analysis and modelling of the risk associated with LNG was conducted in Ref. [46]. The safety and risk aspects of LNG are also analyzed in Ref. [5].

In case of a spill or leakage of LNG, a fire or explosion is the main hazard related to LNG. The consequences of leaks are shown graphically in a so-called event tree, which is shown in Figure 6 for a leakage of LNG near atmospheric and at elevated pressure. As shown in this figure, the consequences of spills depend on several facts like type of release, direct or delayed ignition. According to these facts, different kinds of fire occur like pool fire, jet fire, flash fire, or boiling liquid expanding vapor explosion (BLEVE). The presence of pure oxygen or oxygen-enriched streams, low temperatures, and high-pressure streams are associated with the main hazards in air separation plants. In Ref. [48], the following four main hazards are related to air separation units: rapid oxidation, embrittlement, and pressure excursions due to vaporizing liquids and oxygen-enriched or deficient atmospheres. A survey of accidents at Japanese air separation plants conducted [51] and categorized them according to the following types: explosion, burn, frost bite, and suffocation. The component with the highest number of accidents is the reboiler. Mainly, these accidents are explosions due to the accumulation of hydrocarbons within the liquid oxygen.

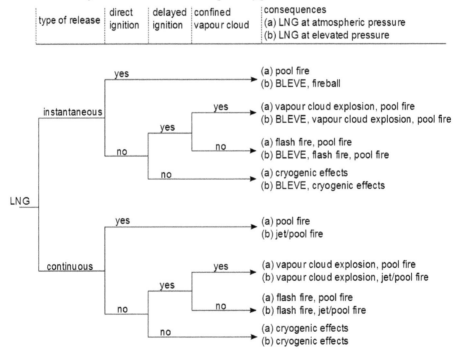

Figure 6. Event tree for the release of LNG at atmospheric and elevated pressure (based on Ref. [49]).

In the discussed cases with the integration of the LNG regasification, the simultaneous presence of LNG and oxygen increases the hazards potential.

SIMULATION

The simulation of the three discussed cases has been conducted using AspenPlus. The Peng-Robinson equation of state is selected, because it is appropriate for low-temperature processes. Table 1 shows the assumptions for the two incoming streams: air and LNG. Main assumptions for the simulation of the different types of components are shown in Table 2. The detailed description of the simulation is reported in Ref. [27].

Table 1. Assumptions for the incoming streams

Parameters	Unit	Air value	LNG Value
T	°C	15	−162
p	bar	1.0134	1.3
$\dot{m}$	kg/s	16.4	10
x_i	kmol/kmol	$x_{N_2} = 0.772; x_{O_2} = 0.208$	$x_{CH_4} = 0.8698; x_{C_2H_6} = 0.0935$
		$x_{Ar} = 0.0095; x_{H_2O} = 0.0102$	$x_{C_3H_8} = 0.0233; x_{C_4H_{10}} = 0.0063$
		$x_{CO_2} = 0.0003$	$x_{N_2} = 0.0071$

RESULTS AND DISCUSSION

Energy Analysis

Figures 7 and 8 show the power consumption/generation within turbomachinery and the heat rate in the heat exchangers, respectively. The total power consumption is $\dot{W}_{tot,\ CA}$ = 18.5 MW for Case A. It decreases to $\dot{W}_{tot,CAD1}$ = 12.0 MW and $\dot{W}_{tot,\ CAD2}$ = 6.9 MW, which corresponds to a reduction in the power consumption of 35.2% (Case AD1) and 62.8% (Case AD2).

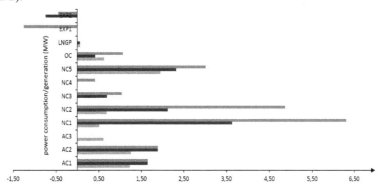

Figure 7. Power consumption/generation (MW).

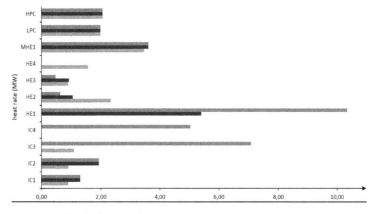

Figure 8. Heat rate within the heat exchangers (MW).

A decrease in the power consumption of more than 50%, if the regasification of LNG is introduced into an air separation process, has been reported in Refs. [20, 50]. Thus, the authors' results are in the range of the data reported by other scientists.

The results show that NC1 in Case A has the highest power consumption, followed by NC2 and NC5. In Case AD1, the power consumption of NC1 and NC2 is decreased by 50% (for each compressor). For Case AD2, the power consumption of the air compressors decreases as well due to the interstage cooling with LNG instead of water.

The heat rate in the heat exchangers varies significantly in the different systems. The HE1 in Case A is the component with the highest heat rate followed by the IC3 and IC4 in the nitrogen liquefaction block of the same system. The MHE has the same heat rate in Case A and AD1, because the air enters and leaves the MHE with the same temperatures. In Case AD2, the heat rate decreases slightly, because the air entering the MHE has a lower temperature. In addition, the heat rate in IC1 and IC2 is reduced from Case AD1 to Case AD2. In Cases A and AD1, the air is compressed within a two-stage compression process. In Case AD2, the air is compressed within a three-stage compression process, which decreases the temperature after each compressor, and, thus, results in a lower heat duty in the following interstage coolers.

Exergetic Analysis

The definitions of the exergy of fuel and exergy of product for each component as well as for the overall systems are reported in Ref. [27]. The results of the overall system for Cases A, AD1, and AD2 are shown in Table 3. The exergetic efficiency increases form 34.7% in Case A to 42.2% in Case AD1 and to 54.1% in Case AD2. This corresponds to an increase in the exergetic efficiency by 21% from Case A to Case AD1 and an increase in the exergetic efficiency of 56% from Case A to Case AD2.

Table 2. Selected assumptions for different types of components

Parameter	Unit	Value
Compressors, expanders		
η_{is}	–	0.8
η_{mech}	–	0.99
Column block		
Stages (HPC)	–	54
Stages (LPC)	–	96
Stage pressure drop	bar	0.003
Reflux ratio (HPC)	kg/s/kg/s	0.75
Bottom rate (LPC)	kg/s	0.5
Heat exchangers		
Pressure drop	%	3

Table 3. Results obtained from the exergetic analysis of the overall systems

System	$\dot{E}_{F,tot}$, MW	$\dot{E}_{P,tot}$, MW	$\dot{E}_{D,tot}$, MW	$\dot{E}_{L,tot}$, MW	ε_{tot}, %
Case A	18.6	6.4	11.9	0.2	34.7
Case AD1	20.6	8.7	11.7	0.2	42.2
Case AD2	15.5	8.4	7.0	0.09	54.1

Figures 9–11 show the exergy balances for all productive components of Cases A, AD1, and AD2, respectively. Each diagram has two axes: the left one is related to the exergy of fuel (MW) as the sum of exergy of product and exergy destruction, and the right one shows the exergetic efficiency (%).

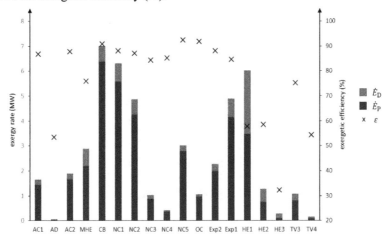

Figure 9. Results obtained from the exergy analysis of Case A.

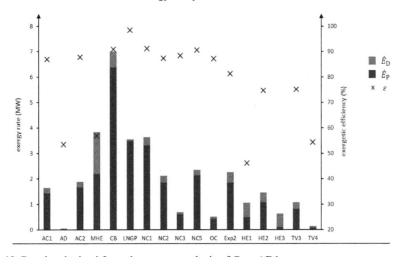

Figure 10. Results obtained from the exergy analysis of Case AD1.

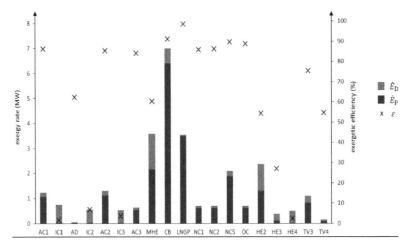

Figure 11. Results obtained from the exergy analysis of Case AD2.

The results obtained from the exergy analysis show that the exergetic efficiencies are around 90% for turbomachinery; however, for the heat exchangers, this value varies between 2% and 76%.

In Case A (Figure 9), the HE1 and the MHE are of particular interest. The HE1 is the component with the highest exergy destruction in this system. However, the component with the lowest exergetic efficiency is HE3. The exergetic efficiency of the MHE is 76%. This value is decreased in Case AD1 to 57% (Figure 10). In Case AD2, the IC1, IC2, and IC3 are productive components, but they have a very low exergetic efficiency between 2% and 7% (Figure 11). The air should not be cooled to the very low temperatures that are provided by LNG. It results in the low exergetic efficiency.

Figures 12–14 show the distribution of the exergy destruction among most important components for the Cases A, AD1, and AD2, respectively. The remaining components are lumped under "others."

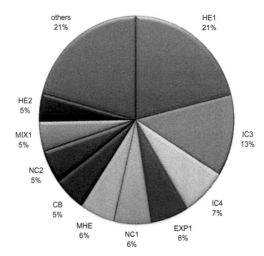

Figure 12. Distribution of the exergy destruction among components of Case A.

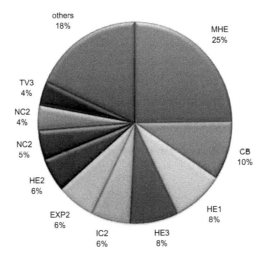

Figure 13. Distribution of the exergy destruction among components of Case AD1.

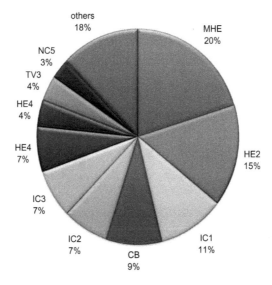

Figure 14. Distribution of the exergy destruction among components of Case AD2.

In Case A, HE1 is the component with the highest exergy destruction, which accounts for 21% of the total exergy destruction. The second component is the IC3 in the nitrogen liquefaction block with 13%. The structural changes from Case A to Case AD1 lead to a different priority. Hence, in Case AD1, the MHE is the component with the highest exergy destruction, i.e., 25% of the total exergy destruction. Of particular interest is also the CB with an exergy destruction of 10%. In Case A, however, both components (MHE and CD) play a minor role (around 5–6%). In Case AD2, the MHE is the component with the highest exergy destruction followed by HE2 and IC1. The contribution of the column block is only 9%.

Advanced Exergetic Analysis

Figures 15–17 show the results obtained from the advanced exergetic analysis, for Cases A, AD1, and AD2, respectively. For all productive components, the exergy destruction is divided into unavoidable and avoidable exergy destructions.

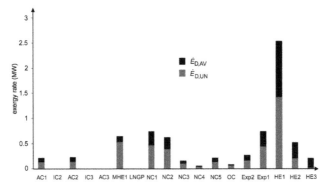

Figure 15. Results obtained from the advanced exergy analysis of Case A (MW).

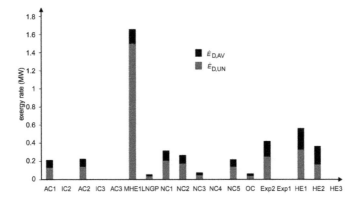

Figure 16. Results obtained from the advanced exergy analysis of Case AD1 (MW).

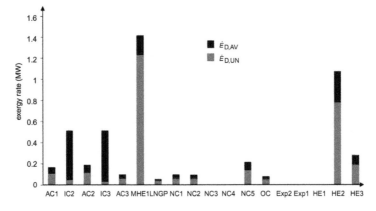

Figure 17. Results obtained from the advanced exergy analysis of Case AD2 (MW).

Plant facilities investment 2 (40% of FCI)	23.4	22.6	18.4
Interest for PFI 1 and PFI 2	9.7	9.4	7.6
TCI	68.2	65.8	53.7

Unfortunately, the economic results cannot be compared with the data reported by other scientists because of the lack of such information in the literature.

CONCLUSIONS

In this chapter, the concept of the LNG-based industrial park is discussed. This means the integration of LNG regasification into different processes, where low temperatures are required in industrial plants. One option is the utilization of the low-temperature exergy of LNG during the liquefaction of air within an air separation unit. Exergy-based methods (conventional and advanced exergetic analyses) are applied to identify the potential for improvement of the discussed systems. The exergoeconomic and exergoenvironmental analyses will be reported later. The authors are also working on safety-related issues. A novel exergy-based method, the exergy-risk-hazard analysis, will be applied in order to identify the differences in the potential hazards for the proposed concepts.

REFERENCES

1.   International Energy Agency. IEA: Key World Energy Statistics 2016. Available from: http://www.iea.org/publications/freepublications/publication/KeyWorld2016.pdf [Accessed: May 26, 2016]

2.   International Gas Union. IGU: World LNG Report 2016. Available from: http://www.igu. org/publications/2016-world-lng-report [Accessed: May 26, 2016].

3.   BP: Statistical Review of World Energy. 65th ed. Available from: https://www.bp.com/content/dam/bp/pdf/energy-economics/statistical-review-2016/bp-statistical-review-ofworld-energy-2016-full-report.pdf [Accessed: February 28, 2017].

4.   International Group of Liquefied Natural Gas Importers. GIIGNL: The LNG Industry. 2016 ed. Available from: http://www.giignl.org/sites/default/files/PUBLIC_AREA/Publications/giignl_2016_annual_report.pdf [Accessed: May 26, 2016].

5.   Mokhatab S, Mak J, Valappil J, Wood D. Handbook of Liquefied Natural Gas. Amsterdam: Elsevier/Gulf Professional Publishing; 2013. ISBN: 9780124045859

6.   Yang CC, Huang Z. Lower emission LNG vaporization. LNG Journal. 2004;11-12:24-26

7.   Koku O, Perry S, Kim JK. Techno-economic evaluation for the heat integration of vaporization cold energy in natural gas processing. Applied Energy. 2014;114:250-261. DOI: 10.1016/j.apenergy.2013.09.066

8.   Angelino G. The use of liquid natural gas as a heat sink for power cycles. ASME Journal of Engineering and Power. 1978;100:160-177

9.   Morosuk T, Tsatsaronis G. LNG-based cogeneration systems: Evaluation using exergybased analyses. In: Natural Gas—Extraction to End Use. InTech; 2012. pp. 235-266. DOI: 10.5772/51477

10. Invernizzi CM, Iora P. The exploitation of the physical exergy of liquid natural gas by closed power thermodynamic cycles. An overview. Energy. 2016;105:2-15

11. Xia G, Sun Q, Cao X, Wang J, Yu Y, Wang L. Thermodynamic analysis and optimization of a solar-powered transcritical CO2 (carbon dioxide) power cycle for reverse osmosis

desalination based on the recovery of cryogenic energy of LNG (liquefied natural gas). Energy. 2014;66:643-653. DOI: 10.1016/j.energy.2013.12.029

12. Cao W, Beggs C, Mujtaba I. Theoretical approach of freeze seawater desalination on flake ice maker utilizing LNG cold energy. Desalination. 2015;355:22-32. DOI: 10.1016/j. desal.2014.09.034

13. La Rocca V. Cold recovery during regasification of LNG part one: Cold utilization far from the regasification facility. Energy. 2010;35(5):2049-2058. DOI: 10.1016/j.energy.2010.01.022

14. La Rocca V. Cold recovery during regasification of LNG part two: Applications in an agro food industry and a hypermarket. Energy. 2011;36(8):4897-4908. DOI: 10.1016/j. energy.2011.05.034

15. Messineo A, Panno G. LNG cold energy use in agro-food industry. A case study in Sicily. Journal of Natural Gas Science and Engineering. 2011;3(1):356-363. DOI: 10.1016/j. jngse.2011.02.002

16. Otsuka T. Evolution of an LNG terminal: Senboku terminal of Osaka gas. In: Proceedings of the 23rd World Gas Conference. Amsterdam, IGU (International Gas Union) 2006. pp. 1-14

17. Yamanouchi N, Nagasawa H. Using LNG cold for air separation. Chemical Engineering Progress. 1979;75(7):78-82

18. Nakaiwa M, Akiya T, Owa M, Tanaka Y. Evaluation of an energy supply system with air separation. Energy Conversion and Management. 1996;37(3):295-301. DOI: 10.1016/0196-8904(95)00787-3

19. Jieyu Z, Yanzhong L, Guangpeng L, Biao S. Simulation of a novel single-column cryogenic air separation process using LNG cold energy. Physics Procedia. 2015;67:116-122. DOI: 10.1016/j.phpro.2015.06.021

20. Mehrpooya M, Moftakhari Sharifzadeh M, Rosen M. Optimum design and exergy analysis of a novel cryogenic air separation process with LNG (liquefied natural gas) cold energy utilization. Energy. 2015;90:2047-2069. DOI: 10.1016/j.energy.2015.07.101

21. Mehrpooya M, Kalhorzadeh M, Chahartaghi M. Investigation of novel integrated air separation processes, cold energy recovery of liquefied natural gas and carbon dioxide power cycle. Journal of Cleaner Production. 2016;113:411-425. DOI: 10.1016/j. jclepro.2015.12.058

22. Agrawal R. Liquefied natural gas refrigeration transfer to a cryogenics air separation unit using high pressure nitrogen stream. US Patent No. 5,137,558 (August 11, 1992)

23. Agrawal R, Ayres C. Production of liquid nitrogen using liquefied natural gas as sole refrigerant. US Patent No. 5,139,547A (August 18, 1992)

24. Ogata S, Yamanoto Y. Process for liquefying and rectifying air. US Patent No. 4,192,662 (March 11, 1980)

25. Perrotin G, Anselmini JP. Processes for the production of nitrogen and oxygen. US Patent No. 3,886,758 (June 3, 1975)

26. Takagi H, Nagamura T. Method of using an external cold source in an air separation. European Patent No. 0304355 B1 (April 17, 1991)

27. Tesch S, Morosuk T, Tsatsaronis G. Advanced exergy analysis applied to the process of regasification of LNG (liquefied natural gas) integrated into an air separation process. Energy. 2016;117:550-561. DOI: 10.1016/j.energy.2016.04.031

28. Tesch S, Morosuk T, Tsatsaronis G. Exergetic and economic evaluation of safety-related concepts for the regasification of LNG integrated into an air separation processes. Energy. 2017. DOI: 10.1016/j.energy.2017.04.043 [in print].

29. Cornelissen R, Hirs G. Exergy analysis of cryogenic air separation. Energy Conversion and Management. 1998;39(16-18):1821-1826. DOI: 10.1016/S0196-8904(98)00062-4

30.   Jain R, Piscataway N. Pre-purification of air for separation. US Patent No. 5,232,474A (August 3, 1993)

31.   Agrawal R, Herron DM. Air liquefaction: Distillation. In: Encyclopedia of Separation Science. Editor Wilson ID, Elsevier Science Ltd, Amsterdam, Netherlands: 2000. pp. 1895-1910. DOI: 10.1016/B0-12-226770-2/04821-3

32.   Bejan A, Tsatsaronis G, Moran M. Thermal Design and Optimization. New York: Wiley; 1996. ISBN: 978-047-1584-67-4

33.   Tsatsaronis G, Morosuk T. Understanding and improving energy conversion systems with the aid of exergy-based methods. Exergy. 2012;11(4):518-542

34.   Tsatsaronis G, Morosuk T. Understanding the formation of costs and environmental impacts using exergy-based methods. In: Energy Security and Development. The Global Context and Indian Perspectives. Editors. Reddy BS, Ulgiati S, New Delhi, India: Springer; 2015. pp. 271-292

35.   European Industrial Gases Association and Industriegaseverband. EIGA and IGV: Safe Practices Guide for Cryogenic Air Separation Plants. Available from: https://www. eiga.eu/ fileadmin/docs_pubs/Doc_147_13_Safe_Practices_Guide_for_Cryogenic_Air_ Separation_ Plants.pdf [Accessed: December 16, 2016].

36.   Aspen Plus. The Software is a Proprietary Product of AspenTech, V8.6. 2014. Available from: http://www.aspentech.com

37.   Ulrich G, Vasudevan P. Chemical Engineering Process Design and Economics. A Practical Guide. 2nd ed. Durham, New Hampshire, US: Process Publishing; 2004

38.   Smith R. Chemical Process Design and Integration. Chichester, West Sussex, England: Wiley; 2005

39.   Peters M, Timmerhaus K, West R. Plant Design and Economics for Chemical Engineers. 5th ed. New York: McGraw-Hill; 2003

40.   Kerry F. Industrial Gas Handbook. Gas Separation and Purification. Boca Raton, Florida: CRC Press; 2007. ISBN: 9780849390050

41.   Häring HW. Industrial Gases Processing. Weinheim: Wiley; 2008. ISBN: 978-3-527-31685-4

42.   Ebrahimi A, Meratizaman M, Akbarpour Reyhani H, Pourali O, Amidpour M. Energetic, exergetic and economic assessment of oxygen production from two columns cryogenic air separation unit. Energy. 2015;90:1298-1316. DOI: 10.1016/j.energy.2015.06.083

43.   Bachmann C, Gerla J, Yang Q. Smaller is Better—New 3-in-1 Internals Reduce Air Separation Column Heights. Available from: https://www.sulzer.com/en/-/media/Documents/Cross_ Division/STR/2013/STR_2013_3_16_19_Bachmann.pdf [Accessed: October 2, 2016].

44.   Epifanova V, Akselrod L. Air Separation Using Deep Cooling Methods: Technologies and Equipment. Moscow, USSR: Machinostroenie; 1976

45.   Guthrie KM, Grace WR. Data and techniques for preliminary capital cost estimating. Chemical Engineering. 1969:114-143

46.   Woodward JL, Pitblado R. LNG Risk Based Safety. Modeling and Consequence Analysis. Hoboken, New Jersey: John Wiley & Sons Inc. Publication; 2010. ISBN: 978-0-470-31764-8

47.   Pitblado RM, Baik J, Hughes GJ, Shaw SJ. Consequence of LNG marine incidents. In: Proceedings of the CCPS Conference; 29 June–1 July 2004; California Energy Commission, Orlando, USA. Available from: http://www.westernsunsystems.comorwww.gosolarcalifornia. org/lng/documents/CCPS_PAPER_PITBLADO.PDF [Accessed: April 6, 2017].

48.   Schmidt WI, Winegardner KS, DennehyI M, Castle-Smith H. Safe design and operation of a cryogenic air separation unit. Process Safety Progress. 2001;20(4):269-279

49.   Ramsden N, Roue R, Mo-Ajok B, Langerak G-J, Watkins S, Peeters R. Rahmenplan
       Flüssigerdags für Rhein-Main-Donau. 2015. Available from: https://www.portofrotterdam.
       com/de/file/5263/download?token=2wwYWvFk [Accessed: December 12, 2016].

50.   Sharratt C. LNG terminal cold energy integration opportunities offered by contractors. LNG
       Journal. 2012:22-24

51.   Kitagawa T. Survey of accidents at the air separation plants. The Journal of Ammonium Sulphate
       Engineering. 1964;17(3):47 [in Japanese, official translation by NASA Technical, Washington
       1970]. Available from: https://archive.org/stream/nasa_techdoc_19710003182/19710003182_
       djvu.txt [Accessed: January 20, 2017].

6

Making a Global Gas Market: Territoriality and Production Networks in Liquefied Natural Gas

Gavin Bridge[1] and Michael Bradshaw[2]

[1]Department of Geography, Durham University, Durham DH1 3LE, UK
[2]Warwick Business School, University of Warwick, Coventry CV4 7AL, UK

ABSTRACT

Energy markets are an important contemporary site of economic globalization. In this article we use a global production network (GPN) approach to examine the evolutionary dynamics of the liquefied natural gas (LNG) sector and its role in an emerging global market for natural gas. We extend recent work in the relational economic geography literature on the organizational practices by which production networks are assembled and sustained over time and space; and we address a significantly underdeveloped aspect of GPN research by demonstrating the implications of these practices for the territoriality of GPNs. The article introduces LNG as a techno-material reconfiguration of natural gas that enables it to be moved and sold beyond the continental limits of pipelines. We briefly outline the evolving scale and geographic scope of LNG trade, and introduce the network of firms, extraeconomic actors, and intermediaries through which LNG production, distribution, and marketing are coordinated. Our analysis shows how LNG is evolving from a relatively simple floating pipeline model of point-to-point, binational flows orchestrated by producing and consuming companies and governed by long-term contracts, to a more geographic and organizationally complex production network that is constitutive of an emergent global gas market. Empirically the article provides the first systematic analysis within economic geography of the globalization of the LNG sector and its influence on global gas markets, demonstrating the potential of GPN (and related frameworks) to contribute meaningful analysis of the contemporary political economy of energy. Conceptually the article pushes research on GPN to realize more fully its potential as an analysis of network territoriality by examining how the spatial configuration of GPNs emerges from the organizational structures and coordinating strategies of firms, extraeconomic actors and intermediaries;

and by recognizing how network territoriality is constitutive of markets rather than merely responsive to them.

Keywords: *Global production networks, Territoriality, Network practices, Liquefied natural gas*

INTRODUCTION

Spatially dispersed production networks are widely acknowledged as a significant organizational form within the global economy. The territorial configuration of global production networks (GPNs) and value chains, however, remains an underdeveloped analytical theme in the economic geography literature. As a consequence, the relationship between network territoriality and practices of network coordination is not well understood. A better understanding of the territoriality of production networks, and how territoriality emerges from the coordinating strategies of firms, extraeconomic actors, and intermediaries, is necessary if economic geography is to provide richer analyses of their geoeconomic/geopolitical consequences and the mutually constitutive character of spatial and organizational form. In this article, we use a GPN approach to examine the evolutionary dynamics of the liquefied natural gas (LNG) supply chain and its role in an emerging global market for natural gas.

Energy markets are an important contemporary site of political–economic change, shaped by a combination of economic policy goals (e.g., market liberalization and supply competition), geopolitical and geoeconomic shifts in power (with associated concerns about energy security), and environmental objectives (e.g., climate change mitigation and urban air quality). An earlier generation of geographic researchers recognized the significance of energy markets and the importance of understanding their structural and dynamic features in accounting for the geographies of economic activity. Manners (1964), for example, placed market demand at the center of his survey of *The Geography of Energy* and its influence on economic development; the eight editions of Odell's (1970) classic *Oil and World Power* highlighted the role of oil markets in shaping geopolitical relations during one of the most turbulent periods in the sector's history; and Chapman's (1989) *Geography and Energy: Commercial Systems and National Policies* examined the organizational and spatial structure of electricity, oil, and gas markets. However, despite the enduring importance of energy markets, it is only recently that they have again become a focus of attention within geography (for a recent review, see Calvert 2016). International markets for natural gas are currently undergoing profound change. Gas consumption worldwide has grown 25 percent in the last decade, with projections of a *Golden Age of Gas* buoyed by surging shale gas production in the United States, large conventional gas discoveries (e.g., offshore East Africa, eastern Mediterranean, and Australia), and fuel switching in power and urban transport sectors. In many national contexts, the shift toward gas has been facilitated by energy market deregulation, major infrastructural investment (e.g., in pipelines and import terminals), and environmental regulation that valorizes the lower particulate and greenhouse gas emissions of gas relative to coal or oil (International Energy Agency [IEA] 2011, 2014). However, the most significant process transforming international gas markets—and the focus of this article—is the increasing integration of geographically discrete markets for gas and, for the first time, the prospect of a global gas market emerging similar to that for oil. Central to this process has been a growing seaborne natural gas trade, in the form of LNG, which increasingly enables gas to be moved and sold beyond the continental limits of pipelines. As we show, however, growth in LNG trade is accompanied by a deeper process of integration associated with cross-border production networks for making, selling, and transporting LNG—what is commonly referred to as the LNG supply chain. These GPNs for LNG stretch from upstream gas extraction to downstream gas consumption via intermediate processes of gas processing, liquefaction, shipping, and regasification. We show how the territorial form of these production networks is evolving, along with the organizational practices through which they are held together, and how the manner of their evolution is bringing a global gas market into being.

The contributions of the article, therefore, are threefold. The article provides the first systematic analysis within economic geography of the globalization of the LNG sector and its influence on global gas markets. In doing so, it demonstrates the potential of GPN to contribute meaningful analysis of the contemporary political economy of energy. Second, this article critically extends recent work in the relational economic geography literature on the organizational practices by which production networks are assembled and sustained over time and space. We agree with Murphy (2012, 211) that GPN/global value chain (GVC) research has yet to develop fully an "empirically informed exposition of how different production network configurations develop through the actions of agents," and we see value in his call for a "process-sensitive approach" attuned to the "process(es) through which network linkages are established, sustained, and reorganized over time and space" (ibid.). The article responds to this call, examining how LNG production networks are scaled and sustained by focusing on the practices that hold together different network actors. Third, by foregrounding the concept of territoriality, we address an underrealized potential of the GPN approach for examining the implications of network practices for the territorial configuration of GPNs. We concur with Coe and Yeung (2015, 35) that, to date, "the territoriality of global production networks is elusive and under-developed." By paying attention to the spatial configuration of LNG production networks, we are able to show how, in the case of natural gas, GPNs are constitutive of markets—market making—rather than merely responsive to them.

The remainder of the article is organized into four sections. The next section contextualizes the article's conceptual and empirical contributions via a review of recent work in GPN. Following that, we provide a brief introduction to the LNG sector and outline our methods and approach. The penultimate section presents our analysis of geographic and organizational change in LNG production networks. We identify three organizational trends reshaping the spatial configuration of LNG production network, and show how they are eroding the dominance of a long-established business model in LNG (what we refer to as the floating pipeline). We examine contract terms and other *network development practices* (Murphy 2012) associated with these organizational changes, and explain how they introduce significant sources of geographic flexibility and uncertainty into the LNG production network. The final section concludes by considering the wider implications of the article's analysis of organizational and geographic shifts in LNG production networks.

UNFINISHED BUSINESS: EXTENDING TERRITORIALITY, MATERIALITY, AND NETWORK PRACTICES WITHIN GPN RESEARCH

Contemporary social science has a rich set of heuristics for understanding the political economy of globalization and, in particular, for examining how spatially distributed economic activity is functionally coordinated. Some derive from studies of international trade and take the commodity as their analytical unit; others emerge from industry studies and focus on issues of value chain management, innovation, and sectoral governance; still others highlight the dialectical interplay of territorial and network coherence, and allow for a broad range of *economic* actors beyond the firm. As readers of this journal will know well, economic geographers have played a significant role in developing a broad family of relational approaches for understanding the interconnectedness, organization, and coordination of industrial sectors that includes work on global commodity chains (GCCs, e.g., Hughes and Reimer 2004), GVCs (e.g., Ponte and Gibbon 2005) and GPNs (Coe 2012). The GPN approach is the most spatially sensitive member of this family with its embrace of multiple geographic scales, recognition of a plurality of economic actors extending beyond the firm, and attentiveness to the unevenness of regional development outcomes. A GPN approach focuses on the relationship between the geographic extensification of economic activities and the activities' organizational integration and coordination. It was initially developed as a tool for understanding changes in the geographic organization of manufacturing and services at the world scale, and examining the implications for regional development of the internationalization of economic activity (Henderson et al. 2002; Coe et al. 2004; Dicken 2015). Consistent with its materialist origins, the GPN approach seeks to understand how existing interactions—around price formation or product design, for example—are outcomes of the distribution of power within a production network and, furthermore, how these interactions are generative of new organizational and geographic forms. Production networks, then, are understood as "organisational platforms through which actors in different regional and national economies compete and co-operate for a greater share of value creation, transformation, and capture though geographically dispersed economic activity" (Yeung and Coe 2015, 30). The point here is not simply that production networks are dynamic over space and time, but that network spatio-temporality is an emergent property and arises from interactions among a network's constituent parts.

The GPN approach's capacity for understanding the mutually constitutive character of spatial configuration and network organization makes it well suited to analyzing economic sectors whose organizational and geographic structures are in a state of flux. So far, the center of gravity of the GPN research framework has been manufacturing, where it has been adopted to understand functional and geographic integration in a range of sectors from aircraft (Bowen 2007) and automobiles (Isaksen and Kalsaas 2009) to textiles (Tokatli, Wrigley, and Kizilgün 2008) and wood products (Murphy 2012; Gibson and Warren 2016). However, recent work has taken GPN into less familiar terrain, to examine producer services such as temporary staffing (Coe, Johns, and Ward 2011), freight forwarding (Bowen and Leinbach 2006; Rodrigue 2006), the creative sector (Johns 2006; Yoon and Malecki 2010), and extractive industries (Bridge 2008; Steen and Underthun 2011; Bridge and Le Billon 2013; MacKinnon 2013). These studies have expanded the sectoral reach of GPN research but have also highlighted some of its conceptual limits and opportunities for further development. We are drawn to GPN's spatially sensitive relational approach and its advantage in this regard over GCC and GVC approaches: we think GPN's geographic sensitivity has the capacity to generate novel insights about the evolution of the LNG sector that make an original contribution to energy studies. However, we also think GPN's potential as a distinctively *geographic* mode of analysis is underdeveloped and can be enhanced by attending to three conceptual elements: GPN's account of territoriality, understanding of materiality and material transformation, and interest in network practices. The case of LNG foregrounds these limitations, while at the same time suggesting how attending to them can advance research utilizing GPN and other relational approaches.

Territoriality

The spatial reordering of manufacturing at the global scale provided the initial impetus for early work on *global shift* and the exercise of *global reach* in fragmented economic networks (Dicken 1986). However, explicit attention to the spatial configuration of networks has more recently taken a backseat in GPN research in preference for more parsimonious modes of explanation and theory-building in relation to network organization and processes of strategic coupling between leading global firms and local actors (e.g., Lee, Heo, and Kim 2014; Mahutga 2014). We think the concept of territoriality is an underdeveloped conceptual resource for more closely examining the territorial configuration of networks and the value activities of which they are comprised. In general terms, territoriality describes "the process by which individual and collective social actors define, bind, reify and control space toward some social end" (Steinberg 1994, 3). The concept draws attention to the way in which particular geographies (i.e., a specific territorial configuration, combining elements of both geographic reach and interaction with place) are integral to the exercise of economic and political power (Brenner et al. 2003). Territoriality initially piqued interest within political geography as a way of thinking about the practices that produce and maintain territory (see, e.g., Taylor 1994; Paasi 1998). Its capacities for de-naturalizing spatial form, and for linking spatial form with strategic practice, subsequently encouraged its application within a wider range of political–economic accounts. The potential for economic geography of theorizing "the territoriality behind territory" was noted early on by Steinberg (1994) in the context of the *new industrial geography*, although it was not directly taken up. The concept's capacity for hinging spatial form with political–economic power was enough to give territoriality a fleeting role within the first generation of GPN research (e.g., Hess 2004). Yet it remained a marginal term within GPN 1.0, overshadowed by GPN 1.0's conceptual trinity of power, embeddedness, and value.

Coe and Yeung (2015) recently highlighted territoriality's analytical potential as part of a GPN 2.0. For them, territoriality comprises vertical and horizontal dimensions of production networks: the former refers to the *spatial scope* or geographic reach of different economic actors (on a scalar continuum from global to local) within a production network; and the latter refers to the *territorial interfaces* among value activities that have different spatial expressions (for example, some may be highly localized and others expressed as regional clusters). Schematic and provisional, we nonetheless find this framework a useful starting point as it recenters the question of spatial configuration within GPN research. It has long been acknowledged within GPN research that GPNs are spatially fragmented and *discontinuously territorial*, but the problem of global shift—that is, how the territorial configuration of production networks evolves in relation to the generation and capture of value—has not been a core research focus in recent years. The analytical value of territoriality in this task, we suggest, is that it foregrounds the particularity of a network's territorial configuration (why *this* spatial form, why *now*?) and links this form to strategic intent (for what *ends*, with what *effects*?). It is, then, more than a fancy synonym for describing a network's complex spatial form as we retain the processual and evolutionary understanding associated with its initial application—that is, territoriality points to the practices undertaken by network actors to establish, maintain, and adapt a production network's territorial form.

As we will show, the LNG production network is rapidly evolving: its organizational structures are diversifying and the *spatial rules* that have characterized LNG production and consumption for nearly fifty years are changing in ways that are economically and geopolitically significant (cf. Glassman 2011). Importantly, these organizational, territorial, and geopolitical dimensions are not captured by conventional analyses that understand the geographies of LNG through the lens of binational trade flows. Conventional analyses readily show LNG consumption to be growing, and the number of producing and consuming countries and firms to be increasing, but say very little about how the global shift under way in LNG (and gas markets more generally) arises from significant organizational changes in LNG production networks. The concept of territoriality provides a way to think about the evolving spatial configuration of LNG production networks, its relationship with the relative power of different network actors, and geographic and geopolitical consequences.

Materiality

A significant strand of recent work in economic geography has called for greater attention to the material transformations at the heart of GPNs and commodity chains. Building on calls to better understand the "influence materiality exerts on industrial organization" (Bridge 2008, 415; see also Boyd, Prudham, and Schurman 2001; Prudham 2005; Hudson 2008), this work explores the significance of materials, and biological, chemical, and mechanical processes, within GVCs. The central provocation of these accounts is that the heterogeneity of materials and the variability of biophysical processes enables and shapes a production network's spatial and organizational form in ways that are economically significant, yet underappreciated. A logical starting point for investigating how materials matter has been *nature-facing* primary sectors, such as forestry, fisheries, mining, and agriculture, which are strongly characterized by seasonality, biological reproduction times, and geological and ecological variability. Ciccantell and Smith (2009) argued that material and locational attributes of the primary sector influence production networks in distinctive ways: they highlight, for example, how large and *lumpy* capital investments are frequently required to mobilize raw materials via ports and pipelines, and the dynamic interaction of scale economies in raw material production and transportation (see also Bunker and Ciccantell 2005). Gibson and Warren's (2016) description of a "resource-sensitive global production networks" showed how shortages of traditional hardwoods (which have prized qualities of resonance, strength, and beauty) and environmental regulation influence the organization and spatiality of acoustic guitar manufacturing, leading to both fragmentation and concentration within the production chain. In a similar way, Crang et al.'s (2013) research on economies of waste highlighted the profound heterogeneity of materials encountered in waste flows and how the corresponding need for fine-grained sorting gives intermediary brokers (rather than large lead firms) a key role within waste value chains because of their capacity for assessing material quality.

The primary insight of these different studies is to problematize accounts of production, exchange, and consumption by emphasizing how production networks are organized around moments of material transformation, in which the (biological, chemical, physical) qualities of materials shape strategies for value capture. To call attention to materiality in this context, then, is to emphasize the *political–economic possibilities* and limitations of material qualities, and their influence on the organizational and spatial structures of energy regimes (Birch and Calvert 2015). In the case of LNG, for example, production networks are structured around the flow of gas from the upstream wellhead to the downstream consumer as part of an overall value creation process.Footnote[1] At the core of the production network are material exchanges and transformations associated with extracting, processing, liquefying, shipping, regasifying, distributing, and consuming gas (Figure 1). Representing the production network as a series of physical input–output structures enables consideration of how infrastructural assets and the technological division of labor associated with long-distance gas supply are territorially embedded. Figure 1 illustrates how gas extraction and liquefaction stages, for example, are shaped by the developmental aspirations of the host state (Territory 1), for which gas extraction and LNG export are typically part of a strategy of resource-based development. Similarly, downstream elements are strongly influenced by the differential ways in which gas is embedded in municipal and national energy markets (Territory 2), via electricity generation, for example. We are aware that others have found this stage-based model of production limiting because it may overlook differences among firms within individual stages as well as how some actors may be involved in several stages in different ways (Coe and Yeung 2015). However, a stage-based model of gas production based around key moments of material transformation is well suited to analysis of LNG production networks. Historically the LNG production chain has conformed to a simple organizational model in which upstream and downstream stages have been internalized within the organizational structures of two different firms (Firms A and B in Figure 1). By starting with a stage-based model, we are able to show how, following processes of vertical and horizontal integration by lead firms, the organizational structures of the production network no longer map straightforwardly onto an underlying technical division of labor between upstream extraction and processing and downstream distribution and consumption. Moreover, we are able to show how these organizational shifts are, simultaneously, introducing significant new territorial forms to LNG production networks.

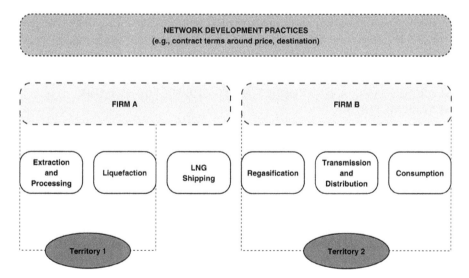

Figure 1. Conceptualizing the LNG production network.

Network Practices

GPN research has a comparatively granular approach to the organization of economic activity, focusing on the "intra-firm, inter-firm and extra-firm networks that characterize contemporary production systems" (Hess and Coe 2006, 1207). The capacities of GPN's relational network perspective are well known for situating economic actors in social and institutional context, emphasizing the significance of their interaction, and understanding the contingency of economic processes (Bathelt and Glückler 2003). However, the organizational practices that link buyers and sellers, align their interests, and reproduce these relations over time and space—that is, which constitute relational networks as networks (as opposed to intrafirm hierarchies, for example)—require further elaboration. In the context of GPN research, for example, Murphy (2012) highlighted a need for greater attention to the ways in which network agents establish, maintain, and adapt network linkages. In his work on the international Bolivian wood products industry, Murphy identified a range of ways in which actors develop ties to international markets. He drew attention to the different strategies that Bolivian supplies adopt in aligning their interests with international buyers and clients, highlighting the importance of these *network development practices* to enhancing relational proximity and creating network structures.

We take up Murphy's call for greater attention to the socioeconomic process that hold production networks together and maintain spatially distributed elements as a functional whole. We agree that grounded "empirically informed exposition(s) of how different production network configurations develop through the actions of agents" can shed light on the processes behind emergent spatial forms (ibid., 210). Focusing on practices of interaction and coordination complements the processual and evolutionary understanding of territoriality, outlined above, in that it makes it possible to understand the production network as a set of competing agendas and asymmetric power relations through which the territorial configuration of a production network takes shape. Paying attention to devices through which practices are negotiated and prescribed, such as contract terms, enables an assessment of how spatial ties are created and modified over time. Accordingly, the concept of network development practices (Figure 1) provides a way to focus our analysis on key interactions between sellers and buyers that sustain the LNG production network, and that are important in understanding its changing organizational structures and geographic form.

RESEARCHING LNG: AN INTRODUCTION TO THE SECTOR AND OUR RESEARCH METHODS

In comparison to oil, natural gas consumption remains strikingly localized: nearly three quarters of the natural gas consumed worldwide (70.5 percent in 2015, see Figure 2) is consumed in the country where it was produced, in comparison to the 64.4 percent of global oil production that is exported (BP 2016). However, the proportion of natural gas traded internationally has been increasing every year. A growing proportion (32.4 percent in 2015) of the just over 1 trillion cubic meters of gas traded internationally each year does so as LNG (Figure 2). Unbound by the fixed infrastructure of pipelines, LNG introduces much greater geographic flexibility to international gas trade and offers, for the first time, the prospect of a global gas market analogous to that for oil. An increasing supply of flexible and relatively inexpensive LNG is anticipated to be one of the most significant developments in the global energy system in the remainder of this decade (IEA 2016). Footnote[2] The growth of international trade and cross-border investment in LNG is, then, part of a larger process of deepening globalization under way within international energy markets such that national systems of energy provision are increasingly porous (Bridge and Bradshaw 2015; Overland 2016).

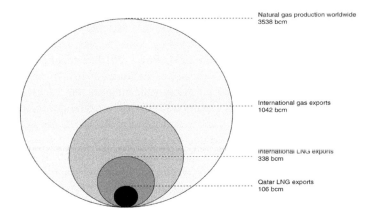

Natural gas production worldwide
3538 bcm

International gas exports
1042 bcm

International LNG exports
338 bcm

Qatar LNG exports
106 bcm

Figure 2. World production and exports of natural gas and LNG, 2015 (billion cubic meters).

At the core of the LNG production network is a process of capital-intensive material transformation that upgrades the value of gas per unit volume. Liquefaction is achieved by cooling natural gas to below its boiling point (−163°C), increasing its energy density six-hundred–fold (to about 65 percent that of crude oil), and substantially improving the economics of gas transportation beyond the limits of the pipeline network (i.e., by road tanker or by ship). Liquefaction is an example of a broad suite of technological interventions that seek to overcome diseconomies of space (Bunker and Ciccantell 2005), effectively creating a commodity by transforming materials from one physical state to another. Its effect is to mobilize and globalize natural gas in unprecedented ways. Ocean-borne LNG enables gas producers to monetize historically *stranded* gas reserves and access large markets *beyond the pipeline*; it creates opportunities for arbitrage between regional markets, and enables utilities and other gas users to diversify sources of supply. By mobilizing gas beyond the continental limits of pipelines, the growth of LNG trade is disrupting established practices among buyers and sellers along the gas supply chain and driving new patterns of uneven development at the regional and global scale. Footnote[3] Although LNG's growing significance can be interpreted as the inexorable evolution of a commodity market (Pirrong 2014), such accounts leave much unexplained. Where, when, and how (in a contractual sense) LNG moves worldwide depends on how a diverse group of economic agents—including international oil companies, state-owned oil and gas producers, sovereign governments, municipal utilities, shipping companies, and gas traders—are sustained in relation with one another. Understanding the structures and practices that create and maintain GPNs for LNG is essential, therefore, if we are to assess how LNG will reshape existing geographies of gas and its implications for energy security, low carbon energy transition, and other areas of policy concern. For gas importing states, for example, LNG can provide a way to offset physical and price risks associated with pipeline gas and other fuels: in a European context, the possibility of LNG imports from North America is seen as a means of reducing reliance on Russian pipeline gas imports and adding greater competition (Bordoff and Houser 2014; Coote 2016; European Commission 2016). The case of LNG, then, readily captures how GPNs are influenced by geopolitical considerations (cf. Glassman 2011).

To date, analysis of the geopolitical economy of LNG has been limited. There is good quality trade literature (e.g., GIIGNL 2015; International Gas Union [IGU] 2015) and several high-quality assessments conducted by consultancies, international agencies, and independent research centers (Jensen 2004; Pöyry 2010; Standard Chartered 2011; Stern 2012; IEA 2014; Rogers 2015; Corbeau and Ledesma 2016). However, such work tends to either focus on trade flows between states (reflecting a methodological nationalism common to work on international commodity trade) or provides empirically rich assessments of key trends that eschew conceptualization or theoretical development. At the same time, industry research tends to be uncritical in the sense that it seeks to *talk up* the future prospects for the industry, and often specific regions and projects, to reassure current and potential investors in the supply chain. Within economic geography, there is growing interest in understanding the geographic political economies of natural gas (e.g., Steen and Underthun 2011; Zalik 2011; Fry 2013; Andrews and McCarthy 2014; Bouzarovski, Bradshaw, and Wochnik 2015; Bradshaw, Dutton, and Bridge 2015). To date, however, there has been no systematic effort to analyze the structures and dynamics of the LNG sector and their territorial consequences. Studies that have applied GPN to the natural gas sector have used it to describe existing networks within a region rather than analyze their dynamic evolution: Leung (2014) adopted the framework to evaluate the role of gas in China's energy transition and characterize its organizational forms, and Stephenson and Agnew (2016) deployed a GPN framework to describe hydrocarbon production in the Russian Arctic.

The analysis in this article is informed by a two-year period of research focused on understanding the changing position of the United Kingdom within global gas markets associated with declining domestic gas production (from the North Sea) and growing dependency on imported gas since 2004. The LNG component of this research examined the organizational structures through which LNG arrives in the United Kingdom, the impact that significant changes in international gas markets had on LNG flows, and the role of organizational structures and coordination strategies in modifying these impacts in terms of the volume and timing of LNG imports.Footnote[4] The project brought together economic geographers, other social scientists, and energy analysts with specialist gas industry expertise. It involved desk-based research using secondary sources (including annual corporate and sector overviews); sustained interactions with industry specialists and senior level corporate representatives (via bespoke research meetings, participation in international industry conferences, and the integration of gas analysts as project partners); site visits to Qatar Petroleum's facilities at Ras Laffan and the UK's LNG import terminals; and interviews (in the United Kingdom, United States, and Qatar) with firms active in the United Kingdom and other gas markets. In structure and purpose, both research meetings and interviews adhered to a model of *close dialog* with industry practitioners as a means of deriving knowledge and "mak(ing) sense of economic diversity in relation to broader … processes of economic change" (Clark 1998, 74). Interviews followed an open-ended and semistructured approach, and were designed to develop an understanding of industry structures and observed practices associated with investment in the LNG production network. Since gas contracts are proprietary and their terms are rarely disclosed as a matter of public record, corporate interviews and frequent discussions with industry specialists were an essential element of the research, and enabled understanding to be built up through conversational exchange and iteration as well as via more formal modes like triangulation.

These methods underpin the article's analysis of the interconnected agents, processes, and structures through which LNG is produced and distributed.

FROM LNG TRADE TO PRODUCTION NETWORKS

In this section we briefly review the evolution of the global LNG sector and highlight significant changes in its territorial form since 2000. We then explain in the following section how cross-border investment in network infrastructure and changing contract terms are enabling a global market for LNG to emerge. Early commercial uses of liquefaction were in local gas markets as a way to store gas in order to meet peaks in demand—a process known as peak shaving. The application of LNG to address spatial (rather than temporal) discontinuities in supply developed initially in the 1950s, although large-scale commercial shipments of LNG began with the commissioning of exports from Algeria to the United Kingdom and France in 1964. The early Mediterranean/Atlantic focus of LNG trade was supplemented in the 1970s by deliveries from Alaska, Brunei, Indonesia, and Abu Dhabi (and later, Malaysia and Australia) into the Japanese market. From the mid-1970s onward, Japan and the intra–Pacific Basin trade came to dominate LNG flows (over 70 percent in the early 1980s), and most new export capacity developed in this period was associated with Japan's diversification away from oil (Vivoda 2014). The complexity of the global LNG trade slowly increased with the emergence of Korea (1986) and then Taiwan (1990) as significant LNG importers toward the end of the 1980s, and the entry of Trinidad and Tobago and Qatar as LNG exporters in the late 1990s. Although the scale of LNG flows was significant for the countries involved, the industry as a whole had a small number of players and was regarded as a high-cost, niche sector reserved primarily for countries with limited access to pipeline gas. Historically, then, LNG has been a point-to-point trade from "dedicated reserves to dedicated markets" so that the *global* LNG sector has consisted of regionally discrete and largely independent projects (Tusiani and Shearer 2006, 67).

Since 2000, the scale and significance of LNG has grown markedly, and we briefly outline here how LNG trade has increased in complexity and geographic scope (Figures 3 and 4). The volume of LNG trade has more than doubled—from around 100 million metric tonnes per anum (MMTPA) in 2002 to over 248 MMTPA in 2015—growing at average of 6 percent per annum between 2000 and 2014 (IGU 2016). Global growth in liquefaction capacity has been led by Qatar, which experienced an 80 percent increase between 2006 and 2011 (Flower 2011). Qatar now accounts for a third of all LNG exports, eclipsing the role of historic exporters (such as Algeria, Indonesia, and Malaysia) in scale and reach through exports into both Atlantic and Pacific basins. However, Australia is expected to surpass Qatar as the world's largest LNG exporter in 2018, following major capacity expansion (an additional sixty-five million tons—equivalent to 25 percent of current trade—are planned to come on stream in the next few years) (Ledesma, Palmer, and Henderson 2014; Ripple 2014). A similar build-up of export capacity is occurring in the United States, which became an LNG exporter in early 2016 (IGU 2016).Footnote[5] Other new exporters have also entered the LNG market since 2000—Russia, Yemen, Angola, Peru, Norway, Equatorial Guinea, Papua New Guinea—raising the number of exporting countries to seventeen. At the same time, the number of LNG importing countries doubled to thirty (including new flows to Latin America [Brazil, Argentina, Chile] and the Middle East [Oman]). New regasification capacity has run ahead of liquefaction and now stands at around three times the volume of annual trade. Figures 3 and 4 summarize the growing extent and intensity of LNG trade between 2002 and 2015, which has eroded, although not replaced, the long-standing regional structure of LNG trade. Overall, LNG trade is anticipated to increase more rapidly than pipeline gas in the remainder of the decade, although the situation in the early 2020s is uncertain, since the current low oil price and the changing nature of LNG trade itself are deferring investment in new gasification capacity (IEA 2015).

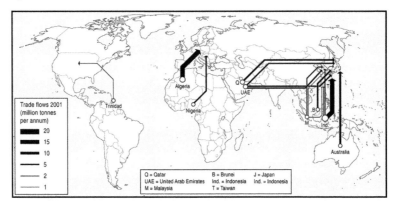

Figure 3. Worldwide LNG Trade, 2001.

Source: authors, based on data from BP Statistical Review of World Energy 2002.

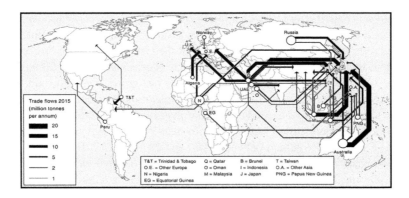

Figure 4. Worldwide LNG Trade, 2015.

Source: authors, based on data from International Gas Union.

The expanding network of LNG infrastructure provides foundations for a more globally integrated market in natural gas to emerge, similar to that for oil. Growth in regasification capacity, for example, has enabled a significant spot market to develop, along with a growing proportion of short-term (four years or less) agreements for the sale and purchase of gas: together these now represent 29 percent of global LNG trade (71.9 MMTPA) compared to less than 5 percent of the LNG market by volume in 2000 (IGU 2016). However, a series of shocks have disrupted a general trajectory of increasing gas market integration via LNG (Bradshaw, Dutton, and Bridge 2015). Three shocks, in particular, have exacerbated the geographic unevenness of gas market globalization, and LNG flows and pricing terms continue to be strongly regionalized. At the same time, these shocks have also contributed to new patterns of LNG trading, the emergence of production networks that adopt nontraditional organizational forms, and a diversification of contracts to include more flexible terms.

The loss of the United States as a potential LNG market constitutes the first shock. Much of the new LNG export capacity put in place in the early 2000s was underpinned by anticipated gas sales in the United States. However, US shale gas production since 2008 has driven down natural gas prices in North America, undermining the case for large-scale LNG imports. In the short term, the reassertion of North America as a largely self-contained *gas island* resulted in a surplus of LNG in the Atlantic basin, with much of this gas finding its way into Europe (and Spain and the United Kingdom, in particular), where it served to undermine the traditional long-term pricing system that had evolved around pipeline gas. In the longer term, the availability of domestic shale gas has encouraged the development of LNG export projects in both the United States and Canada (Boersma 2015). As we explain below, the significance of these export projects goes beyond the volumes of gas involved, since the terms under which gas is sold from these projects effectively internationalizes the US domestic gas price (Henry HubFootnote[6]) as a global benchmark.

The Tohuku earthquake and resulting tsunami in Japan in March 2011 constitutes a second shock, since it overwhelmed the Fukushima-Daichi nuclear power plant and led to the shutdown of Japan's nuclear electricity-generating capacity. The effect was to substantially increase the demand for gas in power generation, driving up the price for gas in the Japanese market and compounding a regional price divergence begun with the decline of the US gas price as a result of the *shale gale*. At its peak, the spot price in Japan was around $19 per million BTU, approximately double the price in European markets and over four times that in the United States. The effect was to reassert the dominance of Japan in LNG markets, draw spot cargoes toward Asian markets, and drive LNG importers in Japan (and elsewhere in Asia) to seek alternative and more sustainable pricing structures.

A third shock has been the fall in the price of oil since mid-2014. The drop in oil price has consequences for LNG for two reasons: most LNG projects are undertaken by oil and gas firms that have slashed expenditures on new project development; and most gas sold in Asian markets (and around 40 percent of gas sales in European markets) is indexed to the price of oil (rather than being based on gas-on-gas competition). Traditionally LNG projects have utilized oil-indexed pricing as a way to cover the relatively high costs of building liquefaction facilities. From a developer's perspective, the fall in the price of oil since 2014 "undermine(s) the rationale for relying on this pricing basis as the 'gold standard' for underpinning the economics of high cost-base LNG projects" (Rogers 2015, 47). Ironically, the previous period of high oil prices had led LNG importers—particularly in Japan—to question the logic of oil indexation and to explore alternative benchmarks for pricing gas, such as the US Henry Hub.

LNG PRODUCTION NETWORKS: EROSION OF THE TRADITIONAL *FLOATING PIPELINE* MODEL

Increases in LNG production and slowing demand growth have resulted in a period of significant oversupply, creating opportunities for new actors and a diversification in the organizational and territorial forms of LNG's production network. LNG's traditional organizational model integrated core upstream phases of gas production, liquefaction, and shipping within the structure of a single entity (Kay and Roberts 2012). In early LNG projects (such as those of Pertamina in Indonesia or Sonatrach in Algeria) resource production, liquefaction, and shipping were vertically integrated within the structure of the national oil company. The production and export of LNG effectively extended the developmental state's role in securing value from sovereign resources. In parallel, downstream stages of regasification, transmission, and gas consumption were also often integrated within a single organizational structure: in Korea, for example, this has taken the form of a national monopoly buyer, KOGAS (until recently the world's largest LNG buyer); in Japan it has been municipal or regional gas and electric utility companies (such as Tokyo Electric Power Company, Chubu Electric Power Company, and Shizuoka Gas Co).

Since the capital costs of liquefaction are very high (and represent about 50 percent of total chain costs), and LNG plants have limited operational flexibility with regard to output volumes, commercial production of LNG is dependent on securing downstream markets able to absorb supply (Pöyry 2010).Footnote[7] LNG production networks have therefore tended to assume a *project* character: the capital-intensive liquefaction stage is developed in association with both upstream (extractive) infrastructure and downstream import terminals, and underwritten by the value of long-term contracts (twenty-five years) committing buyers to take specified volumes of gas. Such long-term contracts have been essential to securing project finance to cover the cost of building the LNG plant and associated infrastructure as "without a meaningful commitment of a buyer (or buyers) to purchase the requisite volumes of LNG at an acceptable price and for the intended project duration, there would be no project" (Kay and Roberts 2012, 20; see also Douglass 2012). LNG projects, then, have traditionally brought together two territorial entities—a national seller and a national or regional buyer—via long-term, *take-or-pay* sale and purchase agreements. In these projects, integrated oil companies (IOCs) provide access to technology, often via a third-party engineering company (such as the German company Linde in the case of the cryogenic elements of the LNG plant), and project management and gas marketing experience. In regard to pricing, the balance of power between buyers and sellers in the traditional model rested largely with LNG producers, with buyers willing to pay a premium to secure supplies. This model was a direct product of the dominance of Japanese buyers in the expansion of the LNG sector where there was no pipeline alternative. Contracts allocated volume risk to buyers and price risk to suppliers, acting as "linchpins" linking the different elements of the LNG chain (Farmer and Sullivan 2012, 29).Footnote[8]

This organizational model has characterized LNG since its establishment in the 1960s. It has given the industry its distinctive structure of "a series of virtually self-contained projects made up of interlinking chains of large-scale facilities, requiring huge capital investments, bound together by long-term contracts, and subject to intensive oversight by host governments and international organizations at every stage of the process" (Tusiani and Shearer 2006, 4). The combination of integrated organizational structures, limited infrastructure, and contract terms binding a high proportion of production to particular buyers meant LNG production networks functioned, in effect, as a *floating pipeline* ferrying gas from a discrete source of supply to a discrete market (Tusiani and Shearer 2006): in other words, the potential spatial flexibility afforded by oceangoing gas trade was, in practice, highly constrained.

DIVERSIFICATION OF PRODUCTION NETWORK STRUCTURES

The traditional model (A in Figure 5) has been eroded over time and is on the cusp of significant change. In this section, we identify three significant organizational trends (B, C, and D in Figure 5) in the contemporary global LNG sector and consider their implications. First, a *process of vertical disintegration and specialization* (B) has increased the number of actors in LNG production networks. In the critical area of shipping, for example, independent LNG shipping fleets—that is, not owned, managed, or operated by upstream gas producers (e.g., Mitsui O.S.K. Lines, Teekay, Golar, Dynagas, and Höegh)— increasingly supplement the large fleets constructed and financed as part of major LNG projects and managed by LNG producers (e.g., Qatar Gas, Shell, BP). Independent carriers conclude long-term shipping and service agreements (time charter contracts) with LNG producers for the transport of their gas. They facilitate the growing market for short-term and spot gas sales, and are central to the growing geographic flexibility of LNG trade.

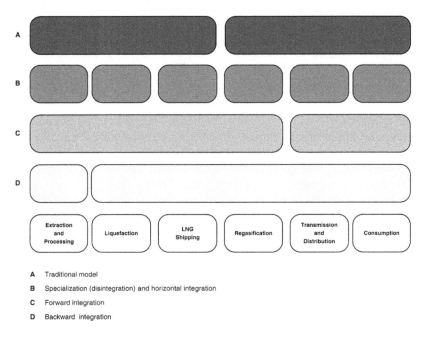

Figure 5. Organizational trends in the LNG production network.

The process of specialization and vertical disintegration in LNG extends beyond shipping to liquefaction and regasification, with the emergence of business models in which these facilities are operated on either a *merchant* or *tolling* basis (Miles 2013). In liquefaction, for example, merchant and tolling models separate the ownership of the liquefaction facility from the ownership of upstream gas supply: in the merchant model, the owner of the LNG plant purchases gas and sells the resulting LNG; in the tolling model, the owner of the LNG plant does not take ownership of the gas but is paid a fee for the option to access physical processing capacity. The nascent US LNG export market is emerging around a tolling model with owners of gas paying a service fee for access to liquefaction capacity.Footnote[9] Tolling models are emerging at the regasification end of the LNG production network, with regasification and storage capacity constructed by companies that are neither LNG producers nor downstream gas consumers and operated on a fee-for-service basis.Footnote[10] The growth of infrastructure and the emergence of big price differentials in regional markets have also created conditions for the entry of third parties. New network participants include banks (Merrill Lynch, Barclays Capital, Société

Générale, and JP Morgan) and commodity trading houses (Vitol, Trafigura, and Gunvor) that operating outside of long-term contracts, seek to capture value from the spatial flexibility that LNG affords, moving gas to markets with temporary shortages (ICIS 2010). Overall, the fragmentation described above has increased the number and diversity of actors in the LNG production network, enhancing its organizational and territorial flexibility relative to the traditional model.

Second, the traditional binational character of LNG projects *has been eroded in a significant way by cross-border investments along the production network.* This reflects, in part, the liberalization of national policies governing energy investment enabling nondomestic companies to take an equity stake and assume operational control of key assets such as liquefaction and regasification plants and the infrastructures of gas consumption (utilities, power generation). Transnational investments in the liquefaction phase of the LNG production network are dominated by joint-venture arrangements between national oil companies and the IOCs—notably Shell, BP, Total, Exxon Mobil, Chevron, and ENI. A number of state oil and gas firms, such as Malaysia's Petronas and PetroChina (both partners in proposed LNG export plants in British Columbia, for example), are also active as transnational investors in upstream LNG. The growing significance of cross-border investment also reflects a process of forward and backward integration (C and D, respectively, in Figure 5) occurring along the LNG production network, since downstream firms invest in assets upstream (and vice versa) in order to share risk and capture value. Examples include gas trading and marketing firms taking equity positions in new LNG plants (e.g., Japan-based Mitsubishi and Mitsui in Sakhalin Energy or similarly Mitsubishi's participation as an upstream investor in LNG projects around the world), and participation by utilities (e.g., Tokyo Gas, Osaka Gas, Engie, Gas Natural Fenosa) in shipping and/or liquefaction stages via equity holdings such as the stake of South Korea's KOGAS in the Prelude (10 percent) and Gladstone (15 percent) LNG projects in Australia (Tusiani and Shearer 2006). This pattern of transnational coventuring in LNG projects is largely obscured by conventional *national* analyses of upstream assets: for example, over 90 percent of LNG imports to the United Kingdom come from Qatar, but the LNG project from which the bulk of these imports are sourced (Qatargas II) is a coventure of Total, Exxon Mobil, and Qatar Petroleum. The process of forward integration involves owners of resource and liquefaction assets acquiring market access by taking equity positions in, or concluding capacity agreements with, owners of regasification terminals.Footnote[11]

Third, the discrete, point-to-point character of current LNG trade is also being reworked through a process of horizontal integration, since upstream and downstream companies take positions across multiple LNG projects. At the upstream end, IOCs, like Shell and BP, have well-established LNG trading arms (e.g., Shell Eastern Trading, BP Singapore) that source supply from the various projects in which they are partners. These arrangements are reflected in the emergence of an *aggregator* business model in which suppliers use portfolio flexibility to source gas from anywhere rather than from a single captive project. The BG Group (now part of Shell) adopted the aggregator model, building downstream market positions in the United Kingdom, United States, and Singapore, and a portfolio of flexible LNG volumes that could be sourced from north Africa, west Africa, and the Caribbean. By not being tied to a single project, the portfolio reduces supply risks for LNG buyers—especially when contracting to new liquefaction projects that are frequently delayed, and enables suppliers to optimize across a suite of assets. The portfolio organizational form is the clearest expression of an alternative to the floating pipeline model, which has characterized the historic evolution of LNG.

CHANGING NETWORK PRACTICES

The volume, timing, and destination of LNG flows are governed by the contracts concluded between buyers and sellers of LNG. Contracts are a critical "network development practice" in the sense implied by Murphy (2012, 211): that is, they are "mutually coherent, recognizable, and legitimated practices (through which) businesspeople develop relational proximity with each other" (ibid.). It is through contracts that the relational proximity that defines the LNG production network is achieved, with power relations between buyers and sellers shaping contract terms. The diversification of organizational forms and the growing complexity of LNG production networks described above are changing long-established contract practices with significant implications for the geographies of LNG trade. In general terms, these changes reflect a shift in market power within LNG production networks toward buyers associated with growing depth and liquidity of LNG markets: however, as we illustrate below, this is geographically very uneven. Contract terms are becoming more variegated over time as new practices around destination flexibility, volume flexibility, and price emerge (Table 1). Taken together, these nontraditional network development practices are causing LNG production networks to function less like floating pipelines, contributing to a more geographically integrated and liquid market. We focus here on two: destination flexibility and pricing.

Table 1 Changing Network Practices: Comparison of Traditional and Emergent Contract Characteristics

Traditional Contract Characteristics	Emergent Contract Characteristics
Long-term, take-or-pay obligations	Shorter-term, options on delivery
Limited off-take flexibility	Flexibility in off-take volumes
No destination flexibility	Flexibility in delivery points
Oil-indexation of prices (outside United States/ United Kingdom)	Pressure on oil indexation, hub benchmarking
Limited options for review/reopening	Contract reopening

Destination Flexibility

A growing number of LNG contracts allow for flexibility in cargo destination. In the historic mode, buyers were prohibited, by the terms of the contract, from landing a cargo at any other import terminal than that named in the contract (i.e., the buyer's facilities). This primarily reflected the interests of sellers who, whether for pricing, marketing, or financial reasons (e.g., export credit agency support for LNG plant construction was conditional on a proportion of cargoes being landed in a domestic market) wanted to restrict the ability of buyers to sell the cargo in a different market (Ashurst 2009). However, buyers are increasingly negotiating into contracts the right to divert cargoes, enabling them to trade LNG more widely. This process is more advanced in the Atlantic market, particularly in relation to contracts concluded for LNG export from the United States, but the process is also growing in significance in the Pacific basin. It is also associated with a greater use of free on board (FOB) terms in sale and purchase agreements, which give the buyer responsibility for delivery and destination. The traditional model, which still dominates sales in Asian and most European markets, specified delivery ex-ship (DES) and made the seller responsible for delivery (typically to a specified point). Although it is possible to write destination flexibility into DES contracts, the buyer is still beholden to the seller for delivery, and so diversion requires the seller's agreement. The growing use of FOB terms places destination within the buyer's control, affording flexibility in where the cargo is traded and enabling buyers to seek out arbitrage opportunities (Kay and Roberts 2012). National and international policy commitments to liberalize energy markets have also taken aim at destination clauses: the G7 has committed to "promote flexible gas markets" via relaxation of destination clauses, and under EU competition law, sale and purchase agreements involving the European Union cannot contain destination restrictions (Platts 2014; see also Weem n.d.; Farmer and Sullivan 2012). The effect of growing destination flexibility in the contract terms that structure LNG production networks is that a growing proportion of LNG is tradeable, since it is no longer bound to a particular destination.

Pricing Innovation

The territorially embedded character of LNG markets—derivative of regional energy histories and the availability of alternative sources (such as pipeline gas)—has given rise to regionally distinctive pricing regimes. The LNG sold in Asia, and in continental Europe (apart from the Netherlands and Belgium), has traditionally been priced against crude oil. In the United States and the United Kingdom, however, gas prices are disclosed through the market and reflect an energy infrastructure that enables gas-on-gas competition: LNG pricing in the United States references the physical gas trading point of Henry Hub in Louisiana; in the United Kingdom, prices reference the national balancing point, a virtual location in the national transmission system. These different pricing regimes mean that two broad patterns of LNG production networks have emerged, differentiated by the markets into which LNG is sold: one linked to oil indexation and representing the bulk of LNG trade and a cornerstone of the *traditional model* described above; the other—an *emergent model*—linked to hub pricing in relatively liquid markets. In the latter case, the LNG importer has to accept the prevailing domestic market price, and the United Kingdom, for example, tends to be the market of last resort.

Since 2008 prices between the Henry Hub and Asia (JCC) have sharply diverged, driven initially by growing domestic US production of shale gas (Bradshaw, Dutton, and Bridge 2015) and compounded by the shutdown of the nuclear power fleet in Japan and South Korea (which created an additional demand for gas). The scale and persistence of this price difference (which was as much as $15 per MMBTU) has encouraged innovation in LNG pricing. On the one hand, it spurred gas importers in Asia to review prevailing pricing structures, develop alliances that increase their market power, and seek greater transparency around price in the Asian markets (e.g., the Japan OTC Exchange, and Platts Japan-Korea Marker Price). In 2015, for example, Chubu Electric and Tokyo Electric Power Company, two of the largest buyers in Japan, created a downstream LNG purchasing alliance with a combined annual volume of around 35–40 MMTPA. On the other hand, buyers like Chubu Electric sought to offload the volume risk associated with the traditional model, pursuing greater destination flexibility, negotiating FOB contract terms, and by entering into joint procurement with overseas buyers. More generally, the growing depth of the LNG market has encouraged buyers to seek mid- to short-term contracts once long-term contracts come up for renewal and to turn for an increasing proportion of their demand to the spot market. Most recently, and most significantly, the Japanese government has used its presidency of the G7 to put forward a strategy to promote the development of a flexible and liquid LNG market to establish an LNG trading hub in Asia (Ministry of Economy, Trade, and Industry [METI] 2016). Unsurprisingly, traditional suppliers have sought to defend oil indexation, and there is now the potential for significant commercial conflict over pricing between producers and purchasers in Asian markets (Stern 2016), exacerbating the uncertainty facing those seeking to invest in new liquefaction capacity in the early 2020s.

Innovations in pricing are significant because they exemplify a process of experimentation currently under way in LNG production networks as suppliers and buyers seek to reallocate risk. They are also a product of a shift in the power balance in favor of LNG purchasers. Experimentation, in the form of emergent network practices—such as destination flexibility and pricing discussed here—is eroding the regionalized character of LNG production networks. The appearance of Henry Hub pricing in LNG contracts for sale in Japan (which has been dominated by oil indexation) indicates how LNG is respatializing gas markets: the reference to Henry Hub carries material and infrastructural conditions that are characteristic of one highly regionalized market (the United States) into another (Japan). Although this trend has been slowed by the impact of falling oil prices, it shows how production networks and network development practices, rather than simply physical commodity trade, are driving gas market integration.

CONCLUSION

A global gas market is emerging enabled by major investments in the infrastructures for producing, shipping, and consuming LNG. Although claims for a global gas market are premature, the LNG sector is at a pivotal moment in its evolution. Most analyses of this sector—and of international energy markets more generally—focus on international trade flows in energy commodities, rather than on the cross-border production networks through which this trade is organized. In this article we have adopted a GPN approach focused on the actors and relational practices that influence where, when, and how gas moves beyond the limits of continental pipelines. This approach has enabled us to show how a dominant *traditional* model is being rapidly reworked in the context of growing LNG supply, identifying a process of organizational and territorial experimentation as buyers, suppliers, and other actors have sought new ways to reallocate risk and capture value. Although an LNG production network has been around for over fifty years, we have shown how it is only recently that organizational structures and network development practices have emerged that depart from the floating pipeline model and enable LNG's *potential* geographic flexibility to be realized.

To account for the processes shaping the globalization of gas markets, our analysis has mobilized three conceptual elements: territoriality, materiality, and network practices. The LNG production network is an exemplar par excellence of how the materiality of commodities is integral (rather than incidental) to the geographies of their circulation, presenting barriers to and opportunities for the rescaling of markets. We have approached LNG as a particular techno-material configuration of natural gas that enables it to be moved and sold beyond the traditional limits of pipeline. Material transformation (from gas to liquid, from liquid to gas) and material stabilization (e.g., maintaining gas as a liquid for transport and storage) create opportunities for value capture, although the technical challenges and large capital costs involved restrict these opportunities to particular actors. A techno-material perspective, focused on how the material properties of natural gas enable and constrain the pursuit of value, therefore, sheds light on the expansion of international markets for natural gas and the organization of LNG production networks. In its own, however, it is unable to account for significant recent changes in the organization and territorial configuration of the LNG production network. A key material aspect of LNG (the creation of discrete, oceanborne cargoes) has always given it a much higher degree of potential spatial flexibility than pipeline gas, but in practice this potential has been highly constrained and the LNG production network has operated as a set of largely separate floating pipelines. The concept of territoriality provides a way to understand how and why LNG's long-established territorial form is now changing. In turning to territoriality we have endeavored to retain something of the processual and explanatory (rather than spatially descriptive) meaning associated with its early application to geographic political economy. As a top-level concept, the value of territoriality is that it simultaneously leans forward to highlight a significant *global shift* under way in the geographies of the LNG production network and backward to the strategies and practices of network actors through which these spatial configurations are made. Our account of territoriality in the LNG production network is empirically grounded in the multiple activities of buyers, sellers, and other actors. The concept of network development practices provides a finer-grained analytical tool for sorting through these detailed activities, identifying key practices that hold the production network together and that have a key influence on its emergent territorial form.

The article has provided the first systematic analysis within economic geography of the globalization of the LNG sector and its influence on global gas markets. It makes two significant contributions. First, adopting a GPN approach and foregrounding the question of territoriality discloses significant changes in organizational structures and network territorial forms that a focus on energy technologies, resources, or patterns of gas trade is unable to reveal. The new organizational structures and network practices emerging in the LNG production network are integral to the ways in which gas is becoming globalized, and they have significant geoeconomic and geopolitical implications. Contract flexibility and the growth of tradeable LNG create new uncertainties that are strategically significant for gas exporters and importers, and for future investment in network infrastructure. Increased flexibility around contracts and pricing may promote an increasingly globalized market, but it is unclear whether the associated lack of surety (in terms of future income streams) can finance the next generation of LNG projects: accordingly, there is potential for supply shortages in the 2020s if demand growth picks up as expected. Moreover, the erosion of the traditional model is geographically uneven. Importers in Japan and South Korea have evolved *dedicated* supply structures for which they pay a premium, whereas in Europe—and increasingly in China—LNG competes against domestic sources and pipeline gas. There is a growing commitment in Europe to marshal the flexibility of LNG to counter dependence on Russian pipeline gas imports, but LNG flows into Europe wax and wane depending on the relative price of alternative gas sources, providing limited supply security. From an LNG importing country policy perspective, there is a balance to be struck between achieving physical gas security through network practices that *lock in* dedicated supply (the Asian model) compared to a market-based form of security where the critical determinant is the price necessary to secure LNG imports (as in the United Kingdom). In sum, our analysis of the LNG production network demonstrates the potential of GPN for contributing new insights into the emergence, organization, and scaling of contemporary energy markets, and their economic and political implications.

Second, we have shown how an emergent territorial form (a *global* gas market) is enabled and shaped by the actors and relations internal to a production network. Our analysis identifies how actors in the LNG sector, and the organizational structures and network practices through which they are functionally integrated, have a central role in the emergence of a global market for gas. The practices of buyers and sellers in the LNG production network—to align interests, allocate risk, and capture value—make the market and shape its emergent territorial form (cf. Hamilton, Petrovic, and Senauer 2011). Their combined effects are changing the way gas is bought and sold and, at the same time, creating new geographies of gas that encompass international trade, cross-border investment, and price formation. A global gas market, in short, is neither self-organizing nor an ineluctable force, but rather an emergent property of the LNG production network. The article has responded to calls for more *process-sensitive* accounts of GPNs by focusing on the relationship between organizational structures, network practices, and territorial form. In doing so, we hope to have realized more fully GPN's potential for analyzing network territoriality by recognizing how network territoriality is constitutive of markets, rather than merely responsive to them.

Acknowledgments

We thank Jim Watson and Paul Ekins for welcoming us to the UKERC fold. The Oxford Institute for Energy Studies acted as a consultant on the project and we thank Jonathan Stern and Howard Rogers for their support and input at various stages. Thanks to Nicky Gregson at Durham for comments and Chris Orton for producing the graphics; to Neil Coe for productive GPN-themed conversations during the Summer Institute of Economic Geography (Kentucky); to audiences at the Open University (Development Policy and Practice Group), Linköping University, Durham Energy Institute, and the British Institute of Energy Economics who engaged with earlier versions of the paper; and to all respondents who, during the research, shared their time and expertise. We also acknowledge the work and insight of the anonymous reviewers and Editor. This work was supported by NERC's UKERC Phase 2 Grant: RP 1390198 "The Geopolitical Economy of Global Gas Security and Governance: Implications for the UK."

NOTES

1. The *difficulty* of natural gas (a mixture of different gases that contains impurities, is highly flammable and readily dissipates) is a staple feature of industrial accounts of the sector's evolution. Kaup's analysis (2008) of the Bolivian gas sector noted that because natural gas requires modes of extraction, separation, transport, and technological innovation that are capital intensive (and, accordingly, large scale), there are only limited opportunities for local firms and/or the domestic state to control technological innovations that enhance value capture (such as investment in gas-to-liquids technology to address local deficits in liquid fuels such as diesel).

2. A recent analysis of global LNG markets by the Oxford Institute for Energy Studies talks of *the great reconfiguration* (Corbeau and Ledesma 2016).

3. Although we focus here on the growth of the international seaborne LNG trade, small-scale liquefaction is also increasingly associated with an inland truck-based

retail trade in some gas markets where distribution pipelines are weakly developed (e.g., in China). This LNG retail trade—supplying industrial users that are *off grid* and the trucking industry—is frequently promoted by the LNG industry as a potential growth market. The French-based multinational ENGIE (formerly GDF-Suez), for example, estimates it could account for about 20 percent of the overall LNG market in 2030.

4. The funded research consisted of three linked elements, and focused on (1) the implications of the boom in US shale gas production, (2) European pipeline networks, and (3) LNG. The project team included specialist partners in the Gas Programme at the Oxford Institute for Energy Studies (https://www.oxfordenergy.org).

5. The *entry* of the United States into the ranks of LNG exporters (as it is popularly described) in January 2016, with the first shipments from Cherniere's Sabine Pass terminal on the Gulf Coast, refers only to the lower–forty-eight states, since the United States has exported LNG from Alaska to Japan since 1969 via the Kenai LNG plant on the Cook Inlet. As of January 2016, sixty-two million tons of new capacity is planned in the United States.

6. Henry Hub is a key trading point for natural gas in the United States. Occupying a central node in the gas transmission system, and located near Erath in Louisiana, Henry Hub has been the delivery point for the NYMEX gas futures contract since 1990.

7. Capital costs have risen sharply in the last decade: in 2013 they stood at around $1,200 per tonne LNG per year, implying a large liquefaction train (around 8 MMTPA) may cost in the range of $8–9 billion (Songhurst 2014). Pöyry (2010) indicated capital expenditure for an 8 MMTPA liquefaction plant at $6–10 billion, with this component significantly larger than shipping ($1–2.5 billion) or regasification ($1–1.5 billion).

8. In the dominant Asian market, for example, contracts price LNG against the so-called Japanese Crude Cocktail (or more properly the Japanese Custom Cleared Crude Oil Price, a weighted average price for crude imports to Japan) and the inclusion of a pricing cap—the so-called s-curve—protects buyers and sellers against large price swings (Farmer and Sullivan 2012).

9. This model is being adopted, for example, at Cheniere Energy's terminal at Sabine Pass in Louisiana and is also the framework for a number of the country's other proposed export plants (Persilly 2013). The tolling model for liquefaction is enabled by the liquidity of the US gas market and the density of gas supply infrastructure. It also reflects the way proposed US LNG export facilities are essentially a strategic response to changed market conditions not by upstream resource holders but by companies owning land and facilities originally intended as LNG import terminals, and that have access to venture capital seeking relatively short-term returns.

10. The Grain import terminal in the United Kingdom, for example, is run by the national transmission system operator (National Grid) on a commercial tolling basis: National Grid neither imports LNG into Grain nor sells gas from it on its own account, but it sells capacity rights to a range of upstream LNG producers

and downstream utilities. A similar model is associated with the rapid growth of floating storage and regasification units (FSRU). Moored offshore, these units allow municipal, regional, or national gas networks to expand and diversify gas imports by tapping into global LNG. Specialist companies (e.g., Höegh LNG, Excelerate Energy) build and operate the FSRU and market regasification capacity to those owning LNG or seeking to import gas.

11. A similar process of overseas downstream investment to secure market access characterized LNG import terminal construction in the United States in the 1990s and early 2000s. Prior to the growth of domestic shale gas production: Qatar Petroleum, Exxon Mobil, and Conoco Phillips, for example, constructed Golden Pass, one of the world's largest LNG import terminals, at Sabine Pass, Texas (Golden Pass has subsequently sought to redevelop the facilities as an LNG export terminal on a merchant model [Miles 2013]).

REFERENCES

1. Andrews, E., and McCarthy, J. 2014. Scale, shale, and the state: Political ecologies and legal geographies of shale gas development in Pennsylvania. *Journal of Environmental Studies and Sciences* 4 (1): 7–16.

2. Ashurst. 2009. Destination restrictions in LNG sale and purchase agreements. https://www.ashurst.com/doc.aspx?id_Content=4413.

3. Bathelt, H., and Glückler, J. 2003. Toward a relational economic geography. *Journal of Economic Geography* 3 (2): 117–44.

4. Birch, K., and Calvert, K. 2015. Rethinking 'drop-in' biofuels: On the political materialities of bioenergy. *Science and Technology Studies* 28 (1): 52–72.

5. Boersma, T. 2015. *Energy security and natural gas markets in Europe: Lessons from the EU and the United States*. Abingdon, Oxon, UK: Routledge.

6. Bordoff, J., and Houser, T. 2014. *American gas to the rescue: The impact of US LNG exports on European security and Russian foreign policy*. New York: Centre on Global Energy Policy, Columbia University.

7. Bouzarovski, S., Bradshaw, M., and Wochnik, A. 2015. Making territory through infrastructure: The governance of natural gas transit in Europe. *Geoforum* 64 (August): 217–28.

8. Bowen, J. 2007. Global production networks, the developmental state and the articulation of Asia Pacific economies in the commercial aircraft industry. *Asia Pacific Viewpoint* 48 (3): 312–29.

9. Bowen, J., and Leinbach, T. 2006. Competitive advantage in global production networks: Air freight services and the electronics industry in Southeast Asia. *Economic Geography* 82 (2): 147–66.

10. Boyd, W., Prudham, W. S., and Schurman, R. A. 2001. Industrial dynamics and the problem of nature. *Society & Natural Resources* 14 (7): 555–70.

11. BP. 2016. Statistical review of world energy. https://www.bp.com/content/dam/bp/pdf/energy-economics/statistical-review-2016/bp-statistical-review-of-world-energy-2016-full-report.pdf.

12. Bradshaw, M., Dutton, J., and Bridge, G. 2015. The geopolitical economy of a globalising gas market. In *Global energy: Issues, policy, and implications*, ed. P. Ekins, M. Bradshaw, and J. Watson, 291–305. Oxford: Oxford University Press.

13. Brenner, N., Jessop, B., Jones, M., and Macleod, R., eds. 2003. *State/space: A reader*. Oxford: Blackwell.

14. Bridge, G. 2008. Global production networks and the extractive sector: Governing resource-based development. *Journal of Economic Geography* 8 (3): 389–419.

15. Bridge, G., and Bradshaw, M. 2015. Deepening globalisation: Economies, trade and energy systems. In *Global energy: Issues, policy, and implications*, ed. P. Ekins, M. Bradshaw, and J. Watson, 52–72. Oxford: Oxford University Press.

16. Bridge, G., and Le Billon, P. 2013. *Oil*. Cambridge: Polity Press.

17. Bunker, S., and Ciccantell, P. 2005. *Globalization and the race for resources*. Baltimore: Johns Hopkins University Press.

18. Calvert, K. 2016. From 'energy geography' to 'energy geographies': Perspectives on a fertile academic borderland. *Progress in Human Geography* 40 (1): 105–25.

19. Chapman, J. D. 1989. *Geography and energy: Commercial energy systems and national policies*. Harlow, UK: Longman Scientific & Technical.

20. Ciccantell, P., and Smith, D. 2009. Rethinking global commodity chains: Integrating extraction, transport, and manufacturing. *International Journal of Comparative Sociology* 50 (3–4): 361–84.

21. Clark, G. 1998. Stylized facts and close dialogue: Methodology in economic geography. *Annals of the Association of American Geographers* 88 (1): 73–87.

22. Coe, N. 2012. Geographies of production II: A global production network A–Z. *Progress in Human Geography* 36 (3): 389–402.

23. Coe, N., Hess, M., Yeung, H., Dicken, P., and Henderson, J. 2004. 'Globalizing' regional development: A global production networks perspective. *Transactions of the Institute of British Geographers* 29 (4): 468–84.

24. Coe, N., and Yeung, H. 2015. *Global production networks: Theorizing economic development in an interconnected world*. Oxford: Oxford University Press.

25. Coe, N. M., Johns, J., and Ward, K. 2011. Variegated global expansion: Internationalization strategies in the temporary staffing industry. *Geoforum* 42 (1): 61–70.

26. Coote, B. 2016. *Surging liquefied natural gas trade: How US exports will benefit European and global gas supply diversity, competition and security*. New York: Atlantic Council.

27. Corbeau, A.-S., and Ledesma, D., eds. 2016. *LNG markets in transition—the great reconfiguration*. Oxford: Oxford University Press.

28. Crang, M., Hughes, A., Gregson, N., Norris, L., and Ahamed, F. 2013. Rethinking governance and value in commodity chains through global recycling networks. *Transactions of the Institute of British Geographers* 38 (1): 12–24.

29. Dicken, P. 1986. *Global shift: Industrial change in a turbulent world*. London: Harper and Row.

30. Dicken, P. 2015. *Global shift: Mapping the changing contours of the world economy*. 7th ed. London: Sage.

31. Douglass, J. 2012. Financing LNG projects. In *Liquefied natural gas: The law and business of LNG*, ed. P. Griffin, 203–36. 2nd ed. London: Globe Law and Business.

32. European Commission. 2016. *On an EU strategy for liquefied natural gas and storage*. Brussels: European Commission. https://ec.europa.eu/energy/sites/ener/files/documents/1_EN_ACT_part1_v10-1.pdf.

33. Farmer, S. H., and Sullivan, H. W. Jr. 2012. LNG sale and purchase agreements. In *Liquefied natural gas: The law and business of LNG*, ed. P. Griffin, 29–54. 2nd ed. London: Globe Law and Business.

34. Flower, A. 2011. LNG in Qatar. In *Natural gas markets in Middle East and North Africa*, ed. B. Fattouh, and J. Stern, 343–85. London: Oxford University Press.

35. Fry, M. 2013. Urban gas drilling and distance ordinances in the Texas Barnett Shale. *Energy Policy* 62 (1): 79–89.

36. Gibson, C., and Warren, A. 2016. Resource-sensitive global production networks: Reconfigured geographies of timber and acoustic guitar manufacturing. *Economic Geography* 92 (4): 430–54.

37. GIIGNL. 2015. *The LNG industry in 2014*. Neuilly-sur-Seine, France: International Group of Liquefied Natural Gas Importers. http://www.giignl.org/sites/default/files/PUBLIC_AREA/Publications/giignl_2015_annual_report.pdf.

38. Glassman, J. 2011. The geo-political economy of global production networks. *Geography Compass* 5 (4): 154–64.

39. Hamilton, G., Petrovic, M., and Senauer, B., eds. 2011. *The market makers: How retailers are reshaping the global economy*. Oxford: Oxford University Press.

40. Henderson, J., Dicken, P., Hess, M., Coe, N., and Yeung, H. 2002. Global production networks and the analysis of economic development. *Review of International Political Economy* 9 (3): 436–64.

41. Hess, M. 2004. Spatial 'relationships? Towards a reconceptualization of embeddedness. *Progress in Human Geography* 28 (2): 165–86.

42. Hess, M., and Coe, N. 2006. Making connections: Global production networks, standards, and embeddedness in the mobile telecommunications industry. *Environment and Planning A* 38 (7): 1205–27.

43. Hudson, R. 2008. Cultural political economy meets global production networks: A productive meeting? *Journal of Economic Geography* 8 (3): 421–40.

44. Hughes, A., and Reimer, S., eds. 2004. *Geographies of commodity chains*. New York: Routledge.

45. ICIS. 2010. Banks seize their moment in LNG. http://www.icis.com/resources/news/2010/09/17/9394397/focus-banks-seize-their-moment-in-lng/.

46. IGU 2015. World LNG report. http://www.igu.org/sites/default/files/node-page-field_file/IGU-World%20LNG%20Report-2015%20Edition.pdf.

47. IGU. 2016 World LNG report. http://www.igu.org/publications/2016-world-lng-report.

48. International Energy Agency. 2011. *Are we entering a golden age of gas? World energy outlook special report*. Paris: IEA. http://www.worldenergyoutlook.org/media/weowebsite/2011/WEO2011_GoldenAgeofGasReport.pdf.

49. International Energy Agency. 2014. *World energy outlook*. Paris: IEA. https://www.iea.org/publications/freepublications/publication/WEO_2014_ES_English_WEB.pdf.

50. International Energy Agency. 2015. *World energy outlook*. Paris: IEA. http://www.worldenergyoutlook.org/weo2015/.

51. International Energy Agency. 2016. *Medium term gas market report*. Paris: IEA.

52. Isaksen, A., and Kalsaas, B. 2009. Suppliers and strategies for upgrading in global production networks: The case of a supplier to the global automotive industry in a high-cost location. *European Planning Studies* 17 (4): 569–85.

53. Jensen, J. T. 2004. The development of a global LNG market. http://www.oxfordenergy.org/2004/01/the-development-of-a-global-lng-market-is-it-likely-if-so-when/.

54. Johns, J. 2006. Video games production networks: Value capture, power relations and embeddedness. *Journal of Economic Geography* 6 (2): 151–80.

55. Kaup, B. 2008. Negotiating through nature: The resistant materiality and materiality of resistance in Bolivia's natural gas sector. *Geoforum* 39 (5): 1734–42.

56. Kay, J., and Roberts, P. 2012. Structuring LNG projects—Evolution or revolution in the LNG supply value chain? In *Liquefied natural gas: The law and business of LNG*, ed. P. Griffin, 13–28. 2nd ed. London: Globe Law and Business.

57. Ledesma, D., Palmer, N., and Henderson, J. 2014. Future of Australian LNG exports—Will domestic challenges limit the development of future LNG export capacity? http://www.oxfordenergy.org/wpcms/wp-content/uploads/2014/09/NG-90.pdf.

58. Lee, Y.-S., Heo, I., and Kim, H. 2014. The role of the state as an inter-scalar mediator in globalizing liquid crystal display industry development in South Korea. *Review of International Political Economy* 21 (1): 102–29.

59. Leung, C.-K. 2014. Fueling the dragon: A geopolitical economy of natural gas transition in China. PhD diss., Durham University.

60. MacKinnon, D. 2013. Strategic coupling and regional development in resource economies: The case of the Pilbara. *Australian Geographer* 44 (3): 305–21.

61. Mahutga, M. 2014. Global models of networked organization, the positional power of nations and economic development. *Review of International Political Economy* 21 (1): 157–94.

62. Manners, G. 1964. *The geography of energy*. London: Hutchinson University Library.

63. Miles, S. 2013. Legal structures and commercial issues for LNG export projects—North America and beyond. Paper presented at the Seventeenth International Conference and Exhibition on Liquefied Natural Gas (LNG 17), Houston, TX, January 15. http://docslide.us/documents/-2013-legal-structures-and-commercial-issues-for-lng-export-projects-north.html.

64. Ministry of Economy, Trade, and Industry. 2016. *Strategy for LNG market development: Creating a flexible LNG market and developing an LNG trading hub in Japan*. Tokyo: METI. http://www.meti.go.jp/english/press/2016/pdf/0502_01b.pdf.

65. Murphy, J. 2012. Global production networks, relational proximity, and the sociospatial dynamics of market internationalization in Bolivia's wood products sector. *Annals of the Association of American Geographers* 102 (1): 208–33.

66. Odell, P. R. 1970. *Oil and world power: A geographical interpretation*. Harmondsworth, UK: Penguin.

67. Overland, I. 2016. Energy: The missing link in globalization. *Energy Research & Social Science* 14 (3): 122–30.

68. Paasi, A. 1998. Boundaries as social processes: Territoriality in the world of flows. *Geopolitics* 3 (1): 69–88.

69. Persilly, L. 2013. Tolling model a new option for LNG plant ownership. Alaska natural gas transportation projects. http://www.arcticgas.gov/tolling-model-new-option-lng-plant-ownership.

70. Pirrong, C. 2014. Fifty years of global LNG: Racing to an inflection point. http://www.trafigura.com/media/1350/fifty-years-global-lng-craig-pirrong-research-trafigura-2.pdf.

71. Platts. 2014. Chubu Electric's 20-year LNG deal with Shell Eastern allows for resell. http://www.platts.com/latest-news/natural-gas/tokyo/chubu-electrics-20-year-lng-deal-with-shell-eastern-26799136.

72. Ponte, S., and Gibbon, P. 2005. Quality standards, conventions and the governance of global value chains. *Economy and Society* 34 (1): 1–31.

73. Pöyry. 2010. Global gas and LNG markets and GB's security of supply. Report to UK Department of Energy and Climate Change, June 2010. Oxford: Pöyry Energy Consulting. http://www.poyry.com/sites/default/files/globalgasandlngwithbgsecurity-june2010-energy.pdf.

74. Prudham, W. S. 2005. *Knock on wood: Nature as commodity in Douglas fir country*. New York: Routledge.

75. Ripple, R. 2014. Australia emerging as top LNG supplier. *Oil and Gas Journal*, May 5.

76. Rodrigue, J.-P. 2006. Transportation and the geographical and functional integration of global production networks. *Growth and Change* 37 (4): 510–25.

77. Rogers, H. 2015. The impact of lower gas and oil prices on global gas and LNG markets. OIES Paper NG 99. Oxford: Oxford Institute for Energy Studies.

78. Songhurst, B. 2014. LNG plant cost escalation. OIES Paper NG 83. Oxford: Oxford Institute for Energy Studies. https://www.oxfordenergy.org/wpcms/wp-content/uploads/2014/02/NG-83.pdf.

79. Standard Chartered. 2011. LNG: The second coming. https://www.yumpu.com/en/document/view/48592598/lng-the-second-coming-standard-chartered-bank-research/3.

80. Steen, M., and Underthun, A. 2011. Upgrading the 'petropolis' of the North? Resource peripheries, global production networks, and local access to the Snøhvit natural gas complex. *Norskgeografisktidsskrift—Norwegian Journal of Geography* 65 (4). 212–25.

81. Steinberg, P. 1994. Territory, territoriality and the new industrial geography. *Political Geography* 13 (1): 3–5.

82. Stephenson, S., and Agnew, J. 2016. The work of networks: Embedding firms, transport, and the state in the Russian Arctic oil and gas sector. *Environment and Planning A* 48 (3): 558–76.

83. Stern, H., ed. 2012. *The pricing of internationally traded gas*. Oxford: Oxford University Press.

84. Stern, J. 2016. *The new Japanese LNG strategy: A major step towards hub-based gas pricing in Asia*. Oxford: Oxford Institute for Energy Studies. https://www.oxfordenergy.org/wpcms/wp-content/uploads/2016/06/The-new-Japanese-LNG-strategy-a-major-step-towards-hub-based-gas-pricing-in-Asia.pdf.

85. Taylor, P. 1994. The state as container: Territoriality in the modern world-system. *Progress in Human Geography* 18 (2): 151–62.

86. Tokatli, N., Wrigley, N., and Kizilgün, Ö. 2008. Shifting global supply networks and fast fashion: Made in Turkey for Marks & Spencer. *Global Networks* 8 (3): 261–80.

87. Tusiani, M., and Shearer, G. 2006. *LNG: A non-technical guide*. Tulsa, OK: PennWell.

88. Vivoda, V. 2014. *Energy security in Japan: Challenges after Fukushima*. Surrey, UK: Ashgate Publishing.

89. Weem, P. n.d. Evolution of long-term LNG sales contracts: Trends and issues. http://ksintranet.kslaw.com/Library/publication/evolutionoflngsales.pdf.

90. Yeung, H.-W., and Coe, N. 2015. Toward a dynamic theory of global production networks. *Economic Geography* 91 (1): 29–58.

91. Yoon, H., and Malecki, E. 2010. Cartoon planet: Worlds of production and global production networks in the animation industry. *Industrial and Corporate Change* 19 (1): 239–71.

92. Zalik, A. 2011. Shipping the next prize: The trade in liquefied natural gas from Nigeria to Mexico. In *Dangerous trade: Histories of industrial hazard across a globalizing world*, ed. C. Sellers, and J. Melling, 87–98. Philadelphia: Temple University Press.

Factors Controlling Natural Gas Accumulation in the Southern Margin of Junggar Basin and Potential Exploration Targets

Jianping Chen[1], Xulong Wang[2], Yongge Sun[3], Yunyan Ni[1], Baoli Xiang[2] and Jiande Liao[2]

[1]PetroChina Research Institute of Petroleum Exploration and Development, Beijing, China
[2]PetroChina Xinjiang Oilfield Company, Karamay, China
[3]School of Earth Sciences, Zhejiang University, Hangzhou, China

ABSTRACT

In this paper, factors controlling natural gas accumulation in the southern margin of Junggar Basin were mainly discussed by a comparison with natural gas generation and accumulation in the Kuqa Depression of Tarim Basin. The southern margin of Junggar Basin and the Kuqa Depression of Tarim Basin are located on the north and south sides of the Tianshan Mountains respectively, and they share the similar sedimentary stratigraphy and tectonic evolution history. In recent several decades, many large gas fields have been found in the Kuqa Depression of Tarim Basin, but no great breakthrough in the southern margin of Junggar Basin. Our results suggest that natural gas in the southern margin of Junggar Basin is mainly thermogenic wet gas, and can be divided into three types as coal-derived gas, mixed gas and oil-associated gas, of which the former two types are dominated. The Jurassic coal measures are the main source rocks of natural gas, and the main gas generation time from this set of source rocks matched well with the formation time of the anticline structures, resulting in favorable conditions for natural gas accumulation. In the western part of the southern margin in the Junggar Basin, the Permian lacustrine and the Upper Triassic lacustrine-swamp source rocks could be important sources of natural gas, and the main gas generation time also matched well with the formation time of traps. Compared with the Kuqa Depression of Tarim Basin, natural gas sources are better in the southern margin of Junggar Basin, and the geologic conditions are favorable for the formation of large oil and gas fields in the southern margin of Junggar Basin. The deep Permian-Jurassic-Cretaceous petroleum system is the most favorable petroleum system for natural gas exploration in the southern margin of Junggar Basin. The western part and the central part of the southern margin in the Junggar Basin could be the first targets for the discovery of the Jurassic coal-derived oil and gas reservoirs. The shallow Cretaceous-Neogene petroleum system is the second target for natural gas exploration.

Keywords: *Southern margin of Junggar Basin, natural gas, genetic type of natural gas, Jurassic coal measures, natural gas accumulation, favorable exploration target, Kuqa depression*

INTRODUCTION

The southern margin of Junggar Basin mainly includes the southern depression zone in the Junggar Basin (Figure 1), with an area of 2.1×10^4 km² and a maximum strata thickness of 15 km. In the southern margin of Junggar Basin, five sets of possible source rocks were identified in the Permian, Triassic, Jurassic, Cretaceous, and Paleogene, respectively (Wang et al., 2013; Chen et al., 2015a), and many structural traps were well developed, where different types of oils and gases have been found (Wang et al., 2013; Chen et al., 2015b; Chen et al., 2016a; Chen et al., 2016b; Chen et al., 2016c; Chen et al., 2016d; Chen et al.,2016e). Therefore, the southern margin of Junggar Basin has long been considered as the most potential area for natural gas exploration (He et al., 2004; Wu et al., 2007; Lei et al., 2012). However, no great breakthrough occurred in last several decades in terms of oil and gas exploration in this area. On the other hand, the southern margin of Junggar Basin and the Kuqa Depression of Tarim Basin, located on the north and south sides of the Tianshan Mountains respectively, share very similar sedimentary stratigraphy and tectonic evolution history (Fang et al., 2005; Fang et al., 2007; He et al., 2009; Wang, 2014). A breakthrough of natural gas exploration in the Kuqa Depression of Tarim Basin has been achieved in last 3 decades, including the discovery of large gas fields KL-2, Dabei, Dina, Keshen, and others (Wang, 2014). The natural gas in the Kuqa Depression was derived mainly from the Jurassic coal-measures, and probably minor from the Upper Triassic Taliqike coal measures (Liang et al., 2002; Zhao et al., 2002; Liang et al., 2003; Liang et al., 2004; Liu et al., 2007; Qin et al., 2007). In the southern margin of Junggar Basin, coal-measures in the Middle-Lower Jurassic strata, the Upper Triassic Huangshanjie Formation and Haojiagou Formation were also well-developed. More important is that the Permian, Cretaceous and Paleogene source rocks were found in the southern margin of Junggar Basin. Furthermore, the multiple sets of source rocks in the southern margin of Junggar Basin are at highly to over mature stages, and large amounts of natural gas could be theoretically generated (Wang et al., 2013; Chen et al., 2015a, Chen et al., 2016c). For example, theoretical calculation suggested that the gas generation intensity of the Jurassic coal-measures can be $3–8 \times 10^9$ m³/km², and even up to 10×10^9 m³/km² in some areas (Wu et al., 2007), which is basically equivalent to that of the Jurassic coal measures from the Kuqa Depression (Du et al., 2006). This result indicates that the gas generation intensity is not the limited factor to control the formation of large gas fields. Although previous studies have clearly concluded that the natural gas discovered in the southern margin of Junggar Basin is mainly from the Jurassic coal-measures (Li et al., 2004; Liao et al., 2011; Dai et al., 2012; Wang et al., 2013; Chen et al., 2016d; Liu et al., 2016), only two commercial gas fields were discovered to date, namely the Hutubi gas field in the Hutubi anticline and the Mahe gas field in the Manas anticline in the central part of the southern margin in the Junggar Basin, with a total proved geological gas reserve of 32.96×10^9 m³ (Du et al., 2019). The scale of natural gas reserve discovered to date in the southern margin of Junggar Basin is unexpected and much smaller than that in the Kuqa Depression. Previous study by Kuang and Liu (2001) indicated that, in the southern margin of Junggar Basin, there are sufficient gas sources, numerous fold anticlines and effective regional cap rocks, but no faults to connect the deep Jurassic gas source with the upper traps, while in the Kuqa Depression of Tarim Basin, there are not only abundant gas sources, but also high quality reservoir rocks, well-developed faults, and good preservation conditions (gypsum-salt cap rocks), and all together result in natural gas accumulation. Thereafter, a general view is that the gas accumulation conditions in the southern margin of Junggar Basin are not as good as those in the Kuqa Depression.

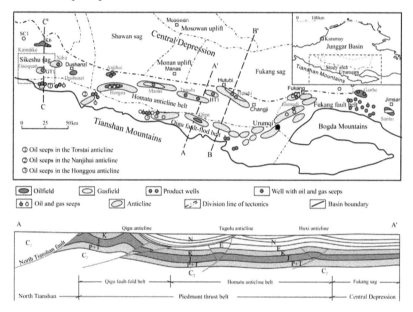

Figure 1. Distribution of structural traps and of oil and gas fields in the southern margin of Junggar Basin.

In the southern margin of Junggar Basin, petroleum geologists and prospectors got confused by many problems for a long time. For examples, is there any possibility for the discovery of large gas fields in the southern margin of Junggar Basin? Where are the favorable exploration areas and targets? What are the factors to induce the great difference in natural gas discovery between the southern margin of Junggar Basin and the Kuqa Depression of Tarim Basin which are located at the north and south depressions of the Tianshan Mountain?

In January 2019, high-product oil and gas flow were obtained from Well GT1 in the Gaoquan anticline of the Sikeshu sag, west part of the southern margin in the Junggar Basin, with 1,213 m^3/d oil and 321.7 × 10^3 m^3/d natural gas from the deep Cretaceous strata (Chen et al., 2019; Du et al., 2019; Zhang et al., 2020). The daily oil and gas production from this well is the highest in the Junggar Basin so far. In December 2020, once again, high-product oil and gas flow were obtained from the Well HT1 at the depth of 7,367 to 7,382 m in the Huxi anticline (Figure 1) in the middle part of the southern margin in the Junggar Basin, with 610 × 10^3 m^3/d natural gas and 106 m^3/d oil. The great breakthrough in these two wells showed a great potential of oil and gas exploration in the southern margin of Junggar Basin.

In this study, based on our previous results about the genetic type of natural gas and its sources in the southern margin of Junggar Basin (Chen et al., 2019), we investigated the geological and geochemical conditions for natural gas generation and accumulation in the southern margin of Junggar Basin, and conducted a comparative study between the southern margin of Junggar Basin and the Kuqa Depression of Tarim Basin in terms of factors controlling the natural gas accumulation. Also, the favorable natural gas exploration areas and targets were discussed for strategy-making reference.

GEOLOGICAL BACKGROUND

Structural Characters

The southern margin of Junggar Basin starts from the Fukang fault zone in the east, extending to the Sikeshu sag in the west, and connects with the Shawan sag, Monan uplift and Fukang sag in the north, and with the north Tianshan Mountain in the south. It is 500 km in length from east to west, 40–60 km in width from south to north, and 21×10^3 km^2 in area. In terms of regional tectonic background, the southern margin of Junggar Basin belongs to the piedmont thrust belt of the north Tianshan Mountain (Figure 1), and is the youngest and most complex fold belt in the Junggar Basin. Also, it is a secondary tectonic unit developed during the Late Hercynian, Indosinian-Yanshanian, and Himalayan periods (Yang et al., 2004; Kuang and Jia, 2005; Kuang and Qi, 2006; Chen et al., 2007). Based on the structural styles and their formation mechanisms, the southern margin of Junggar Basin can be further divided into four sub-tectonic units as the Sikeshu sag, the Homatu structural belt, the Qigu fault fold belt and the Fukang fault zone (Yang et al., 2004; Figure 1). From the Qigu fault fold belt to the Homatu structural belt, three rows of anticlines were developed from south to north. The first row includes the Torstai, Nananjihai, Honggou, Qingshuihe, and Qigu anticlines, etc., the second row is the Horgos, Manas and Tugulu anticlines, and the third row has the Anjihai, Huxi, and Hutubi anticlines, etc. In terms of geographic background, the southern margin of Junggar Basin can be divided into three parts as the west, the central and the east (Figure 1).

Sedimentary Strata

Six sets of sedimentary strata occur in the southern margin of Junggar Basin, including the Permian, Triassic, Jurassic, Cretaceous, Paleogene, and Neogene (Figure 2). In the central part, the gross thickness of sedimentary strata is up to 15 km, and relatively thin in the west and east parts, generally 8–12 km (Wang et al., 2013; Chen et al., 2015a; Chen et al., 2016c). Previous studies showed that the Permian source rock was one of the most important source rocks in the Junggar Basin. In the southern margin of Junggar Basin, the Middle Permian source rock deposited in the semi-deep to deep lacustrine facies, with a thickness of 600–1,600 m. Oil shale deposit in the east part of the southern margin was well-developed in the Lucaogou Formation in the Middle Permian (Graham et al., 1990; Carroll et al., 1992; Gao et al., 2016; Bai et al., 2017; Cao et al., 2017). The Upper Permian strata were mainly deposited in the fluvial-swamp to semi-deep lacustrine facies. The Middle-Lower Triassic strata are mainly composed of fluvial-shallow lacustrine coarse clastic deposits, while the Upper Triassic strata deposited in the shore-shallow to semi-deep lacustrine facies with a thickness of 300–800 m, interbedded with thin carbonaceous mudstone and coal seam of swamp facies. The Badaowan, Sangonghe, Xishanyao, and Toutunhe formations of Middle-Lower Jurassic strata are mainly coal-bearing deposits of fluvial and limnetic facies, which are widely distributed in the Junggar Basin, with a maximum thickness of 3,000 m in the southern margin, and generally 1,000–2,000 m. This set of coal measures is the main oil and gas source rocks in the southern margin of Junggar Basin (Wang et al., 2013; Chen et al., 2015a; Chen et al., 2016c). The Upper Jurassic strata include the Qigu Formation and the Karaza Formation, and it is a set of red coarse clastic deposits, which is widely distributed in the southern margin with a thickness of more than 600 m. The Lower Cretaceous strata are a set of semi-deep to shallow lacustrine deposits, which is widely distributed in the whole basin with the thickness of 1,594 m in the southern margin of Junggar Basin. It is relatively well-developed in the central part of the southern margin in respect to oil and gas generation potential (Wang et al., 2013; Chen et al., 2015a; Chen et al., 2016c). The Upper Cretaceous strata are mainly composed of fluvial coarse clastic deposits, with a thickness of 46–813 m, and generally 300–600 ms. The Paleocene-Eocene strata are fluvial-shallow lacustrine deposits, with a thickness of 15–855 m, and generally >450 m. The Eocene-Oligocene Anjihaihe Formation is mainly composed of deep-semi, deep-shallow lacustrine facies, with a thickness of 44–800 m and generally 350–650 m. Dark mudstone is relatively well developed in the west part of the southern margin. The Oligocene-Pliocene strata are mainly dominated by shallow lacustrine and fluvial deposits, with a thickness of 2,000–2,300 m. The Quaternary Xiyu Formation is composed of piedmont proluvial-alluvial fan-fluvial conglomerate and glutenite deposits, which is widely distributed in the southern margin of Junggar Basin, with a thickness of 350–2046 m, and generally >1,300 m. The thickness of the Quaternary Xiyu Formation in the west part is greater than that in the central and east parts.

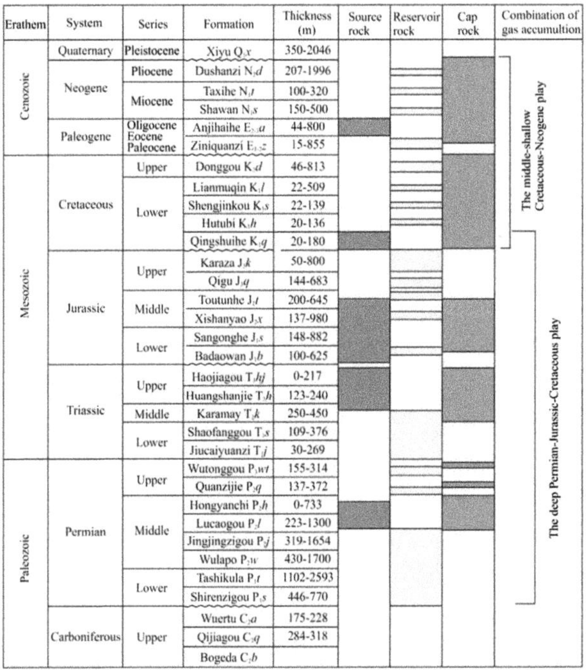

Erathem	System	Series	Formation	Thickness (m)	Source rock	Reservoir rock	Cap rock	Combination of gas accumultion
Cenozoic	Quaternary	Pleistocene	Xiyu Q_1x	350-2046				The middle-shallow Cretaceous-Neogene play
	Neogene	Pliocene	Dushanzi N_2d	207-1996				
		Miocene	Taxihe N_1t	100-320				
			Shawan N_1s	150-500				
	Paleogene	Oligocene Eocene	Anjihaihe $E_{3-2}a$	44-800				
		Eocene Paleocene	Ziniquanzi $E_{1-2}z$	15-855				
Mesozoic	Cretaceous	Upper	Donggou K_2d	46-813				
		Lower	Lianmuqin K_1l	22-509				
			Shengjinkou K_1s	22-139				
			Hutubi K_1h	20-136				
			Qingshuihe K_1q	20-180				
	Jurassic	Upper	Karaza J_3k	50-800				The deep Permian-Jurassic-Cretaceous play
			Qigu J_3q	144-683				
		Middle	Toutunhe J_2t	200-645				
			Xishanyao J_2x	137-980				
		Lower	Sangonghe J_1s	148-882				
			Badaowan J_1b	100-625				
	Triassic	Upper	Haojiagou T_3hj	0-217				
			Huangshanjie T_3h	123-240				
		Middle	Karamay T_2k	250-450				
		Lower	Shaofanggou T_1s	109-376				
			Jiucaiyuanzi T_1j	30-269				
Paleozoic	Permian	Upper	Wutonggou P_3wt	155-314				
			Quanzijie P_3q	137-372				
		Middle	Hongyanchi P_2h	0-733				
			Lucaogou P_2l	223-1300				
			Jingjingzigou P_2j	319-1654				
			Wulapo P_2w	430-1700				
		Lower	Tashikula P_1t	1102-2593				
			Shirenzigou P_1s	446-770				
	Carboniferous	Upper	Wuertu C_2a	175-228				
			Qijiagou C_2q	284-318				
			Bogeda C_2b					

Figure 2. Sedimentary strata as well as combination of source rock, reservoir rock, and cap rock in the southern margin of the Junggar Basin.

DISTRIBUTION AND SOURCES OF NATURAL GAS

Distribution of Natural Gas

Although many oil and gas seeps occur in the southern margin of Junggar Basin, and natural gas shows have also been found in lots of exploration wells (Wang et al., 2013; Chen et al., 2016b; Liu et al., 2016; Zheng et al., 2017), only two commercial gas fields have been discovered in the Hutubi anticline (the Hutubi gas field) and in the Manas Anticline (the Mahe gas field) in the central part (Figure 1). The natural gas fields discovered in other structures are mainly small-scale gas reservoirs or associated gas of oil reservoirs revealed by individual well drilling, including the Mazhuang gas field in the Santai, east part.

In these gas fields or gas-bearing structures, the natural gas reservoirs in the Hutubi, Tugulu, Manas, Horgos, and Anjihai anticlines in the central part are mainly located in the Paleogene Ziniquanzi and Anjihaihe formations, and minor in the Neogene Shawan Formation and the Upper Cretaceous Donggou Formation. The natural gas reservoirs in the Nananjihai structure are distributed in the Jurassic Badaowan Formation, while the natural gas reservoirs from the Qigu oilfield mainly distributed in the Triassic and Jurassic strata. The oil and gas reservoirs in the Dushanzi anticline, located in the west part of the southern margin, are mainly distributed in the Neogene Shawan Formation and Taxihe Formation. Two condensate gas layers in the Neogene Shawan Formation have been penetrated in Well Du1 and Well XC2.

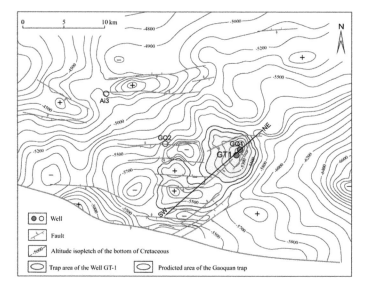

Figure 3. Structural map of Gaoquan anticline and adjacent Cretaceous bottom boundary in west of southern margin.

The oil and gas reservoirs in the Kaindick, Xihu, and Gaoquan anticlines in the west part are mainly distributed in the Jurassic Qigu Formation and the bottom of the Lower Cretaceous Qingshuihe Formation. The natural gas reservoirs in the Mazhuang gas field in the east part are mainly in the Upper Jurassic strata. Vertically, oil and gas discovered in the central part are mainly in the middle-shallow Upper Cretaceous-Neogene, while oil and gas discovered in the west part are much deeper, mainly in the Upper Jurassic-Lower Cretaceous.

Recently, high-product oil and gas flow was discovered in Well GT1 in the Gaoquan anticline of the Sikeshu sag (Figure 1), west part of the southern margin in the Junggar Basin (Chen et al., 2019; Du et al., 2019), and the oil and gas reservoirs are located in the Toutunhe Formation of Middle Jurassic (Figures 3, 4). Although it is difficult at moment to determine the boundary and scale of oil and gas reservoirs, it was predicted that the structural high trap area of the Gaoquan anticline is about 69 km^2 with the closure height is 450 m, and the Cretaceous structural high trap area where Well GT1 was drilled is about 28 km^2. Thereafter, large oil and gas field is being expected in Gaoquan anticline. More recently, a high-product commercial oil and gas field was discovered in Well HT1 at the depth of 7,367–7,382 m in the Huxi anticline in the middle part of the southern margin (Figure 1). It was estimated to be 100 billion cubic meters of natural gas reserve.

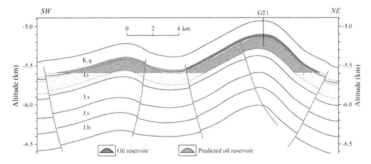

Figure 4. Predicted reservoir profile (through Well GT1) of Gaoquan anticline in west of southern margin (Its location is indicaten in Figure 3).

Genetic Types and Sources of Natural Gas

The stable carbon and hydrogen isotopic compositions of gasoline hydrocarbons is considered to be closely related to the sedimentary environments, organic matter types and thermal maturity, and can be widely used to determine the genetic types and sources of natural gas (Stahl, 1974; Schoell, 1980; Schoell, 1983; Bernard et al., 1977; James, 1983; James, 1990; Whiticar, 1994; Whiticar, 1996; Whiticar, 1999). Previously, a large body of publications have been focused on the geochemical characters and sources of natural gas discovered in the southern margin of Junggar Basin (Wang et al., 2009; Hu et al., 2010; Wang et al., 2013; Liu et al., 2016; Zheng et al., 2017; Chen et al., 2019), and it is now generally accepted that natural gas discovered in the southern margin of Junggar Basin is thermogenic gas (Chen et al., 2019).

In respect to genetic types and sources of natural gas in the southern margin of Junggar Basin, previous studies by Wang et al. (2009), Hu et al. (2010), Wang et al. (2013), and Liu et al. (2016) suggested that it is mainly coal-derived gas from the Jurassic coal-measures. However, Chen et al. (2019) recently conducted a systematic comparative study on the components and the stable carbon isotopic compositions of natural gas from different anticline structures in the southern margin, and found that the geochemical characters of natural gas from different structures in the southern margin of Junggar Basin were quite different. They can be divided into three types as coal-derived gas, mixed gas and oil-associated gas, of which coal-derived gas and mixed gas are dominated (Figure 5). The main genetic types of natural gas are coal-derived gas and mixed gas in the Kaindick, Xihu, and Dushanzi anticlines in the west part of the southern margin, while mixed gas in Well GT1 at the Gaoquan anticline. In the central part, the coal-derived gas is dominated in the Anjihai, Horgos, Manas, Tugulu, and Hutubi anticlines, and mixed gas and coal-derived gas are dominated in the Qigu anticline, while the oil-associated gas in the Nananjihai Anticline. In the Mazhuang gas field from the Santai, Fukang fault fold belt in the east part of the southern margin, the oil-associated gas is the main genetic type.

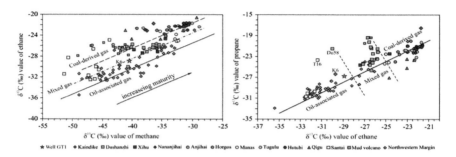

Figure 5. Carbon isotopic composition and types of natural gas in southern margin (Modified from Chen et al., 2019. The data regarding mud volcano are cited from Dai et al., 2012, and the data for the Northwestern margin is provided by the Research Institute of Xinjiang Oilfield Company).

Gas-source correlation results suggested that natural gas from the Kaindick, Xihu, and Dushanzi anticlines in the west part of the southern margin was derived mainly from the Jurassic coal-measures, and minor from the Permian lacustrine source rocks (Chen et al., 2019). The natural gas from Well GT1 was sourced from the Jurassic coal measures and the Permian lacustrine source rocks. The natural gas from the second and third row anticlines in the Homatu anticline belt in the central part of the southern margin was derived mainly from the Jurassic coal-measures, while the natural gas from the first row anticlines in the Qigu fault fold belt was sourced mainly from the Permian lacustrine source rocks and the Jurassic coal-measures, minor from the Upper Triassic lacustrine-limnetic source rocks. In the Mazhuang gas field in the Santai, Fukang fault fold belt in the east part of the southern margin, the natural gas was derived mainly from the Permian lacustrine source rocks, and minor from biogenetic gas due to biodegradation of crude oil generated from the Permian source rocks. The results clearly showed that in the southern margin of Junggar Basin, the Jurassic coal-measures is the most important source rock of natural gas, and the Permian lacustrine source rock is the second one. The Triassic lacustrine-limnetic source rock may also be regionally important gas source rocks.

GEOCHEMICAL CONSTRAINTS ON NATURAL GAS GENERATION

Bulk Characters of Source Rocks

Five sets of source rocks from the Permian, Triassic, Jurassic, Cretaceous, and Paleogene strata occurred in the southern margin of Junggar Basin, and the thickness of source rocks mainly depends on its location. In the central part of the southern margin, there are 5 sets of source rocks, while 2-4 sets in east and west parts (Wang et al., 2013; Chen et al., 2015a; Chen et al., 2016c).

The Middle Permian Lucaogou Formation lacustrine source rocks are mainly distributed in the areas from the east part to the central part of the southern margin, with a thickness of 50–250 m, and the maximum thickness up to >700 m in the east part (Carroll, 1998; Wang et al., 2013). The organic carbon content of source rocks ranges from 0.50 to 34.27%, with an average of 6.60%. The average hydrocarbon generation potential (S_1+S_2) is 36.99 mg/g.rock. The organic matters are dominated by sapropelic type (type I) and humic-sapropelic type (type II_A). The Middle Permian Lucaogou Formation lacustrine source rock is now at the low-mature stage at the outcrops in the east part of the southern margin (Wang et al., 2013; Hou et al., 2021). In the sags of the Homatu anticline belt, the Permian source rock is buried greater than 10 km and reached the highly to over mature stage, and was considered to be an effective gas source rock (Wang et al., 2013; Chen et al., 2015a). Crude oils from the Permian source rocks have been previously found in the Dushanzi anticline (Wang et al., 2013; Chen et al., 2016a; Chen et al., 2016b). In Well GT1 and Well K6, half of the natural gas with lighter carbon isotope composition was derived from the Permian source rocks (Chen et al., 2019). These results suggested that the Permian lacustrine source rocks could be an important source rock in the west part of the southern margin. Therefore, further study using seismic and drilling data to determine the distribution and scale of the Permian lacustrine source rocks is needed.

The lacustrine source rock in the Upper Triassic Huangshanjie Formation is also widely distributed in the southern margin of Junggar Basin (Chen et al., 2003; Kang et al., 2012; Wang et al., 2013; Chen et al., 2015a; Chen et al., 2016c), with a thickness of 50–300 m. The total organic carbon is lower than that of the Permian Lucaogou Formation, with an average TOC of 2.89%. The organic matters are mainly type II and type III. The burial depth of the Huangshanjie Formation is now up to >9 km in the central sag, and reaches highly to over mature stage, resulting in an effective source rock. This set of source rock is relatively well developed and is an important candidate as natural gas source rock in the central part of the southern margin and the Fukang sag in the east part.

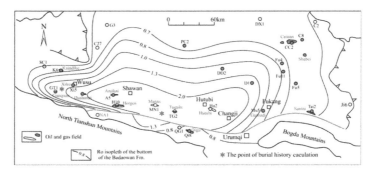

Figure 6. Maturity of source rocks at the bottom of Jurassic and the distribution map of main oil and gas fields (wells) from Jurassic in southern margin of Junggar Basin.

The Middle-Lower Jurassic source rock is widely distributed in the southern margin of Junggar Basin. In Badaowan Formation of the Lower Jurassic, the dark mudstone, carbonaceous mudstone, and coal seam are generally 200–300 m, 1–10 m, and 5–50 m in thickness, respectively. The thickness of dark mudstone ranges from 50 m to 300 m in the Sangonghe Formation. The thickness of dark mudstone, carbonaceous mudstone and coal seam in the Xishanyao Formation is 75–150 m, 2–15 m and 5–30 m, respectively. The total organic carbon of dark mudstone from the Middle-Lower Jurassic strata ranges from 0.5 to 6.0%, with an average of 1–2% in different Formations. The average TOC of carbonaceous mudstone is about 20%, and ~50–60% for coal seam. The organic matters of the Middle-Lower Jurassic source rocks are mainly type II_B and type III, with type II_A limited. Although the vitrinite reflectance of organic matter from the Jurassic outcrop source rocks ranges from 0.5 to 0.7%, it reaches highly to over mature stage in the depression due to burial depth of >8 km (Figure 6). Previous studies concluded it was the most important source rock in the southern margin (Wang et al., 2013; Chen et al., 2015a; Chen et al., 2016c).

The Qingshuihe Formation of Lower Cretaceous lacustrine source rock is widely distributed in the southern margin, but the most developed in the central part of the southern margin with a thickness of 150–200 m, compared to a general thickness of 50–150 m in other parts of the southern margin. The TOC of mudstone ranges from 0.06 to 1.81% with an average of 0.92%. The organic matters are dominated by type I and type II_A. Although organic matter in outcrop samples showed low mature stage, it reaches peak to late oil generation stage in the depression due to burial depth of up to 6–8 km. In the central part of the southern margin, the crude oil was mainly derived from the Qingshuihe source rock (Liao et al., 2006; Wang et al., 2013; Chen et al., 2016b; Chen et al., 2016d; Chen et al., 2016e).

The Paleogene Anjihaihe Formation lacustrine source rock is mainly distributed in the central and west parts of the southern margin, with a thickness of 50 m–200 m. The average TOC is 1.03%, but shows a great change depending on location. Organic carbon content of source rocks from the Sikeshu sag in the west part is much higher, with an average TOC of 1.41%, and the hydrocarbon generation potential is 5.02 mg/g. rock. The organic matter is dominated by type II. In the central and east parts, organic carbon content of dark mudstone is relatively low, and the organic matter is dominated by type III. Organic matter from the outcrop dark mudstone is now at immature stage. However, the thermal maturity of organic matter in source rocks from the Sikeshu Sag to the central part reaches low mature-mature stage in respect to its depth of 5,000–6,500 m. The crude oil in the Paleogene-Neogene reservoirs is sourced from this set of source rock in the Dushanzi, Kaindick, Xihu and Gaoquan anticlines in the west part (Wang et al., 2013; Chen et al., 2016b; Chen et al., 2016d). Therefore, it is an effective oil source rock, with little gas potential.

Conclusively, the effective source rocks for natural gas generation in the southern margin of Junggar Basin are mainly the Middle-Lower Jurassic coal measures, the Upper Triassic limnetic and the Permian lacustrine source rocks.

Thermal Evolution and Hydrocarbon Generation History

Previous studies suggested that the paleo-geothermal field in the southern margin of Junggar Basin experienced a gradual cooling process as revealed by the geothermal gradient from 32.0–36.6°C/km in Permian to 18–22°C/km at present (Wang et al., 2000; Qiu et al., 2001). Within the constraint of measured vitrinite reflectance of drilled source rocks, the thermal evolution and hydrocarbon generation history of source rocks from the sags in the central and west parts were calculated by basin modeling software (Figure 7). In the central part, the burial depths of the Permian, Triassic and Jurassic source rocks are much deeper (Figure 8), and the hydrocarbon generation occurred relatively early. In the southern sag of the Manas anticline in Homatu structural belt, the main oil generation period of the Middle Permian source rock was in Cretaceous (150–60 Ma), and the main gas generation period was in Paleogene-Oligocene (60–20 Ma; Figure 7A). The source rock from the Upper Triassic strata mainly generated oil at the end of Early Cretaceous to Paleogene (110–30 Ma), and the main gas generation period at Miocene (20–5 Ma). The main oil generation period of the Middle-Lower Jurassic source rocks occurred at the Late Cretaceous to Oligocene (100–20 Ma), and the peak oil about 90–25 Ma from the Late Cretaceous to Eocene. Gas generation from kerogen-cracking (R_o = 1.0%) started at the beginning of Eocene (40 Ma), and currently reaches peak gas generation stage. The Lower Cretaceous source rock is now mainly at the peak and late oil generation stage.

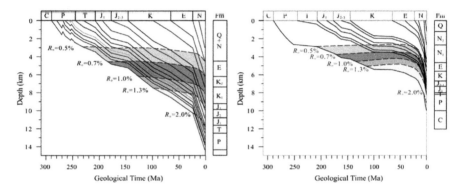

Figure 7. Burial evolution and hydrocarbon generation history of source rocks in the middle and western parts of southern margin. (A) Middle part of sedimentary sag in the middle of southern margin (see Figure 6 for location); (B) Middle and west parts of Sikeshu Sag in the west of southern margin (see Figure 6 for location).

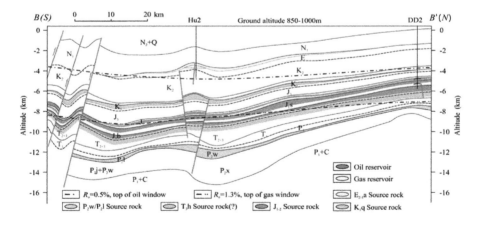

Figure 8. Sketch diagram of structure, source rock burial evolution and hydrocarbon migration and accumulation section in the middle of southern margin.

It is still unclear to date about the distribution of the Permian-Triassic source rocks in the west part of the southern margin in Junggar Basin. According to seismic interpretation, the Permian-Triassic strata are about 1800–2,300 m in thickness, and are 6–8 km in burial depth in the mid-west of the Sikeshu sag (Figure 9), much shallower than that in the central part. Therefore, the main hydrocarbon generation time in the mid-west of the Sikeshu sag could be much later than that in the central part. The Lower Permian source rock (equivalent to the Fengcheng Formation) mainly generated oil during the Late Jurassic to Early Cretaceous (160–100 Ma), and the main gas generation period started from the Late Cretaceous and continues to present (Figure 7B). Because the Cretaceous and Paleogene strata in the Sikeshu sag are much thinner than that in the central part, the hydrocarbon generation period of the Jurassic coal-measures in the Sikeshu sag should be later than that in the central part. The main oil generation stage started from Eocene and continues to present, and it is still at the peak oil to late stage oil generation. The Lower Cretaceous source rock generated oil much later, which was mainly at the mature stage of oil generation. The Paleogene source rock is at immature to early mature stage of oil generation, and basically has no potential for natural gas generation.

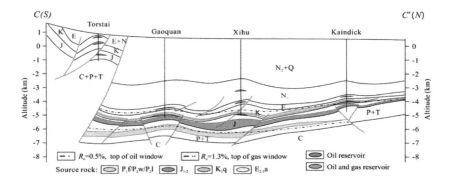

Figure 9. Sketch diagram of structure, source rock burial evolution and hydrocarbon migration and accumulation section in the west of southern margin.

COMPARISON ON GAS ACCUMULATION CONDITIONS BETWEEN THE SOUTHERN MARGIN OF JUNGGAR BASIN AND THE KUQA DEPRESSION

The Kuqa Depression of Tarim Basin and the southern margin of Junggar Basin are located on south and north sides of the Tianshan Mountains, respectively, with similar sedimentary cap rocks and tectonic evolution history in respect to petroleum geological background (Hendrix et al., 1994; Li et al., 2000; Kuang and Liu, 2001; Liang et al., 2002; Liang et al., 2004; Fang et al., 2005; Kuang and Jia, 2005; Kuang and Qi, 2006; Fang et al., 2007; He et al., 2009). Many large gas fields have been discovered to date in the Kuqa Depression, such as KL-2, Dabei, Keshen and Dina gas fields (Wang, 2014). However, in the southern margin of Junggar Basin, only two medium-sized gas fields have been found in the Hutubi and Manas anticlines. The main factors leading to the exploration differences between the Kuqa Depression and the southern margin of Junggar Basin were investigated for a long time and are still unclear to date. Kuang and Liu (2001) made a comprehensive comparison on the hydrocarbon accumulation conditions between the two regions, and concluded that both were excellent gas source, fold anticlines, and effective regional cap rocks. The main difference is that in the Kuqa Depression, the quality of the reservoir rock is much better and faults connected source rocks with reservoirs were well developed. Also, the preservation is better in the Kuqa Depression than that in the southern margin of Junggar Basin. Thereafter, it was considered that natural gas accumulation conditions in the southern margin of Junggar Basin are worse than those in the Kuqa Depression. However, recent discovery of high-product oil and gas flow in the Well GT1 and Well HT1 suggested that gas accumulation conditions in the southern margin are probably not worse than expected previously, and need a deep insight on the factors controlling gas generation and accumulation in the southern margin of Junggar Basin.

Difference in Source Rock Development

It is now generally accepted that the Middle-Lower Jurassic coal-measures are main source rocks in the Kuqa Depression and the southern margin of Junggar Basin, followed by the Upper Triassic lacustrine-limnetic source rocks (Du et al., 2006, Qin et al., 2007; Wang et al., 2013; Chen et al., 2015a; Chen et al., 2016c). In the Kuqa Depression, the cumulative thickness of Middle-Lower Jurassic limnetic mudstone and carbonaceous mudstone is 100–600 m, and the cumulative thickness of coal seams is generally 5–30 m (Liang et al., 2004). The mudstone in the Yangxia and Kizilonur Formations of Lower Jurassic is generally 50–500 m in thickness, and the coal seams can reach a maximum thickness of 52 m. The thickness of mudstone in the Chakemak Formation generally ranges from 50 to 150 m. The dark mudstone and carbonaceous mudstone in the Upper Triassic Taliqike Formation are generally 50–150 m in thickness, and the coal seams are generally 0.5–7 m, with a maximum thickness of 12 m.

In the southern margin of Junggar Basin, the cumulative thickness of the Middle-Lower Jurassic limnetic dark mudstone and carbonaceous mudstone is 200–700 m, and the cumulative thickness of coal seams is 10–50 m with a maximum thickness of 60 m (Wang et al., 2013; Chen et al., 2015a; Chen et al., 2016c). The mudstone in the Badaowan Formation of Lower Jurassic is generally 200–300 m in thickness, and the cumulative thickness of coal seams is generally 5–20 m (up to 50 m). The mudstone of the Sangonghe Formation is generally 50–300 m in thickness; the mudstone of the Xishanyao Formation of Middle Jurassic is generally 75–150 m, and the cumulative thickness of coal seams is 5–30 m with a maximum thickness of >40 m.

Table 1. Comparison of source rocks between southern margin and Kuqa Depression[a]

Time	Source rock type	Southern margin					Kuqa depression				
		Thickness (m)	TOC (%)	HC generation potential (mg/g)	HI (mg/gTOC)	R_o (%)	Thickness (m)	TOC (%)	HC generation potential (mg/g)	HI (mg/gTOC)	R_o (%)
E	Mud	50–200	1.41	5.02	387	0.4–0.8					
K	Mud	150–250	0.92	1.74	189	0.4–1.3					
J	Mud	200–700	1.70	2.41	142		100–600	2.20	2.18	99	
	Coal	10–50	54.22	109.44	210	0.5–2.2	5–30	55.75	89.49	167	0.5–2.5
T_3	Mud	50–300	2.89			0.8–2.5	50–150	1.85			0.6–2.8
	Coal	<5					0.5–7	64.99			0.6–2.8
P	Mud	50–250	6.60			>1.3					

[a]The data in the table are mainly based on the statistics of Liang et al. (2004) and Wang et al. (2013). The abundance of organic matter and hydrocarbon generation potential of Jurassic are the average values of source rocks in low to medium maturity stage.

The lacustrine and limnetic source rocks from the Upper Triassic Huangshanjie and Haojiagou Formations are generally 50–300 in thickness, which is similar to those in the Kuqa Depression, but the distribution of coal-measures in the Haojiagou Formation is not as stable as that in Kuqa Depression. As discussed in *Bulk Characters of Source Rocks*, three sets of source rocks occurred in the southern margin of Junggar Basin, including the Lower Permian/Middle Permian, the Lower Cretaceous and Paleogene source rocks, which were not developed in the Kuqa Depression, suggesting multiple sets of source rocks in the southern margin of Junggar Basin, and even the Middle-Lower Jurassic coal-measures were developed better than those in the Kuqa Depression (Table 1). However, the Upper Triassic lacustrine and limnetic source rocks in the southern margin of Junggar Basin are basically equivalent to or slightly worse than those in the Kuqa Depression.

Difference in Hydrocarbon Generation Potential of Source Rocks

As showed in Table 1, at low-medium maturity, hydrocarbon generation potential of Jurassic dark mudstone, carbonaceous mudstone and coals from the southern margin of Junggar Basin is higher than those of the Jurassic coal measures from the Kuqa Depression (Liang et al., 2004; Wang et al., 2013; Chen et al., 2015a). This is mainly due to the relatively low content of hydrogen-enriched liptinites in coal measures from the Kuqa Depression. The relative percentage of inertinites in mudstone and carbonaceous mudstone from the Kuqa Depression is about 25–50%, and 40–70% vitrinite as well as 3–8% liptinites. However, the relative percentage of inertinites in mudstone and carbonaceous mudstone from the southern margin of Junggar Basin is only 8–10%, and 56–68% vitrinite as well as 25–33% liptinite. This is the same case in coal seams. The relative percentage of inertinites reaches up to 28%, vitrinite to 70%, and liptinites to 2% in coals from the Kuqa Depression. While the relative percentage of inertinites is only 16%, and 64% vitrinite as well as up to 20% liptinites in coals from the southern margin of Junggar Basin (Liang et al., 2004; Qin et al., 2007; Wang et al., 2013). In addition, the average TOC of dark mudstones from the Upper Triassic Huangshanjie and Taliqike Formations in the Kuqa Depression is 1.09 and 1.81%, respectively. However, the average TOC of Upper Triassic mudstone and carbonaceous mudstone is 2.89% in the southern margin of Junggar Basin, higher than that in the Kuqa Depression. Therefore, the hydrocarbon sources in the southern margin of Junggar Basin are better than those in the Kuqa Depression.

The maturity of organic matter in Jurassic coal-measures from the Kuqa Depression is higher than that in the southern margin of Junggar Basin. At present, the maturity of organic matter in Jurassic coal measures from the Kuqa Depression ranges from 0.8 to 2.5% as revealed by vitrinite reflectance, showing an increasing trend from east to west with the highest of 2.8% (Wang et al., 1999; Liang et al., 2004). In the eastern region, the Jurassic coal-measures is mainly at the peak oil to late oil stages, while in the central and west parts, source rocks are mainly at highly to over mature stage (equivalent to wet gas-dry gas stages). However, the maturity of organic matter in Jurassic coal measures from the southern margin of Junggar Basin ranges from 0.7 to 2.2% as revealed by vitrinite reflectance, showing an increasing trend from west to east. The Jurassic coal-measures is mainly at peak oil stage in the west part, but mainly at high-mature wet-gas stage in the central part. No source rock reaches at dry gas stage. Therefore, the maturity of organic matter in source rocks from the Kuqa Depression is much higher than that in the southern margin of Junggar Basin, which may be one of the main factors controlling gas generation and accumulation in the Kuqa Depression.

Basin modeling results showed that the total generated hydrocarbon amount from Jurassic source rocks in the southern margin of Junggar Basin is about 397.3×10^9 t (Du et al., 2019), and the total expelled hydrocarbon amount is about 140.3×10^9 t (including the total expelled oil amount of 38.9×10^9 t, and total expelled gas amount of 127×10^{12} m^3). The average intensity of hydrocarbon generation, hydrocarbon expulsion and gas expulsion were 18.92×10^6 t/km^2, 6.68×10^6 t/km^2 and 6×10^9 m^3/km^2, respectively. Also, the Permian and the Upper Triassic source rocks can contribute hydrocarbon resources, which was not included here. Therefore, the southern margin of Junggar Basin has rich sources for hydrocarbon accumulation.

Difference in Physical Properties of Reservoir Rock

Both the Jurassic and Cretaceous sandstones as reservoir rocks in the Kuqa Depression showed high quality (Kuang and Liu, 2001). The porosity and permeability of Jurassic sandstones are 6–21% and 0.1×10^{-3}–300×10^{-3} μm^2, respectively. While the porosity and permeability of Cretaceous Basjiqike Formation sandstone reaches 8.7–19.2% and 87 $\times 10^{-3}$–696×10^{-3} μm^2, respectively, typical characters of medium porosity and medium permeability reservoir rocks. Furthermore, the Cretaceous Formation sandstone was widely distributed in the Kuqa Depression with huge thickness of 90–500 m (Wang and Hu, 2002). However, compared to the Kuqa Depression, the Jurassic, Cretaceous and Tertiary reservoir rocks are generally poor in quality in the southern margin of Junggar Basin (Kuang and Liu, 2001). In fact, the deep buried reservoirs showed extremely low porosity and ultra-low permeability in the Kuqa Depression, with a porosity of 3–9% (averaging 5.4%) and a matrix permeability of 0.35×10^{-3} to 0.5×10^{-3} μm^2 (Wang, 2014).

Sandstones from the Upper Jurassic Qigu Formation and the Karaza Formation are the effective reservoir rocks in the southern margin of Junggar Basin. The sandstone from the Jurassic Qigu Formation mainly deposited in the braided delta front with an area of >15,000 km^2, resulting in changing physical properties, and thereafter leading to low porosity and low permeability. In the west part of the southern margin, the sandstone from the Jurassic Qigu Formation is relatively thin, with thickness of 100–236 m. The porosity ranges from 3 to 25%, with an average of 10–21%; the permeability ranges from 0.1×10^{-3} to $1,640 \times 10^{-3}$ μm^2, with an average of 4×10^{-3}–162×10^{-3} μm^2 (Zhang et al., 2012). In the central part of the southern margin, sandstone from the Jurassic Qigu Formation is much thicker, with a thickness of 60–384 m. The porosity ranges from 9.27 to 14.38%, with an average of 11.5%, and the permeability ranges from 0.16×10^{-3} μm^2 to 17.68×10^{-3} μm^2. Therefore, sandstone from the Jurassic Qigu Formation has medium porosity and low permeability (Wu et al., 1994). The Jurassic Karaza Formation is mainly distributed in the central and east parts of the southern margin, with relatively limited potentials. Large alluvial fan and braided river delta were well developed, resulting in the formation of a set of very thick massive conglomerate and sandstone. In outcrop area, the thickness of glutenite is usually >150 m, with a maximum thickness up to 860 m in the Karaza area (Du et al., 2019). The exploration results revealed that sandstone from the Jurassic Karaza Formation was 210–450 m in thickness, with an area of 10,000 km^2, and showing mainly medium-low porosity and medium-low permeability. Regionally, high-quality Jurassic Karaza reservoir rocks were well developed, with an average porosity of 16–19%, and permeability of 100×10^{-3}–260×10^{-3} μm^2 (Han et al., 2012; Lei et al., 2012; Du et al., 2019).

The Cretaceous reservoir rock is mainly composed of glutenite and sandstone at the bottom of the Qingshuihe Formation of Lower Cretaceous in the southern margin of Junggar Basin. Previous study by Fang et al. (2006) suggested that this set of reservoir rock was low quality with thin deposit (10–30 m), and was mainly distributed at the basin edge and low uplifts in the central part. However, recent study indicated that the Cretaceous sandstones developed mainly from braided river delta and fan delta front at the bottom of the Qingshuihe Formation, with a thickness of 20–100 m and an area of 15,000 km^2 (Du et al., 2019). The sandstone shows good in the physical properties, with porosity of 9.0–

18.6% (averaging 15–18%), permeability of 97.75×10^{-3}–186.00×10^{-3} μm^2. It can be defined as medium-low porosity and medium-high permeability. The main pore type in sandstone from the Qingshuihe Formation is primary residual intergranular pores, with good connectivity. For example, the porosity of sandstone from the Qingshuihe Formation in Well GT1 ranges from 13.4 to 18.4% at the interval of 5767.5–5774.7 m on the basis of well logging interpretation. High-product oil and gas flow confirmed that sandstone from the Cretaceous Qingshuihe Formation also is the excellent reservoir rocks.

Sandstones from the Paleogene Ziniquanzi Formation and the Neogene Shawan Formation are also the effective reservoir rocks in the southern margin of Junggar Basin, with a thickness generally ranging from 10 to 80 m (Lei et al., 2008; Xiao et al., 2011; Bai et al., 2013a). Sandstone from the Ziniquanzi Formation in Homatu structural belt showed medium-high porosity and medium-high permeability, with a porosity of 1.8–34% (mainly 21–26%, averaging 18.94%). The permeability ranges from 0.06×10^{-3} to $1000 \times 10^{-3} \mu m^2$, and mainly 4×10^{-3} to 640×10^{-3} μm^2, with an average of $197 \times 10^{-3} \mu m^2$. Sandstones from the Ziniquanzi Formation and Shawan Formation in the Sikeshu sag are relatively poor in quality as reservoir rock, with porosity of 9–16% and permeability of 10×10^{-3}–127×10^{-3} μm^2. Therefore, reservoir rocks distributed in the Jurassic to Neogene were relatively well-developed in the southern margin of Junggar Basin, and their quality is similar to those in the Kuqa Depression.

Difference in Migration Pathways and Traps

The strong thrust and compression during Himalayan orogeny in the Kuqa Depression resulted in the development of structures in rows and belts, which can be divided into upper and lower structural layers. Natural gas discovered to date was mainly accumulated in the lower structural layer. The thrust faults directly connected source rocks with the lower structural layer, being good vertical migration pathways (Kuang and Liu, 2001; He et al., 2009; Wang, 2014). In the southern margin of Junggar Basin, structural traps were also well developed (Li et al., 2003; Kuang and Jia, 2005; Kuang and Qi, 2006; Lei et al., 2012), which were not only in the shallow structural layer, but also in the deep structural layer. Total 45 traps have been identified to date in the middle-shallow structural layers of the piedmont thrust belt (Li et al., 2003), and 40–46 traps have been preliminarily identified in the deep layer (Lei et al., 2012; Du et al., 2019), of which 21 traps in the deep layer were confirmed, with a total trap area of 2,486 km^2. Most of these traps are anticlines that were formed during the Neogene period (Hendrix et al., 1994; Deng et al., 1999; Fang et al., 2005; Hu et al., 2005; Guo et al., 2006; Du and Wang, 2007; Fang et al., 2007) and are similar to those in the Kuqa Depression. The trap formation time in the southern margin of Junggar Basin matched well with the time of gas generation from the Jurassic coal-measures, which is also similar to that in the Kuqa Depression.

Previously, Kuang and Liu (2001) argued that no fault system connected deep source rocks with the upper anticline traps in the southern margin of Junggar Basin. However, recent study clearly showed faults connecting deep source rocks with the shallow structural traps in the southern margin of Junggar Basin (Figures 4, 8, 9). This was evidenced by oil and gas shows in outcrops and drilled wells in the southern margin of Junggar Basin, and commercial natural gas fields were also discovered in the shallow Paleogene and Neogene reservoirs from the Manas and Hutubi anticlines. Natural gas was sourced mainly from the deep Jurassic coal-measures, and migrated into shallow layers through fault systems (Wang et al., 2013; Chen et al., 2015b; Chen et al., 2016c; Chen et al., 2017). The results suggested that the fault systems connecting the deep source kitchen with the upper traps were well developed in the southern margin of Junggar Basin, that were favor for the upward migration of deep oil and gas.

Difference in Cap Rocks and Sealing Capability

Two sets of regional cap rocks mainly occurred in the Kuqa Depression. The first one is the Paleogene gypsum-salt rock and gypsum-mudstone cap rock, and the second is the Lower Cretaceous Shushanhe Formation-Jurassic Qigu Formation mudstone. The deposits of cap rocks in the Kuqa Depression were widely distributed with excellent sealing capability, especially for the Paleogene gypsum-mudstone salt rock (Kuang and Liu, 2001; Wang and Hu, 2002). There are also two sets of regional cap rocks developed widely in the southern margin of Junggar Basin. One is the mudstone from the Qingshuihe Formation-Hutubi Formation of Lower Cretaceous, and another is lacustrine mudstone from the Paleogene Anjihaihe Formation. Basically, the quality of the cap rock in the Kuqa Depression is better than that in the southern margin of Junggar Basin in terms of rock characters.

The Qingshuihe Formation in the southern composed of gray and grayish green mudstone, interbedded with thin argillaceous siltstone. A set of thick basal conglomerate is well developed at the bottom of Qingshuihe Formation, with ratio of mudstones to strata of 0.5–1.0. The total thickness of mudstone drilled is 188 m, and the maximum thickness of individual layer is 78 m. The Hutubi Formation is mainly composed of grayish green and brownish red mudstone, with a thickness of 300–700 m, and a maximum thickness of individual layer up to 138 m (Du et al., 2019). The lacustrine mudstone in the Anjihaihe Formation of Paleogene is generally 50–200 m in thickness. Although no gypsum-mud salt rock developed in the Cretaceous and Paleogene strata in the southern margin of Junggar Basin, overpressure occurred in the mudstones of the Middle-Lower Jurassic, Lower Cretaceous, and Paleogene Anjihaihe Formation (Kuang, 1993; Wu et al., 2000; Zha et al., 2000; Wang et al., 2003; Luo et al., 2004; Wu et al., 2006; Luo et al., 2006; Luo et al., 2007). The pressure coefficient ranges from 1.3 to 2.0 with a maximum up to 2.43, and most of them >1.8. Regionally, mudstone system in the west of the southern margin showed high overpressure, while low overpressure in the east. For example, a repeat formation test (RFT) showed pressure coefficients of 2.2 and 2.4 (with an excess pressure of approximately 40–44 MPa) in the lower part of the Cretaceous Qingshuihe Formation and the Anjihaihe Formation from the Gaoquan and Anjihai anticlines in the west, respectively (Luo et al., 2007; Du et al., 2019). The excess pressure in the lower part of the Anjihaihe Formation from the Manas and Tugulu anticlines is approximately 20 MPa, whereas on the Hutubi anticline to the east, the pressure in the same formation and the underlying strata is close to hydrostatic pressure (Luo et al., 2007). The widespread occurrence of overpressure indicates that mudstone system can be good sealing capability in the southern margin of Junggar Basin.

In fact, oil and gas discovered in the Jurassic reservoirs in Kaindick oilfield demonstrated a good sealing capability of mudstones in the Cretaceous Qingshuihe Formation in the southern margin of Junggar Basin. Also, the Dushanzi oil field, Mahe gas field and Hutubi gas field showed good Paleogene and Neogene reservoir–cap rock combination. The exploration facts strongly suggest that the mudstone systems in the southern margin of Junggar Basin can act as good cap rocks for large and medium oil and gas accumulation.

NATURAL GAS ACCUMULATION AND EXPLORATION TARGETS PREDICTED IN THE SOUTHERN MARGIN OF JUNGGAR BASIN

Although source rocks in the Permian, Triassic, Middle-Lower Jurassic, Lower Cretaceous Qingshuihe Formation, and the Lower Tertiary Anjihaihe Formation have been proved to be effective source rocks in the southern margin of Junggar Basin, the main oil and gas generation periods of source rocks are quite different, which strongly depend on the location of source rocks. The relationship between hydrocarbon generation time and the formation time of structural traps is a key factor controlling the formation of large oil and gas reservoirs.

Regionally Tectonic Evolution and Natural Gas Accumulation

The southern margin of Junggar Basin started to uplift greatly since Miocene (25 Ma). Therefore, the anticline structures in this area were developed very late (Fang et al., 2005; Hu et al., 2005; Guo et al., 2006; Du and Wang, 2007; Fang et al., 2007). The Qigu anticline and other anticlines in the first row were formed before ~10–7 Ma; the Horgos anticline and other anticlines in the second row were formed before 3–1.5 Ma; the Anjihai anticline and other anticlines in the third row were formed before 1 Ma, while the Hutubi and Xihu anticlines etc. were formed much later. Therefore, the structures in the first row can only capture the oil and gas formed since ~10 Ma, the structures in the second row can capture oil and gas since ~3 Ma, and the structures in the third row can capture oil and gas since 1 Ma. By comparing the relationship between the oil and gas generation time from five sets of source rocks and the formation time of the anticlines in the southern margin of Junggar Basin, natural gas charging and accumulation process can be deciphered in these anticline structures, and can also interpret the differences in geochemical properties of natural gas from different anticline structures perfectly.

The anticline structures with oil and gas discovery had not formed during the main oil generation stage from the Permian, Triassic and Jurassic source rocks in the central part of the southern margin. Except for the anticlines located at the edge of southern margin where the Permian and Triassic source rock depositions were shallow and can correlated to the initial formation stage of paleo-structures, for most anticline structures in the central part of the southern margin, it is impossible to be charged by crude oil generated from the Permian, Triassic and Jurassic source rocks. Even the main gas generation stage from the Middle Permian and Upper Triassic source rocks, these traps were still not formed, leading to its less possibility to form large gas reservoirs with natural gas from the Permian and Triassic source rocks. Therefore, only a small amount of dry gas generated by the Permian-Triassic source rocks at over mature stage could be captured very late. However, organic matter of the Middle-Lower Jurassic coal-measures began to generate gas (R_o = 1.0%) at the beginning of Eocene (40 Ma), and entered main gas window at 20 Ma. It is now still at the large amount of gas generation stage, suggesting that it matched well with the formation time of the anticlines in the central part. Therefore, the anticline traps in the central part of the southern margin can capture the natural gas generated from the Middle-Lower Jurassic coal-measures. Since the burial depth of Jurassic coal measures is much shallower in the west part, resulting in lower maturity compared to that in the central part (Figure 7), and thereafter, the beginning of a large amount of gas generation was later in the west part. Conclusively, the Jurassic coal measures are now still at the stage of crude oil-condensate -wet gas generation, and the central part at the stage of wet gas generation.

The natural gas captured by the traps in the central part shows a gradually drying trend from west to east and an increased trend of maturity. Because the anticline structures in the second and third rows such as the Tugulu and Hutubi anticlines were formed very late, they mainly captured natural gas generated from the Jurassic coal-measures at a highly to over mature stage, leading to much heavier carbon isotopes than those of the Anjihai anticline.

On the other hand, faults were well developed in the thrust-fault zone of the southern margin (Kuang and Qi, 2006; Chen et al., 2007; Lei et al., 2012). These faults connected the multiple deep source kitchens with the upper reservoirs (Figures 4, 8, 9), resulting in the formation of upward migration channels for oil and gas, and finally in the multiple charging and oil and gas accumulation. Fluid inclusions in sandstones from reservoirs in the Manas anticline and its fluorescence spectrum characteristics suggested that two stages of oil and gas charging occurred in these anticline structures (Bai et al., 2013b). The first stage (11 Ma) was oil charging and accumulation, followed by the second stage (3 Ma) with natural gas charging and accumulation. Other anticline structures in the central part of the southern margin have almost the same structural development background and oil and gas charging history as the Manas anticline The early charged oil in the anticlines from the central part of the southern margin was derived mainly from lacustrine source rocks in the Lower Cretaceous Qingshuihe Formation (Kang et al., 2008; Wang et al., 2013; Chen et al., 2016b; Chen et al., 2016c; Chen et al., 2016d). The late charged natural gas was derived mainly from the Jurassic coal-measures (Wang et al., 2009; Hu et al., 2010; Wang et al., 2013; Liu et al., 2016; Chen et al., 2019). Condensates discovered could be formed by gas charging and secondary reformation of a large amount of Jurassic-derived natural gas to Cretaceous-derived crude oil (Chen et al., 2017).

If the Lower Permian source rocks occurred in the Sikeshu sag in the west part of the southern margin, the main oil generation period started from the Late Jurassic to Early Cretaceous (Figure 7). If the Middle Permian source rocks occurred, the main oil generation period started from the Late Cretaceous to Paleogene. Whatever the occurrence of Lower and Middle Permian source rocks, the anticlines such as the Dushanzi, Xihu, and Gaoquan in the west part of the southern margin had not formed. Therefore, it is impossible for these anticlines to capture the crude oil generated from the Permian lacustrine source rocks. One exclusive is that the Permian source rocks buried in relatively shallow areas might still generate a certain amount of crude oil since Neogene, and then form small-scale hydrocarbon accumulation, such as the crude oil reservoir in Well Du68 in the Dushanzi anticline (Wang et al., 2013; Chen et al., 2016b). However, the main gas generation period of the Permian source rocks started from the Late Cretaceous and continued to present. This matched well with the formation time of anticlines in the west part of the southern margin. Therefore, the natural gas generated from these source rocks can be captured and form oil and gas reservoirs. On the other hand, the Jurassic coal-measures in the Sikeshu sag is still at a large amount of oil generation stage or peak oil generation stage. For example, crude oil from the Qigu and Qingshuihe reservoirs in the Kaindick Oilfield and the Xihu anticline was sourced from the Jurassic coal-measures (Wang et al., 2013; Chen et al., 2016b; Chen et al., 2016d). Also, a large amount of natural gas associated with crude oil could be expected. Therefore, the western anticlines in the southern margin might be charged with oil-associated gas from the Permian source rocks or coal-derived gas from the Jurassic coal measures, or mixed. The natural gases produced from Well GT1 in the Qingshuihe Formation reservoir in the Gaoquan anticline might be the mixture of the gases derived from the Jurassic coal-measures and the Permian lacustrine source rocks (Chen et al., 2019).

Exploration Targets for Natural Gas

Although many structural traps were well developed in the shallow and deep layers in the southern margin of Junggar Basin, (Li et al., 2003; Kuang and Jia, 2005; Kuang and Qi, 2006; Lei et al., 2012; Du et al., 2019), the exploration targets in the southern margin mainly focused on the middle-shallow layers for long time, and the natural gas discovered to date is mainly in the shallow Paleogene and Neogene anticlinal traps. Commercial natural gas fields were only found in the Hutubi anticline and Manas anticline in the central part of southern margin. Recently, the Well GT1 in the Gaoquan anticline in the west part and the Well HT1 in the Huxi anticline in the central part revealed high-product oil and gas flow in the sandstone reservoirs at the bottom of the Qingshuihe Formation of Lower Cretaceous, showing a good prospect for oil and gas exploration in the deep layers in the southern margin of Junggar Basin.

The middle and shallow oil and gas plays discovered to date in the southern margin of Junggar Basin were defined as the Cretaceous-Neogene plays, which were mainly generated from the Cretaceous source rocks in the central part of the southern margin and source rocks from the Paleogene Anjihaihe Formation in the Wusu-Dushanzi area in the west of the southern margin. However, the scales and hydrocarbon generation potentials of these two sets of source rocks are relatively small due to its currently low to medium maturity, and it cannot be the main contributors for the formation of large scale of natural gas reservoirs. The deep-buried Jurassic coal-measures could be the main candidate for large scale natural gas reservoirs. The Hutubi gas field and Mahe gas field, which were discovered recently, are located in the middle-shallow depth, in which the crude oil was derived from the Cretaceous source rocks, and the natural gas from the deep Jurassic coal measures. On the other hand, the anticline traps in shallow depth is relatively small, and the sealing capability of cap rocks was partly destroyed due to complex fault systems in the southern margin, resulting in loss of large amounts of oil and gas. Furthermore, these shallow anticline traps were formed very late, especially the anticlines in the central part, leading to a capture of late stage of gas generation from the highly to over mature Jurassic coal-measures, then limiting the scale of oil and gas accumulations.

On the contrary, the deep buried Permian and the Upper Triassic source rocks and Jurassic coal-measures can be the main contributors for the formation of large scale oil and gas fields in the deep Permian-Jurassic-Cretaceous plays in the southern margin of Junggar Basin. Here the reservoirs were well developed within the Jurassic strata and at the bottom of the Lower Cretaceous, while mudstone within the Jurassic strata and the Cretaceous Qingshuihe Formation is good cap rocks. The overlying thick strata further increased the sealing capability of the cap rocks. Meanwhile, a large number of large-scale structural traps were formed during the Late Yanshanian movement and the Himalayan movement. According to the results of Lei et al. (2012), Du et al. (2019), nearly 40–46 traps have been identified and confirmed in this play, with a total area of 2140–2486 km^2, of which 21 are structural traps with an area greater than 30 km^2, with a total trap area of 1840 km^2. The most important is that the formation period of these structural traps was earlier than gas generation time from the Jurassic coal-measures, and is favor for the large-scale oil and gas accumulation.

Well GT1 drilled recently has confirmed that the oil and gas reservoir in the Cretaceous Qingshuihe Formation in the Gaoquan anticline was typical deep hydrocarbon accumulation pool (Figures 3, 4). Half of the natural gas was derived from the Jurassic coal measures and another half from the Permian lacustrine source rocks (Chen et al., 2019). The reservoir was composed of gravel rock at the bottom of Cretaceous Qingshuihe Formation, and the cap rock is mudstone of the Qingshuihe Formation. In addition, sandstones within the Jurassic strata were also well developed. Therefore, large scale gas reservoirs from the lithologic traps and/or structural-lithologic traps could be one of the main targets in the future exploration. Although deep-buried reservoirs in the Permian-Jurassic-Cretaceous plays resulted in relatively low quality of rock physical properties, the discovery of high-product oil and gas reservoirs at the deep-buried Well GT1 in the Gaoquan anticline and Well HT1 in the Huxi anticline indicated that good reservoirs can be developed in the deep plays for natural gas accumulation.

The oil and gas accumulation conditions and exploration practice and results suggest that the deep Permian-Jurassic-Cretaceous plays in the southern margin are the most favorable gas exploration target. Regionally, the deep play in the west part of the southern margin of Junggar Basin is favorable for discovery of oil and gas reservoirs from the Jurassic coal measures. There is also the possibility to discover gas reservoirs from the Permian lacustrine source rocks. While in the central part, the deep play is favorable for discovery of gas reservoirs from the Jurassic coal measures. The deep play in the east part of the southern margin of Junggar Basin is favorable for discovery of gas reservoirs from the Jurassic coal measures and Permian lacustrine source rocks. The middle-shallow Cretaceous-Neogene play in the central and west parts of the southern margin may be the secondary target for natural gas exploration.

CONCLUSION

(1) Three sets of effective gas source rocks were developed in the southern margin of Junggar Basin. The widely distributed Jurassic coal-measures are the most important oil and gas source rocks, and the Permian and Upper Triassic lacustrine source rocks are important gas source rocks in some area of the southern margin.

(2) In the southern margin of Junggar Basin, the Jurassic coal-measures is mainly at mature to highly mature stage, indicating a main gas generation stage. It matched well with the formation time of anticlines, resulting in the best source-kitchen and trap combination. A series of thrust faults and secondary faults connected the deep source kitchen with the middle-upper traps. All together it made favorable conditions for multiple hydrocarbon migration and accumulation.

(3) Compared studies showed that source rocks in the southern margin of Junggar Basin, were better than those in the Kuqa Depression. Although the maturity of source organic matter, the scale of reservoirs and caps, and sealing capability in the southern margin were slightly lower than those in the Kuqa Depression, the southern margin of Junggar Basin still has good hydrocarbon accumulation conditions, due to multiple source rocks, well-developed faults and traps, good quality reservoirs and sealing conditions.

(4) In the southern margin of Junggar Basin, the deep Permian-Jurassic-Cretaceous play is the most favorable target for natural gas exploration. The middle-shallow Cretaceous-Neogene play is the secondary target for natural gas exploration, with

possibility to discover a certain scale natural gas reservoirs under the supply of deep Jurassic gas sources.

Author Contributions

CJ, article writing; WX, reservoir avaluation; XB, geological background; LJ, natural gas analyses; NY and SY, natural gas geochemistry.

Acknowledgments

We would like to thank PetroChina for permission to publish this work. Liang Digang reviewed the early version of this article and made suggestions.

REFERENCES

1. Bai, Z., Jiang, Z., Song, Y., Zhao, M., Fang, S., and Zhang, J. (2013a). Dynamic hydrocarbon accumulation process in Manasi anticline in the southern Junggar foreland basin. *Nat. Gas Industry* 33 (4), 37–42. [in Chinese with English abstract].

2. Bai, Z., Jiang, Z., Song, Y., Zhao, M., Fang, S., and Zhang, J. (2013b). The reservoir characteristics and its main controlling factor discussion in Ziniquanzi Formation of Homatu tectonic zone, Southern Junggar fold-thrust belt. *Nat. Gas Geosci.* 24, 273–281. [in Chinese with English abstract].

3. Bai, H., Pang, X., Kuang, L., Pang, H., Wang, X., Jia, X., et al. (2017). Hydrocarbon expulsion potential of source rocks and its influence on the distribution of lacustrine tight oil reservoir, Middle Permian Lucaogou Formation, Jimsar Sag, Junggar Basin, Northwest China. *J. Pet. Sci. Eng.* 149, 740–755. doi:10.1016/j.petrol.2016.09.053

4. Bernard, B. B., Brooks, J. M., and Sackett, W. M. (1977). "A geochemical model for characterization of hydrocarbon gas sources in marine sediments," in Proceedings of the ninth annual offshore technology conference, OTC 2934, Houston, May 2–5, 1977. Houston, Texas, USA: Offshore Technology Conference, 435–438.

5. Cao, Z., Liu, G., Xiang, B., Wang, P., Niu, G., Niu, Z., et al. (2017). Geochemical characteristics of crude oil from a tight oil reservoir in the Lucaogou Formation, Jimusar sag, Junggar Basin. *Bulletin* 101 (01), 39–72. doi:10.1306/05241614182

6. Carroll, A. R., Brassell, S. C., and Graham, S. A. (1992). Upper permian lacustrine oil shales, southern Junggar Basin, northwest China. *AAPG Bull.* 76 (12), 1874–1902. doi:10.1306/bdff8b0a-1718-11d7-8645000102c1865d

7. Carroll, A. R. (1998). Upper permian lacustrine organic facies evolution, southern Junggar Basin, NW China. *Org. Geochem.* 28 (11), 649–667. doi:10.1016/s0146-6380(98)00040-0

8. Chen, J., Liang, D., Wang, X., Deng, C., Jin, T., Xiang, S., et al. (2003). The discovery and significance of the crude oils derived from Triassic source rocks in the Junggar Basin. *Geochimica* 32, 582–590. [in Chinese with English abstract].

9. Chen, S., Wang, X., Abulimit, I., and LiWang, Y. L. (2004). Geochemical study of forming gas reservoir in Hutubi field in Zhungeer basin. *Nat. Gas Industry* 24 , 16–18. [in Chinese with English abstract].

10. Chen, S., Qi, J., Yu, F., and Yang, Q. (2007). Deformation characteristics in the southern margin of Junggar Basin and their controlling factors. *Acta Geol. Sin.* 81, 151–157. [in Chinese with English abstract].

11. Chen, J., Wang, X., Deng, C., Zhao, Z., Ni, Y., SunYang, Y. H., et al. (2015a). Geochemical features of source rocks in the southern margin, Junggar Basin, Northwestern China. *Acta Petrolei Sin.* 36, 767–780. [in Chinese with English abstract].

12. Chen, J., Wang, X., Deng, C., Zhao, Z., Ni, Y., SunYang, Y. H., et al. (2015b). Geochemical

features and classification of crude oils in the southern margin, Junggar Basin, northwest China. *Acta Petrolei Sin.* 36, 1315–1331. [in Chinese with English abstract].

13. Chen, J., Wang, X., Deng, C., Zhao, Z., Ni, Y., SunYang, Y. H., et al. (2016a). Oil-source correlation of typical crude oil in the southern margin, Junggar Basin, Northwestern China. *Acta Petrolei Sin.* 37, 160–171. [in Chinese with English abstract].

14. Chen, J., Wang, X., Deng, C., Zhao, Z., Ni, Y., SunYang, Y. H., et al. (2016b). Investigation of typical reservoirs and occurrence regularity of crude oil in the southern margin of Junggar Basin, Northwestern China. *Acta Petrolei Sin.* 37, 415–429. [in Chinese with English abstract].

15. Chen, J., Wang, X., Deng, C., Liang, D., Zhang, Y., Zhao, Z., et al. (2016c). Geochemical features of source rock and crude oil in the Junggar Basin, Northwest China. *Acta Geol. Sin.* 90, 37–67. [in Chinese with English abstract].

16. Chen, J., Wang, X., Deng, C., Liang, D., Zhang, Y., Zhao, Z., et al. (2016d). Oil and gas source, occurrence and petroleum system in the Junggar Basin, Northwest China. *Acta Geol. Sin.* 90, 421–450. [in Chinese with English abstract]. doi:10.1111/1755-6724.13039

17. Chen, J., Deng, C., Wang, X., Ni, Y., Sun, Y., Zhao, Z., et al. (2016e). Source of condensate oil in the middle of southern margin, Junggar Basin, NW China. *Pet. Explor. Dev.* 43 (5), 902–913. doi:10.1016/s1876-3804(16)30108-2

18. Chen, J., Deng, C., Wang, X., Ni, Y., Sun, Y., Zhao, Z., et al. (2017). Formation mechanism of condensates, waxy and heavy oils in the southern margin of Junggar Basin, NW China. *Sci. China Earth Sci.* 60 (5), 972–991. doi:10.1007/s11430-016-9027-3

19. Chen, J., Wang, X., Ni, Y., Xiang, B., Liao, F., Liao, J., et al. (2019). Genetic type and source of natural gas in the southern margin of Junggar Basin, NW China. *Pet. Explor. Dev.* 46 (3), 482–495. doi:10.1016/s1876-3804(19)60029-7

20. Dai, J., Wu, X., Ni, Y., Wang, Z., Zhao, C., Wang, Z., et al. (2012). Geochemical characteristics of natural gas from mud volcanoes in the southern Junggar Basin. *Sci. China Earth Sci.* 55 (3), 355–367. doi:10.1007/s11430-012-4363-x

21. Deng, Q., Feng, X., Zhang, P., Yang, X., Xu, X., Peng, S., et al. (1999). Reverse fault and fold zone in the Urumqi range-front depression of the Northern Tianshan and its genetic mechanism. *Earth Sci. Front.* 6 (4), 191–200.

22. Du, Z., and Wang, Q. (2007). Mesozoic and Cenozoic uplifting history of the Tianshan Region: insight from apatite fission track. *Acta Geol. Sin.* 81, 1081–1101. [in Chinese with English abstract].

23. Du, Z., Wang, F., Zhang, S., Zhang, B., and Liang, D. (2006). Gas generation history of mesozoic hydrocarbon kitchen in Kuqa depression, Tarim Basin. *Geochemica* 35, 419–431. [in Chinese with English abstract].

24. Du, J., Zhi, D., Li, J., Yang, D., Tang, Y., Qi, X., et al. (2019). Major breakthrough of Well Gaotan 1 and exploration prospects of lower assemblage in southern margin of Junggar Basin, NW China. *Pet. Explor. Dev.* 46 (2), 216–227. doi:10.1016/s1876-3804(19)60003-0

25. Fang, S., Jia, C., Guo, Z., Song, Y., and Zhang, Z. (2005). Preliminary determination of the forming time of foreland thrust belt in the Southern Margin of Junggar Basin. *Earth Sci. Front.* 12 (3), 66 [in Chinese with English abstract].

26. Fang, S., Song, Y., Jia, C., Xu, H., Liu, L., and Zhang, J. (2006). Relationship between Cretaceous basal conglomerate and oil/gas reservoiring in the Junggar Basin. *Natural Gas Industry* 26 (5), 13–16. [in Chinese with English abstract].

27. Fang, S., Song, Y., Jia, C., Guo, Z., Zhang, Z., and Liu, L. (2007). Timing of cenozoic intense deformation and its implications for petroleum accumulation, northern margin of tianshan orogenic belt, northwest China. *Earth Sci. Front.* 14 (2), 205–214. doi:10.1016/s1872-5791(07)60018-9

28. Gao, G., Zhang, W., Xiang, B., Liu, G., and Ren, J. (2016). Geochemistry characteristics and hydrocarbon-generating potential of lacustrine source rock in Lucaogou Formation of the jimusaer sag, Junggar Basin. *J. Pet. Sci. Eng.* 145, 168–182. doi:10.1016/j.petrol.2016.03.023

29. Graham, S. A., Brassell, S., Carroll, A. R., Xiao, X., Demaison, G., McKnight, C. L., et al. (1990). Characteristics of selected petroleum source rocks, Xinjiang uygur autonomous region, northwest China. *AAPG Bull.* 74, 493–512. doi:10.1306/0c9b233f-1710-11d7-8645000102c1865d

30. Guo, Z., Zhang, Z., Wu, C., Fang, S., and Zhang, R. (2006). The mesozoic and cenozoic exhumation history of tianshan and comparative studies to the junggar and altai Mountains. *Acta Geol. Sin.* 80 (1), 1–15. [in Chinese with English abstract]. doi:10.1201/9781420004106.ch0

31. Han, S., Li, X., Chen, N., Shen, J., and Xu, Y. (2012). Hydrocarbon reservoirs and their controlling factors in the lower associations of the middle part of southern Junggar Basin, Xinjiang. *Sediment. Geol. Tethyan Geol.* 32 (4), 52–58. [in Chinese with English abstract].

32. He, D., Zhang, Y., Jia, J., and Shi, X. (2004). Plays for giant oil field in Junggar. *Xinjiang Pet. Geol.* 25 (2), 117–121. [in Chinese with English abstract].

33. He, D., Zhou, X., Yang, H., Lei, G., and Ma, Y. (2009). Geological structure and its controls on giant oil and gas fields in Kuqa Depression, Tarim Basin: a clue from new shot seismic data. *Geotetonica et Metallogenia* 33, 19–32. [in Chinese with English abstract].

34. Hendrix, M. S., Dumitru, T. A., and Graham, S. A. (1994). Late Oligocene-Early Miocene unroofing in the Chinese Tian Shan: an early effect of the India-Asia collision. *Geology* 22 (6), 487–490. doi:10.1130/0091-7613(1994)022<0487:loemui>2.3.co;2

35. Hou, L., Ma, W., Luo, X., Liu, J., Liu, S., and Zhao, Z. (2021). Hydrocarbon generation-retention-expulsion mechanism and shale oil producibility of the permian lucaogou shale in the Junggar Basin as simulated by semi-open pyrolysis experiments. *Mar. Pet. Geol.* 125, 104880. doi:10.1016/j.marpetgeo.2020.104880

36. Hu, L., He, D., and Hu, D. (2005). Electron spin resonance dating of the late Cenozoic deformation of the Huoerguosi-Manas-Tugulu reverse faults along southern edge of Junggar Basin. *Acta Geoscientica Sinica* 26, 121–126. [in Chinese with English abstract].

37. Hu, G., Zhang, S., Li, J., Li, J., and Han, Z. (2010). The origin of natural gas in the Hutubi gas field, Southern Junggar Foreland Sub-basin, NW China. *Int. J. Coal Geol.* 84 (3-4), 301–310. doi:10.1016/j.coal.2010.10.009

38. James, A. T. (1983). Correlation of natural gas by use of carbon isotopic distribution between hydrocarbon components. *AAPG Bull.* 67, 1176–1191. doi:10.1306/03b5b722-16d1-11d7-8645000102c1865d

39. James, A. T. (1990). Correlation of reservoired gases using the carbon isotopic compositions of wet gas components. *AAPG Bull.* 74, 1441–1458. doi:10.1306/0c9b24f7-1710-11d7-8645000102c1865d

40. Kang, S., Wang, X., Liao, J., Zhou, N., and Luo, L. (2008). Oil and gas characteristics and charging priority in Huo'erguosi Oilfield of Junggar Basin. *Spec. Oil Gas Reservoirs* 15 (4), 20–23. [in Chinese with English abstract].

41. Kang, S., Xiang, B., Liao, J., Ablimiti, I., and Sun, P. (2012). Organic geochemistry of Triassic source rock in the southern Junggar Basin. *J. Southwest Pet. Univ. (Sci. Tech. Edition)* 34 (2), 43–53. [in Chinese with English abstract].

42. Kuang, J., and Jia, X. (2005). Relationship between himalayan movement and hydrocarbon accumulation in southern margin of Junggar Basin. *Xinjiang Pet. Geol.* 26 (2), 129–133. [in Chinese with English abstract].

43. Kuang, J., and Liu, D. (2001). Comparative analysis on natural gas reservoir formed conditions between Southern Margin of Junggar Basin and Kuche depression of Tarim Basin. *Xinjiang*

Pet. Geol. 22 (4), 287–290. [in Chinese with English abstract].

44. Kuang, J., and Qi, X. (2006). The Structural characteristics and oil-gas explorative direction in Junggar foreland basin. *Xinjiang Pet. Geol.* 27 (1), 5–9. [in Chinese with English abstract].

45. Kuang, J. (1993). The supperpressure mud seams in the southern margin of Junggar Basin and their significance in structural geology. *Exp. Pet. Geol.* 15, 168–172. [in Chinese with English abstract].

46. Lei, D., Tang, Y., and Chang, Q. (2008). The deep and relatively high-quality clastic reservoir bodies and favorable exploration areas in southern margin of Junggar Basin. *Xinjiang Pet. Geol.* 29 (4), 435–438. [in Chinese with English abstract].

47. Lei, D., Zhang, J., Chen, N., and Xiang, B. (2012). Conditions for gas pooling in the lower assemblage in the southern margin of Junggar Basin and the exploration prospect of large hydrocarbon fields. *Nat. Gas Industry* 32 (2), 16–22. [in Chinese with English abstract].

48. Li, W., Wang, C., Gao, Z., and Peng, D. (2000). Sedimentary evolution of mesozoic ear in kuqhe depression, Tarim Basin. *Acta Sedimentol. Sin.* 18, 543–548. [in Chinese with English abstract].

49. Li, X., Shao, Yu., and Li, T. (2003). Three oil-reservoir combinations in southern marginal of Junggar Basin, Northwest China. *Pet. Explor. Dev.* 30 (6), 32–34. [in Chinese with English abstract].

50. Li, Y., Wang, T., Zhang, Y., Chen, S., and Wang, X. (2004). Natural gas genesis and formation of gas pools in the Southern margin of Junggar Basin. *Acta Sedimentol. Sin.* 22, 529–534. [in Chinese with English abstract].

51. Liang, D., Zhang, S., Zhao, M., and Wang, F. (2002). Hydrocarbon sources and stages of reservoir Formation in Kuqa depression, Tarim Basin. *Chin. Sci. Bull.* 47 (S1), 62–70. doi:10.1007/bf02902820

52. Liang, D., Zhang, S., Chen, J., Wang, F., and Wang, P. (2003). Organic geochemistry of oil and gas in the Kuqa depression, Tarim Basin, NW China. *Org. Geochem.* 34 (7), 873–888. doi:10.1016/s0146-6380(03)00029-9

53. Liang, D., Chen, J., Zhang, B., Zhang, S., Wang, F., and Zhao, M. (2004). *Formation of continental oil and gas in Kuqa Depression, Tarim Basin.* Beijing: Petroleum Industry Press [in Chinese].

54. Liao, J., Wu, Y., Zhao, Z., Jing, W., and Dilidaer, (2006). Genesis study of Horgos region, Junggar Basin. *Nat. Gas Explor. Dev.* 29 (1), 21–23. [in Chinese with English abstract].

55. Liao, J., Zhao, Z., Ma, W., Guo, Y., Shen, N., and Zhou, Ni. (2011). Analysis on oil-gas origin and accumulation hydrocarbons in Hutubi gas field, Junggar Basin. *Xinjiang Geology.* 29, 453–456. [in Chinese with English abstract].

56. Liu, Q., Qin, S., Li, J., Liu, W., Zhang, D., Zhou, Q., et al. (2007). Natural gas geochemistry and its origins in Kuqa Depression. *Sci. China Ser. D-Earth Sci.* 51 (S1), 174–182.

57. Liu, J., Zhang, W., Gao, C., Ni, Q., and Yuan, H. (2016). Genetic type and source of the natural gas in Huo-Ma-Tuo articline zone in the Southern Junggar Basin. *Mar. Geol. Quat. Geol.* 26 (3), 135–141. [in Chinese with English abstract].

58. Luo, X., Xiao, L., Li, X., Zhang, L., Zeng, Z., and Wang, Z. (2004). Overpressure distribution and affecting factors in southern margin of Junggar Basin. *Earth Sci. J. Chin. Univ. Geosci.* 29, 404–412. [in Chinese with English abstract].

59. Luo, X., Liu, L., and Li, X. (2006). Overpressure distribution and pressuring mechanism on the southern margin of the Junggar Basin, Northwestern China. *Chin. Sci Bull* 51 (19), 2383–2390. doi:10.1007/s11434-006-2126-9

60. Luo, X., Wang, Z., Zhang, L., Yang, W., and Liu, L. (2007). Overpressure generation and

evolution in a compressional tectonic setting, the southern margin of Junggar Basin, northwestern China. *Bulletin* 91 (8), 1123–1139. doi:10.1306/02260706035

61. Qin, S., Dai, J., and Liu, X. (2007). The controlling factors of oil and gas generation from coal in the Kuqa Depression of Tarim Basin, China. *Int. J. Coal Geol.* 70 (1-3), 255–263. doi:10.1016/j.coal.2006.04.011

62. Qiu, N., Wang, X., Yang, H., and Xiang, Y. (2001). The characteristics of temperature distribution in the Junggar Basin. *Chin. J. Geol.* 36 (3), 350–358. [in Chinese with English abstract].

63. Schoell, M. (1980). The hydrogen and carbon isotopic composition of methane from natural gases of various origins. *Geochim. Cosmochim. Acta* 44 (5), 649–661. doi:10.1016/0016-7037(80)90155-6

64. Schoell, M. (1983). Genetic characterization of natural gases. *AAPG Bull.* 67 (12), 2225–2238. doi:10.1306/AD46094A-16F7-11D7-8645000102C1865D

65. Stahl, W. (1974). Carbon isotope fractionations in natural gases. *Nature* 251 (5471), 134–135. doi:10.1038/251134a0

66. Wang, H., and Hu, J. (2002). Cretaceous petroleum system and high pressure gas reservoir formation in Kuche Depression. *Nat. Gas Industry* 22 (1), 5–8. [in Chinese with English abstract].

67. Wang, F., Zhang, S., Zhang, B., and Zhao, M. (1999). Organic maturity of mesozoic source rocks in Kuqa depression, Tarim Basin. *Xinjiang Pet. Geol.* 20, 221–224. [in Chinese with English abstract].

68. Wang, S., Hu, S., and Wang, J. (2000). The characteristics of heat flow and geothermal fields in Junggar Basin. *Chin. J. Geophys.* 43, 771–779. [in Chinese with English abstract]. doi:10.1002/cjg2.98

69. Wang, Z., Sun, M., Geng, P., Song, Y., and Li, Y. (2003). The development features and formation mechanisms of abnormal high formation pressure in southern Junggar region. *Pet. Explor. Dev.* 30 (1), 32–34. [in Chinese with English abstract].

70. Wang, H., Zhou, N., Zhou, X., Luo, L., and Xie, G. (2009). Petroleum origin in Manas area, Junggar Basin. *Nat. Explor. Dev.* 32 (2), 4–9. [in Chinese with English abstract].

71. Wang, X., Zhi, D., Wang, Y., Chen, J., Qin, Z., Liu, D., et al. (2013). *Geochemistry of source rock and petroleum in the Junggar Basin*. Beijing: Petroleum Industry Press. [in Chinese].

72. Wang, Z. (2014). Formation mechanism and enrichment regularities of Kelasu subsalt deep large gas field in Kuqa Depression, Tarim Basin. *Nat. Gas Geosci.* 25, 153–166. [in Chinese with English abstract].

73. Whiticar, M. J. (1994). "Correlation of natural gases with their sources," in *The petroleum system — from source to trap*. Editors L. Magoon, and W. Dow (Tulsa, OK, United States: AAPG Memoir). 60, 261–284. doi:10.1306/m60585c16

74. Whiticar, M. J. (1996). Stable isotope geochemistry of coals, humic kerogens and related natural gases. *Int. J. Coal Geol.* 32 (1-4), 191–215. doi:10.1016/s0166-5162(96)00042-0

75. Whiticar, M. J. (1999). Carbon and hydrogen isotope systematics of bacterial formation and oxidation of methane. *Chem. Geol.* 161 (1-3), 291–314. doi:10.1016/s0009-2541(99)00092-3

76. Wu, X., Wang, L., and Xu, C. (1994). The stracture characteristics and prospect for hydrocarbon exploration in Qigu-Xiaoquzhi area in southern margin of Junggar Basin. *Pet. Explor. Dev.* 21 (1), 1–7. [in Chinese with English abstract].

77. Wu, X., Wang, L., and Song, Z. (2000). The relations between structural stress field and hydrocarbon migration and accumulation in Southern Margin of Junggar Basin. *Xinjing Pet. Geol.* 21 (2), 97–100. [in Chinese with English abstract].

78. Wu, K., Zha, M., and Zhong, J. (2006). Distribution and evolution of overpressure system in the Junggar Basin. *Chin. J. Geol.* 41, 636–647. [in Chinese with English abstract].

79. Wu, X., Liu, D., Abulimiti, I., and Ding, J. (2007). Potential and field of exploration for natural gas in Junggar Bain. *China Pet. Explor.* 12 (2), 1–6. [in Chinese with English abstract].

80. Xiao, L., Chen, N., Zhang, J., Shen, J., and Zhang, S. (2011). Sedimentary systems of Paleogene Ziniquanzi Formation, south edge of Junggar Basin. *Nat. Gas Geosci.* 22, 426–431. [in Chinese with English abstract].

81. Yang, H., Chen, L., and Kong, Y. (2004). A novel classification of structural units in Junggar Basin. *Xinjiang Pet. Geol.* 25, 686–688. [in Chinese with English abstract].

82. Zha, M., Zhang, W., and Qu, J. (2000). The character and origin of overpressure and its explorational significance in Junggar Basin. *Pet. Explor. Dev.* 27 (2), 31–35. [in Chinese with English abstract].

83. Zhang, J., Li, T., Han, S., Li, X., and Xia, Y. (2012). The development characteristics and distribution of reservoir in jurassic and cretaceous in western part of southern margin of Junggar Basin. *Xinjiang Geol.* 30 (1), 62–66. [in Chinese with English abstract].

84. Zhang, Z., Zhu, G., Chi, L., Wang, P., Zhou, L., Li, J., et al. (2020). Discovery of the high-yield well GT1 in the deep strata of the southern margin of the Junggar Basin, China: implications for liquid petroleum potential in deep assemblage. *J. Pet. Sci. Eng.* 191, 107178. doi:10.1016/j10.1016/j.petrol.2020.107178

85. Zhao, M., Lu, S., and Li, J. (2002). The geochemical features of natural gas in Kuqa Depression and the discussion on the gas source. *Pet. Explor. Dev.* 29 (6), 4–7. [in Chinese with English abstract].

86. Zheng, G., Ma, X., Guo, Z., Hilton, D. R., Xu, W., Liang, S., et al. (2017). Gas geochemistry and methane emission from Dushanzi mud volcanoes in the southern Junggar Basin, NW China. *J. Asian Earth Sci.* 149, 184–190. doi:10.1016/j.jseaes.2017.08.023

8

Organic Geochemistry of Ordovician Ultra-deep Natural Gas in the North Shuntuoguole area, Tarim Basin, NW China: Insights into Genetic Types, Maturity, and Sources

Zhenjie Jia[1,2,3], Dujie Hou[1,2,3], Xiuxiang Zhu[4], Jiejing Bian[1,2,3] and Xiaoxiao Ma[1,2,3]

[1]School of Energy Resources, China University of Geosciences, Beijing, China
[2]Key Laboratory of Marine Reservoir Evolution and Hydrocarbon Accumulation Mechanism, Ministry of Education, China University of Geosciences, Beijing, China
[3]Beijing Key Laboratory of Unconventional Natural Gas Geological Evaluation and Development Engineering, Beijing, China
[4]Northwest Oilfield Company, Sinopec, Urumqi, Xinjiang, China

ABSTRACT

As a gas-rich region in the Tarim Basin, the northern Shuntuoguole area (also known as the Shunbei area) is an attractive prospect. Non-etheless, the debate about the origins of these natural gas continues. The analysis on the geological context, natural gas components, and the carbon and hydrogen isotope ratios prove that methane is the predominate component of alkane gases. Alkane gases' carbon isotope fractionation ($\delta^{13}C_2 < -28‰$ and $\delta^{13}C_3 < -25‰$) shows that they are oil-associated gas, and their parent material type is I kerogen. Natural gas can be broken down further into three subgroups—Type I_1, Type I_2, and Type I_3. Based on the link between the carbon number $1/n$ and $\delta^{13}Cn$ of the gas. Modified plots of lnC_1/C_2 vs. lnC_2/C_3 reveal that kerogen cracking is the primary source of natural gas in the Shunbei area, and that this gas is combined with the contribution of oil cracking gas. Petroleum exploration and development in the Shunbei area can be justified on the basis that natural gas in the area originate primarily from Ordovician source rocks, as shown by carbon isotopic compositions.

INTRODUCTION

Globally there is great focus on exploring deep and ultra-deep gas fields (Dutton et al., 2010; Jia et al., 2015). As for the boundary depth of deep and ultra-deep petroliferous basins, the understanding of different countries, different institutions and different scholars in different periods is still quite different. Ultra-deep oil and gas reservoirs are distributed in two types of basins in the world, namely main rift basin and foreland basin. In foreland basin, ultra-deep oil and gas reservoirs are mainly distributed in foredeep tectonic belt (Huang B. J. et al., 2016). The world's deep oil and gas exploration began in the United States in the 1950s, and by the end of 2018, 68 oil and gas reservoirs with a depth of more than 8,000 m meters had been discovered worldwide (Jia et al., 2015).

At present, a large number of practices and researches have been carried out on the exploration of oil and gas in deep and ultra-deep basins in the world, and a series of major breakthroughs have been made. Especially, the three deepest wells in the world, namely Odoptu OP-11 Well in Sakhalin, Russia (12,345 m, in 2011), Ashosin Well in Qatar (12289 m in 2008) and SG-3 Well in kola peninsula (12,262 m in 1989) (Wu et al., 2006; Zhai et al., 2012), have obtained important information on deep oil and gas generation and reservoir properties. At present, the deepest drilling well in China is Luntan 1 Well (8882 m, in 2019) in Tarim Basin, which can obtain high-yield industrial oil and gas flow in Cambrian below 8,200 m. Some industrial oil and gas reservoirs have also been found in Sichuan Basin and Tarim Basin in China in the depth range of 6,500–8,000 m (Pang et al., 2015), which shows that the ultra-deep still has good oil and gas exploration potential.

Natural gas, crude oil, and hydrocarbon source rocks in the Lower Paleozoic Ordovician and Cambrian reservoirs have been the subject of intense study since the discovery of the Shunbei Oilfield in China (Wang et al., 2003; He et al., 2008; Dai et al., 2014; Chen et al., 2015; Jiao, 2018; Zheng, 2018; Deng et al., 2019; Ma et al., 2020; Ma et al., 2021). However, the origin of these materials has been strongly contested (Zhu et al., 2015; Zhu et al., 2018; Qi, 2021). Palaeohigh in the Tarim Basin has been the target of petroleum exploration efforts in recent years. Insight into the strike-slip fault zone's tectonic history, structural features, active fault evolution process, and petroleum geological conditions has led to the growing understanding that it plays a crucial role in the formation of Tarim Basin's carbonate reservoirs and hydrocarbon accumulation (Zhang et al., 2021, 2019). A significant advancement in recent years has been the discovery of the Shunbei Oilfield (Zhao et al., 2018; Ma et al., 2019). This discovery has furthered the argument that intracratonic strike-slip faults with small displacements are crucial for reservoir development and hydrocarbon accumulation in the Ordovician carbonates (Qi, 2021). Deep oil and gas resources in China have great potential, and the exploration degree of oil and gas is low (13% and 10%, respectively). Deep and ultra-deep are the realistic fields for oil and gas exploration and development in the future (Jia et al., 2015; Pan et al., 2022). The research on the accumulation conditions and accumulation rules of the ultra-deep ancient strata has become a hot topic, and a number of high quality results have been obtained (Zhai and He, 2004; Bai et al., 2014; Ren et al., 2020; Li et al., 2021). It is of great significance to study the controlling effect of deep and ultra-deep natural gas geochemical characteristics on hydrocarbon accumulation and enrichment in order to guide the deep oil and gas exploration and development and meet the important national demand. In this study, we conducted a thorough investigation into the carbon and hydrogen isotopic compositions of the Ordovician natural gas in the Shunbei, and their geochemical properties.

GEOLOGICAL BACKGROUND

China's largest inland oil-gas yielding basin is located in the Tarim Basin, which is a large-scale superimposition basin. It is situated in Xinjiang, Northwest China, and has a size of around 560,000 square kilometers. Seven primary structural units plus a few subsidiary structural units make up the Tarim basin. Northern depression area is home to Shuntuoguole, which sits on secondary structural units. Accordingly, Shuntuoguole is subdivided into four tertiary structural units: the Shunbei gentle slope, the Shundong gentle slope, the Shuntuo low uplift, and the Shunnan gentle slope (Qi, 2021). The Shunbei Oilfield is located in the northern portion of the Shuntuoguole low uplift, and its near neighbors are the Shaya uplift to the north, the Kathak uplift to the south, the Awati depression to the west, and the Mangar depression to the east (Figure 1). From the perspective of tectonic evolution, the Tarim Basin has an ancient evolutionary history, which has undergone several subsidence and uplift movements on the plane.

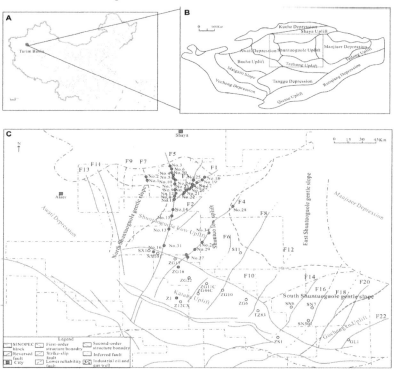

Figure 1. (A) location of the Tarim Basin in China and **(B)** location of the North Shuntuoguole area in Tarim Basin and **(C)** Map showing locations of the oilfield and some sampled wells and structure location of North Shuntuoguole area (Modified from Ma et al. 2021).

It is composed of seven tectonic evolution stages, and the evolution process is very complex (Jia, 1997). Substantial sedimentary layers, some of which are over ten thousand meters thick, and about 800 million years of geological history offer the material basis and objective conditions for the formation of oil and gas resources. Of these, 21 maritime oil and gas fields date back to the Paleozoic era, which is currently the focus of exploration and development (Jia, 1997; Zheng, 2018). To date, 18 main strike-slip faults have been found in the Tarim Basin, providing crucial information regarding the pattern of fault distribution. Overall structural characteristics of the Tarim Basin are governed by three fault types that can be categorized as NWW, NEE, or NNE (Jia, 1997; Deng et al., 2019). An important step forward was achieved in 2016 at the Shunbei Oilfield. Tarim basin has been a hotspot for petroleum exploration due to estimates that 18 strike-slip fault zones spanning 3,400 km² contain oil and gas with a total production of 1.7 billion tons, 70% of which is oil reserves, and natural gas reserves exceeding 5,000 cubic meters (Yang et al., 2017).

MATERIALS AND METHODS

The natural gas and crude oils samples were collected from the Ordovician Fault No. 7 (F7), Fault No. 5 (F5), Fault No.1 (F1) and Fault No.4 (F4) in the Shunbei area. The sample component is determined by HP5980 gas chromatograph. Chromatographic conditions were as follows: MS molecular sieve with column length of 2.4 mm; GDX-502 column of 4 m. The chromatographic temperature rise program is the initial temperature of 30°C, kept for 10 min, and then the temperature rise rate is 10°C/min to 180°C. The carbon isotope value of main alkane in natural gas is determined by Optima isotope mass spectrometer. Natural gas samples are separated into single components in HP5890 gas chromatograph by chromatographic column (HP-PLOTQ column). The natural gas sample was separated into a single component by a HP-PLOTQ column (30 m×0.32 mm×20 µm) in the HP5980 gas chromatograph. The single component hydrocarbons were converted into CO_2 by high temperature, and then directly entered the isotope mass spectrometer to determine the carbon isotope composition. The initial furnace temperature of the chromatograph is 35°C, and the temperature rise rate is 8°C/min to 80°C, and the temperature rise rate is 5°C/min to 260°C, and the temperature rise is maintained for 10 min. The CO_2 experiment utilized a PorparKQ column (2 m×3 mm) with Helium as the carrier gas. The temperature of the GC column was raised from 40 to 100°C in one-minute increments. It took a TDX column (2 m×3 mm) heated at a rate of 20°C per minute from 32°C to 120°C to separate the remaining gases that are not hydrocarbons. By comparing the results to the PDB carbon isotope, the precision of the analysis was found to be ±0.5‰. All the above tests were completed in Sinopec Key Laboratory of Petroleum Accumulation (Wuxi). Using the relationship between Ro and $\delta^{13}C1$, $\delta^{13}C1=21.88\log Ro-45.6$, the corresponding Ro value is obtained.

RESULTS

Molecular Composition of Natural Gas

Natural gas's constituents are a crucial indicator of the genetic types of natural gas that are present. Given that hydrocarbons, which make up more than 70% of the total gas and dominate the molecular composition of the natural gas in the study area, the natural gas are likely mostly derived from organic sources, according to this theory. Methane is the main hydrocarbon gas in natural gas, and the methane content ranges from 12.57% to 87.90% (Table 1), with an average of 67.3%, the main peak between 70% and 90%. The minor ethane content varies between 1.91% and 25.50%, with an average of 9.64%; the trace propane content varies between 0.41% and 21.56%, with an average of 5.18%; and Well No.13 has the highest concentration, at 87.90%. Well No.5 has the lowest concentration, at 12.57%. Natural gas's dryness indices (C_1/C_{1-5}) range from 0.19% on the low end to 0.97% on the high end, with an average of 0.8% (which is typical for wet gas) across faults (Table 1). Nitrogen (N_2), carbon dioxide (CO_2), and hydrogen (H_2) are the most common non-hydrocarbon gases in Shunbei's natural gas, albeit at low amounts. The CO_2 content ranges from 1.65% to 68.21% (11.77% on average), with the majority of the CO_2 content being less than 10% (Table 1). The N_2 content ranges from 0.37% to 11.34% (2.92% on average)

(Table 1), with the majority of the N_2 content being around 2%; and the H_2 content ranges from 0.01% to 1.58% (0.19% on average) (Table 1).

Table 1. Molecular and stable carbon isotopic compositions of natural gases from Shunbei area

Fault no.	Well no.	Components/%							δ¹³C/‰(VPDB)%				δ¹³H/‰(VSMOW)%			Ro	
		H_2	N_2	CO_2	CH_4	C_2H_6	C_3H_8	C_1/C_{1+5}	CO_2	CH_4	C_2H_6	C_3H_8	CH_4	C_2H_6	C_3H_8	Ro	
F7	1	0.15	9.31	8.99	47.92	17.83	10.85	0.61	−5	−46.4	−37.7	−33.2	−208	−205	−152	0.92	
	2	0.76	1.85	6.90	46.89	20.92	14.78	0.52	−14	−48.4	−39	−33.9	n.d.	n.d.	n.d.	0.74	Quoted from Ref Ma et al. (2021)
F5 North	3	0.03	11.34	6.79	58.67	14.54	6.17	0.72	−7.8	−49.2	−39.1	−35.1	−205	−185	−157	0.68	
	4	0.18	5.84	8.06	54.48	17.97	9.43	0.63	−3.7	−48.9	−39.3	−35.6	−207	−180	−141	0.71	
	5	0.02	n.d.	30.00	12.57	17.29	21.56	0.19	−2.5	−49.2	−38.6	−34.1	−217	−173	−133	0.68	
	6	0.19	2.36	5.05	62.06	18.00	8.70	0.67	−2	−49	−37.7	−34.1	n.d.	n.d.	n.d.	0.70	Quoted from Ref Ma et al. (2021)
F5 Middle	7	n.d.	n.d.	68.21	13.64	9.09	4.55	0.43	−9.9	n.d.	n.d.	n.d.	n.d.	n.d.	n.d.	n.d.	
	8	0.19	n.d.	47.80	47.57	2.96	0.81	0.92	n.d.	n.d.	n.d.	n.d.	n.d.	n.d.	n.d.	n.d.	
	9	0.01	1.10	6.11	31.15	25.50	19.59	0.82	−4	−48	−33.83	−31.3	−188	−144	−123	0.78	
	10	0.01	3.82	1.65	80.14	9.34	3.49	0.85	1.2	−47.8	−33.6	−30.9	−182	−131	−110	0.79	
	11	0.01	4.18	2.07	82.21	8.36	2.41	0.88	−1.1	−47.5	−33.5	−30.7	−182	−128	−102	0.82	
	12	0.02	2.52	2.15	83.25	8.15	2.73	0.88	−0.5	−47.6	−33.3	−30.6	−180	−127	−102	0.81	
F5 South	13	0.14	1.71	5.79	87.90	3.21	0.66	0.95	−9	−47.5	−28.6	−25.4	n.d.	n.d.	n.d.	0.82	
	14	0.04	0.87	19.05	74.43	3.57	1.03	0.93	−4.1	−47.3	−32.1	−29.3	n.d.	n.d.	n.d.	0.84	
	15	0.06	4.96	6.49	74.51	7.90	3.08	0.84	−13.8	−47.7	−33.4	−31.7	−159	n.d.	n.d.	0.80	Quoted from Ref Ma et al. (2021)
	16	0.01	n.d.	8.30	84.91	3.12	1.20	0.94	2.7	−51.7	−32.5	−28.2	n.d.	n.d.	n.d.	0.53	
F1 North	17	0.32	1.55	11.01	84.18	2.43	0.41	0.97	n.d.	−44.7	−33.1	−30.8	−174	−129	−116	1.10	Quoted from Ref Ma et al. (2021)
	18	0.01	1.16	2.59	83.73	6.99	3.25	0.87	0.1	−44.7	−33.3	−30.8	n.d.	n.d.	n.d.	1.10	
	19	0.17	1.82	6.87	77.37	8.15	3.55	0.86	−2.8	−46	−34.4	−32.1	−162	−111	−105	0.96	
	20	n.d.	2.20	2.32	80.35	9.05	3.98	0.85	0.5	−47	−33.8	−31.6	−180	−148	−116	0.86	
	21	1.58	2.53	16.36	67.76	7.45	2.54	0.86	−1.6	−48.1	−34.8	−32.3	−178	n.d.	n.d.	0.77	
F1 South	22	0.05	3.05	4.43	77.36	10.11	3.61	0.84	−5.9	−48.8	−34.7	−32.2	−162	−110	−101	0.71	Quoted from Ref. Ma et al. (2021)
	23	0.02	1.99	6.75	78.12	8.32	3.16	0.86	−6.4	−46.6	−34.1	−32	−156	−113	−104	0.90	
F1 Splay	24	0.54	1.81	10.43	74.04	7.82	3.38	0.86	−1.4	−47.2	−33.8	−31.2	−169	−111	−107	0.85	
	25	0.02	1.22	3.73	74.57	9.02	5.81	0.81	−2.85	−46.6	−34.15	−31.9	−167	−119	−107	0.90	
F4	26	0.26	1.93	8.96	86.15	1.91	0.50	0.97	−6.7	−44.2	−29.9	−27.5	−151	−99	−81	1.16	
	27	0.17	0.37	16.16	77.70	3.49	1.10	0.94	−4.7	−47.4	−34.4	−29.8	n.d.	n.d.	n.d.	0.83	
	28	0.04	0.51	6.60	80.65	7.30	2.71	0.88	−7	−45.7	−33.7	−30.9	n.d.	n.d.	n.d.	0.99	
	29	n.d.	n.d.	n.d.	n.d.	n.d.	n.d.	n.d.	n.d.	n.d.	n.d.	n.d.	−146	−99	n.d.	n.d.	

Note: n.d.: no data.

Carbon and Hydrogen Isotopes of Natural Gas

Natural gas in the research area has a standard stable carbon isotope trend, with methane ($δ^{13}C_1$), ethane ($δ^{13}C_2$), and propane ($δ^{13}C_3$) carbon isotope levels increasing with increasing carbon number, starting at a value of −51.7‰ to −44.2‰ (average −47.43‰), −39.3‰ to −28.6‰ (average −34.47‰), −35.6‰ to −25.4‰ (average −31.43‰), respectively.

Carbon dioxide ($\delta^{13}C_{CO2}$) has a $\delta^{13}C$ value that varies from 14 to 2.7‰ (Table 1). The natural gas in the study area has the methane hydrogen isotope (δ^2H-CH_4) values rang from −217‰ to −146‰ (average −177‰), the ethane hydrogen isotope ($\delta^2H-C_2H_6$) values rang from −205‰ to −99‰ (average −133‰), and the propane carbon isotope ($\delta^2H-C_3H_8$) values rang from −157‰ to −81‰ (average −116‰) (Table 1).

DISCUSSION

Genetic Types and Origins of Natural Gas

Oil and gas' geochemical properties are mostly determined by their parent material, degree of maturation, and other processes. Natural gas formation theories center mostly on the peculiarities of light hydrocarbons and various isotopes of carbon and hydrogen. ^{12}C is typically enriched in the low molecular hydrocarbon as a result of organic matter breaking, whereas ^{13}C is significantly enriched in the large molecular hydrocarbon, such that the carbon isotope ratios of natural gas components are ordered from small to large ($\delta^{13}C_1$ < $\delta^{13}C_2$ < $\delta^{13}C_3$ < $\delta^{13}C_4$). The difference in carbon isotope content between neighboring components correlates with the age of the parent rock. When the maturity is low, the difference of carbon isotope is obvious. Differences tend to decrease and sometimes reverse as maturity increases ($\delta^{13}C_1$ > $\delta^{13}C_2$ > $\delta^{13}C_3$ > $\delta^{13}C_4$) (Schoell 1980; Whiticar et al., 1986; Whiticar 1999; Dai et al., 2016; Xie et al., 2017; Ni et al., 2019). Therefore, the carbon isotope ratio index can be adopted to determine the origin and genetic makeup of various parent natural gases at various times in their development. Carbon isotope characteristics of ethane and propane, as well as the geological history of the study area, suggest that the natural gas in the Shunbei area are likely thermogenic gases (Figure 2). Methane's hydrogen isotopic composition varies with its sedimentary context, and this variation can be used as a valuable indication of that environment. For methane, the concentration of hydrogen isotopes is highest in marine environments rich in salt, followed by those rich in brackish water and finally those rich in fresh water.

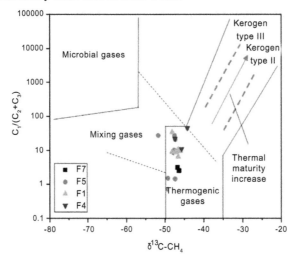

Figure 2. Plot of $\delta^{13}C-CH_4$ vs. $C_1/(C_2+C_3)$ values of natural gases from the Shunbei area (Modified from Bernard 1978).

The value of methane hydrogen isotope is bounded by −180‰, when the value more than −180‰, indicating marine source rocks; otherwise, indicating continental source rocks (Wang et al., 2015). The average δD−CH$_4$ values of the naturally occurring gases in Fault 7, 5, 1, and 4 are −208‰, −190‰, and −168.5‰, and −148.5‰, respectively (Table 1). The carbon and hydrogen isotope properties of methane are used to identify the origin of natural gas, and these measurements showed that the gases in the research area were consistent with a sapropelic-kerogen source (Figure 3). To more accurately determine the genetic types of natural gases based on their isotopic makeup, scientists have discovered that carbon isotopes may be utilized to distinguish between gas originating from coal and gas related with oil. Researchers in Shunbei could tell that the gas was predominantly from zone II and that it was an oil-associated gas by analyzing its carbon isotope composition (Figure 4).

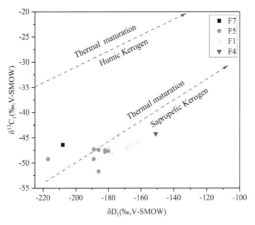

Figure 3. Generalized summary plots of δD −CH$_4$ vs. δ^{13}C −CH$_4$ for the natural gases from Shunbei area (Modified from Wang et al., 2015).

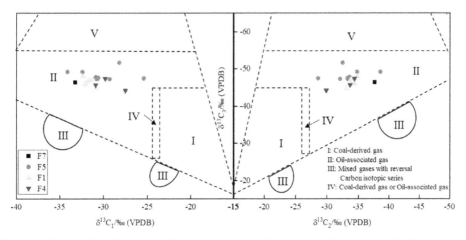

Figure 4. Genetic identification of alkane gases showing that the natural gases from the Shunbei area along the exhibits the characteristics of oil-associated gas (Modified from Dai et al., 1992).

Natural gas genetic kinds can be determined using carbon isotopes contained in gas components as trustworthy indicators. In order to gauge the precision of the method, the reciprocal value of the carbon number associated with methane and pentanes is used (Chung et al., 1988; Dai et al., 2016). In the case when $\delta^{13}Cn$ is proportional to $1/n$, it can be inferred that the carbon isotopic composition of the ancestor is also homologous. However, if this is not the case, it suggests that the genetic source has a complex carbon isotope makeup (Prinzhofer et al., 1995; Zhang et al., 2005; Zou et al., 2007). In the Shunbei, there is a positive trend in the carbon isotopic compositions of alkanes, suggesting that these gases are produced by the cracking of organic materials. This is denoted by the notation $\delta^{13}C_1 < \delta^{13}C_2 < \delta^{13}C_3$. According to the information presented in Table 1, $\delta^{13}C_1$ and $\delta^{13}C_2$ values of natural gases display quite wide ranges of variation, with values ranging from −51.7‰ to −44.2‰ (average −47‰) and −39.3‰ to −28.6‰ (average −34‰), respectively. Natural gases are oil-associated gas and its parent material type is I kerogen in Shunbei, which can be further divided three subcategories. Type I_1, Type I_2 and Type I_3 (Figure 5A). Type I_1 shows a positive trend, $\delta^{13}C_1$ values range from −47.5‰ to −44.2‰ (average −45.85‰), $\delta^{13}C_2$ values range from −28.6‰ to −29.9‰ (average −29.3‰) (Table 1; Figure 5B), the representative wells are No. 26 and No. 13, and $C_1/\Sigma C_{1-5}$ values range from 0.97 to 0.95, respectively, indicating dry gas and oil-associated gas of high maturity. Type I_2 shows a positive trend, $\delta^{13}C_1$ values of the Type I_2 range from −51.7‰ to −44.7‰ (average −47.2‰), $\delta^{13}C_2$ values of the Type I_2 range from −34.8‰ to −32.1‰ (average −33.7‰) (Table 1; Figure 5C). $C_1/\Sigma C_{1-5}$ values of Type I_2 range from 0.81 to 0.97 (average 0.87), the Type I_2 gas is wet gas. The $\delta^{13}C_1$ values of the Type I_3 range from −49.2‰ to −46.4‰ (average −48.51‰), $\delta^{13}C_2$ values of the Type I_3 range from −39.3‰ to −37.7‰ (average −38.6‰) (Table 1; Figure 5D). $C_1/\Sigma C_{1-5}$ values of Type I_3 range from 0.19 to 0.72 (average 0.56), the Type I_3 gas is wet gas. Type I_2 and Type I_3 gases are distinguished from Type I1 gases by having $\delta^{13}C_3$ values typically lower than −28.0‰. In addition, Type I_1 gas exhibits heavier $\delta^{13}C_3$ values than Type I_2 and Type I_3 gas, indicating a greater degree of thermal maturity.

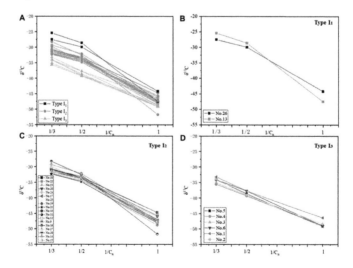

Figure 5. Relationship between carbon number $1/n$ and $\delta^{13}Cn$ of natural gases in Shunbei **(A)** Classification of natural gas types in Shunbei and **(B)** Type I_1 natural gases and **(C)** Type I_2 natural gases and **(D)** Type I_3 natural gases (Modified from Chung et al., 1988; Dai et al., 2003).

Carbon Dioxide

Although CO_2 is widely distributed in nature, its concentration is generally low. If located near to oil fields, large reserves of CO_2 have the potential to be used to enhance oil recovery. Natural gas typically contains a number of components, carbon dioxide being one of the most frequent that is not a hydrocarbon. Most natural gases contain a certain CO_2 content. The CO_2 content is an effective indicator for geologists to understand geochemical processes in natural gases. The starting point for evaluating the regularity of CO_2 enrichment is the source of the gas. Many studies have been conducted to determine where CO_2 first appeared in the atmosphere (Gould et al., 1981; Shang et al., 1990; Tassi et al., 2012; Dai et al., 2016; Mikov et al., 2018). Dai et al. (1996) divided carbon dioxide gas reservoirs into four categories according to the content of CO_2 in gas reservoirs, and believed that the content of CO_2 in gas reservoirs is more than 60%, CO_2 is of inorganic origin, and the content of CO_2 is 15%–60% Mainly of inorganic origin. There is little difference about CO_2 content in Shunbei area. Most of wells have been acidified fracturing in Shunbei, CO_2 content will be increase during the process of acidizing fracturing. The CO_2 produced by the dissolution of acid in the formation water of carbonate rocks is generally low in formation rate and gas production intensity, because the acid in the formation water is generally low in content and concentration. However, the high concentration and quantity of strong acid injected during artificial acid fracturing can quickly react with the carbonate formation to produce a large amount of CO_2 in a short period of time, resulting in high CO_2 content in gas samples collected during this period (Zhang et al., 2010). Therefore, the CO_2 content were related to acidified fracturing in Shunbei. Carbon dioxide origin can be determined by measuring its $\delta^{13}C$ isotope signature, which has been shown to be greater than −8‰ for inorganic carbon dioxide and less than −10‰ for organic carbon dioxide (Dai et al., 1996). Figure 6 shows that the majority of the CO_2 in natural gases in the Shunbei region comes from inorganic sources and exists in a coexisting zone.

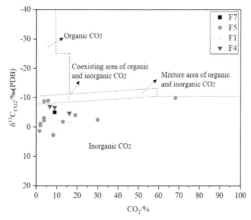

Figure 6. Plot of $\delta^{13}C_{CO2}$ vs. CO_2 content of natural gases from the Shunbei area (Modified from Dai et al., 1996).

Identification of Kerogen Cracking Gas and Oil Cracking Gas

For a complete picture of the natural gas cycle and its origin, it is also important to distinguish between oil-associated gas and coal-type gas, as well as kerogen cracking gas and oil cracking gas (Tissot et al., 1984; Lan et al., 2009; Cheng et al., 2013). If the natural gas is oil cracking gas, then the oil and gas that the source rock produces during the peak phase of oil generation are in the large cracking gas stage when they are trapped to form paleo-reservoirs. Since the oil reservoir created in the early stage of the source rock would have been destroyed, the availability of natural gas would be drastically impacted if it were determined to be kerogen cracking gas (Stahl et al., 1975; Berner et al., 1996; Huang J. et al., 2016). Zhao et al. (2001) proved that there are two kinds of cracking gas in the Tarim Basin, namely, the natural gas in the eastern Tabei Uplift is mainly kerogen cracking gas, and the natural gas in the Hetianhe gas field is mainly crude oil cracking gas; Zhang et al. (2011) proposed that the natural gas in the east Lungu area was mainly crude oil cracking gas.

The natural logarithmic relationship of methane, ethane, and propane ratios shows a positive trend for this ln (C_1/C_2) and ln (C_2/C_3) (Figure 7) (Li et al., 2017). The results show that the values of ln(C_1/C_2) of natural gas in Shunbei area range from 0.20 to 3.81, and the values of ln(C_2/C_3) vary from 0.26 to 1.78, which mainly fall on the evolution curve of kerogen cracking gas, most of which are below 1.5%. Some natural gas is located between the curves of kerogen cracking gas and oil cracking gas, which indicates the contribution of natural gas mixed with oil cracking gas. However, the ln(C_1/C_2) values of natural gas in Shunnan, Gulong and Gucheng areas are mostly greater than 4, and the ln(C_2/C_3) values vary greatly, ranging from 0.5 to 3.04, which falls on the evolution curve of crude oil cracking gas. The maturity of natural gas is mostly between 1.5% and 2.5% (Ma et al., 2021).

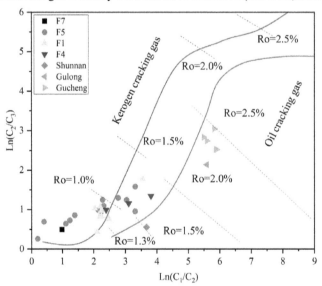

Figure 7. The diagram of ln (C_1/C_2) *versus* ln (C_2/C_3) for source identification of natural gases: kerogen cracking and oil cracking (Modified from Berner et al., 1996; Huang B. J. et al., 2016; Stahl et al., 1975).

From Shunbei to Shuntuo to Shunnan area, the content of methyl adamantane in crude oil shows an increasing trend, which indicates that the cracking degree of crude oil has increased, which provides geochemical evidence that the natural gas is crude oil cracking gas in Shuntuo and Shunnan areas (Ma et al., 2021). The oil cracking degree of Well Shuntuo 1 and Well Shunnan 1 are 96%, 98%, respectively (Ma et al., 2021). The coke bitumen developed in the Ordovician Yingshan Formation reservoir in Shunnan, Gulong and Gucheng area provides petrological evidence for the formation of natural gas as crude oil cracking gas in this area. The high vitrinite reflectance of pyrobitumen indicates a high degree of cracking of the paleo-oil reservoir (Cao et al., 2019; Zhou et al., 2019).

Thermal Maturity of Natural Gas

Since the thermal maturity of natural gas cannot be directly obtained, it is necessary to use its carbon isotope to judge. Methane carbon isotopes in natural gas are closely related to maturity. Important theoretical support for tracing the gas's origins and establishing a gas-source correlation comes from a set of empirical carbon isotope-maturity relationships given for evaluating the maturity of gases and estimated Ro value (Dai, 1989; Huang et al., 1996). There are some discrepancies between the calculated conclusions of the δ^{13}C-maturity models in the Shunbei, however, because of the region's varied geological settings and/or accumulation history. Because of this, Huang (1979) advocated using the δ^{13}C-maturity model, with the equation $\delta^{13}C_1 = 21.88\log Ro - 45.6$ (Huang et al., 1996). The $\delta^{13}C_1$-Ro model was used to calculate the Ro values (Table 1). The carbon isotope of methane and Ro values are displayed in Table 1 in accordance with the dryness coefficient, demonstrating that the maturity of natural gases in the Shunbei area steadily increases from west to east. The southern part of Fault 5 has a higher maturity level than the center and northern parts. The northern portion of Fault 1 is more mature than the southern portion. Natural gas maturity can be determined using a variety of markers, the most popular and reliable of which is the light hydrocarbon component. The light hydrocarbon component's n- and iso-heptane may efficiently discriminate between various maturity stages (Thompson, 1979). Figure 8 shows that the natural gas in Shunbei area is in the mature to high mature stage.

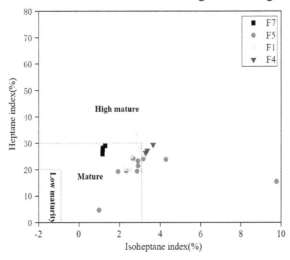

Figure 8. The relationship between the heptane index and the iso-heptane index of natural gases in Shunbei area (Modified from Thompson 1979).

Source of Natural Gas

It is common knowledge that the Cambrian, Lower-Middle Ordovician, and Upper Ordovician were the most productive times for production of the marine source rocks that make up the Tarim Basin (Zhang et al., 2000b). While both the Xishanbulake-Xidashan and Yuertusi Formations contributed to the formation of Cambrian source rocks, the Yuertusi Formation was far more instrumental. Well XH1 uncovered the Cambrian Yuertusi Formation, which has a total thickness of about 40 m and a total organic carbon (TOC) concentration of 1.0%–9.43% (7 samples averaged out to 5.5%) (Yun et al., 2014; Jin et al., 2017). Type I-II organic compounds make up the bulk of all organic materials (Xiao et al., 2000). There is now a stage of extreme maturity in the Cambrian source rocks (Zhan, 2016).

The Heituao and Saergan Formations have the highest concentration of middle and lower Ordovician source rocks (Chen et al., 2014). The presence of kerogen type II in algae and acritarchs causes a wide range of total organic carbon (TOC) values in Middle-Lower Ordovician source rocks (average 1.77%; 7 samples) (Zhao et al., 2012; Zhao et al., 2014). There is a total organic carbon concentration of 0.47–0.56% in the Upper Ordovician source rocks of the North Uplift of the Tarim Basin, and a TOC concentration of 0.5% or higher in rocks with a thickness of 6–28 m. Natural gas in the Shunbei area was determined to be oil-associated gas based on its geochemical features and those of the source rocks. The Ordovician age is largely responsible for the generation of the gas found in oil reservoirs. The evidence is broken down and addressed in detail below.

①The $\delta^{13}C$ properties of the natural gas in the Shunbei exploratory wells show that the oil-associated gas originates from the Ordovician source rocks. Gaseous alkanes from the Middle-Upper Ordovician and Cambrian have been dated using their carbon isotope distribution curves, which have been published by Wang et al. (2014). It is discovered that the wet gases show steep C_1-C_3 alkane carbon isotope distribution curves with negative $\delta^{13}C_1$ values (<− 42.5‰), which are assumed to have originated from Middle-Upper Ordovician source rocks. In contrast, Cambrian natural gas had $\delta^{13}C$ values that were considerably high (>−42.5‰), along with flat distribution curves for carbon isotopes C_1–C_3. Therefore, using the carbon isotopes of gaseous alkanes permits one to determine the origin of gases and establish relationships between gases. The wet gas from the Shunbei correlates well with gases from the Middle-Upper Ordovician, with $\delta^{13}C$ values that range from 44‰ to 52‰ (or <− 42.5‰) and a steep distribution curve of C_1-C_3 alkanes carbon isotopes (Table 1; Figure 9).

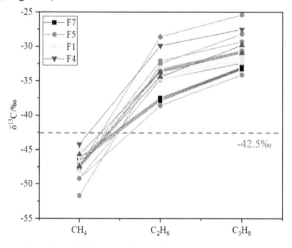

Figure 9. Carbon isotopic series of alkane gas in the Tarim Basin.

②In accordance with the inheritance of isotopes, dispersion of isotopes, and variation of isotopes during the formation and evolution of hydrocarbons, the carbon isotopes can be utilized to correlate oil sources. The majority of Cambrian source rock samples exhibit stable carbon isotopes heavier than −30‰, with the greatest values seen in Well H4 at −25.8‰. The isotopic curve distribution of Cambrian and Ordovician crude oils is shown in Figure 10 and Table 2. Obviously, Cambrian crude oils are consistent with Cambrian source rocks. On the other hand, the isotopes of Ordovician crude oil are obviously lighter and are distributed in −32‰ ~ −36‰ (Song et al., 2016), so it is obviously impossible for them to be derived from Cambrian source rocks.

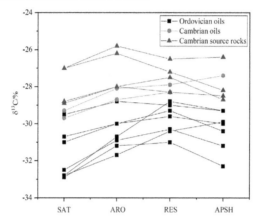

Figure 10. Carbon isotope curves of non-hydrocarbon from the Tarim Basin.

Table 2. Carbon isotope for Cambrian source rock extracts, typical Cambrian oils and typical Ordovician oils from the Tarim Basin

	Wells	Depth/m	Strata	$\delta^{13}C_{PDB}$ (‰)				
				SAT	ARO	RES	ASPH	
Ordovician oils in Shunbei	No.1	7,674–8,024.66	O	−30.70	−30.00	−29.60	−30.00	
	No.30	n.d.	O	−32.50	−30.90	−30.30	−31.20	
	No.14	8,050	O_{2yj}-O_{1-2y}	−32.90	−31.20	−31.00	−32.30	
	No.31	7,438.42	O_{2yj}-O_{1-2y}	−29.50	−28.80	−29.00	−29.30	
	No.32	7,458–7,613.05	O2yj	−32.80	−30.70	−28.80	−29.30	
	No.33	n.d.	O	−32.80	−31.70	−30.40	−30.00	
	No.34	7,531	O_{2yj}-O_{1-2y}	−31.00	−30.00	−29.30	−28.60	
Cambrian source rocks in Tarim basin	KN1	4,994	$\varepsilon_{3q}l$	n.d.	n.d.	n.d.	n.d.	Quoted from Ref. Song et al. (2016) and Jiang et al. (2017)
	KN1	5,188	$\varepsilon_{3q}l$	n.d.	n.d.	n.d.	n.d.	
	H4	4,598–4,599	$\varepsilon_{2q}l$	−27.00	−25.80	−26.50	−26.40	
	TD2	4,772	$\varepsilon_{3}t$	n.d.	n.d.	n.d.	n.d.	
	YL1	4,228	$\varepsilon_{2}m$	−27.00	−26.20	−27.20	−28.20	
	KN1	5,188.5	ε_{3}	−28.90	−28.00	−27.50	−28.70	
	TD2	4,919.2	ε_{1}	−28.8	−28	−28.3	−28.5	
	YL1	4,235	$\varepsilon_{2}m$	n.d.	n.d.	n.d.	n.d.	
	XH1	5,826–5,830	$\varepsilon_{1}y$	n.d.	n.d.	n.d.	n.d.	
Cambrian oils in Tarim basin	TZ26	4,392–440	$O_{3}l$	n.d.	n.d.	n.d.	n.d.	Quoted from Ref. Song et al. (2016) and Tian et al. (2017)
	T904	5,900–5,935	$O_{1}y$	−29.70	−28.70	−28.30	n.d.	
	LK1	4,265–4,305	J	n.d.	n.d.	n.d.	n.d.	
	MA4-2	2017–2041	$O_{3}l$	n.d.	n.d.	n.d.	n.d.	
	TD2	4,561–5,040	ε	−29.30	−28.10	−27.90	−27.40	

Note: SAT= saturated; ARO= aromatics; RES= resins; ASPH= asphaltene.

Oil and Gas Accumulation and Enrichment Patterns

The crude oil in Shunbei area mainly comes from the Lower Cambrian Yuertusi Formation source rocks (Yun et al., 2014), the Ordovician reservoir is mainly controlled by the multi-stage structural rupture of the strike-slip fault zone and the dissolution along the fault (Jiang et al., 2005). The characteristics of hydrocarbon reservoirs revealed in shallow and deep parts of the same fault zone are consistent. For example, deep well SHB1-10H and shallow well SHB1-3 of Shunbei No. 1 fault zone have basically the same crude oil density and gas dryness coefficient of the two Wells, which proves that the oil and gas generated by *in-situ* source rock is mainly formed by vertical transport along the fault in Shunbei area. The movable oil and gas are mainly accumulated since the late Hercynian period, and the fault zone plays an obvious role in controlling reservoir and accumulation. This area is located in the sedimentary area of gentle slope source rocks in the early Cambrian period. In the later period, the pass-source strike-slip fault was developed and the reservoir was dominated by "fault-karst". Therefore, because strike slip faults influence in-reservoir geochemical processes and vertical petroleum migration, strike slip faults play an important role in the ultra-deep fault-karst petroleum systems present in the Shunbei area (Figure 11) (Qi, 2021).

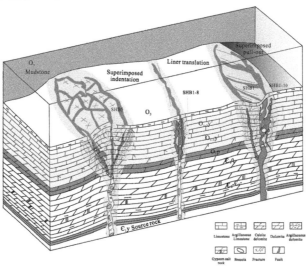

Figure 11. Oil and gas accumulation and enrichment patterns of different segments of strike slip fault zone in Shunbei Oilfield (Modified from Qi 2021).

CONCLUSION

In the Shunbei area, the natural gas is the origin of oil-associated gas and its parent material type is I kerogen. The relationship between carbon number $1/n$ and natural gas $\delta^{13}C_n$ can be further subdivided into I_1, I_2 and I_3 subclasses. The $\delta^{13}C_1$ and $\delta^{13}C_2$ values for Type I_1 gases are highly enriched at $\delta^{13}C$, ranging from $-47.5‰$ to $-44.2‰$ ($-45.85‰$ on average) and $-28.6‰$ to $-29.9‰$ ($-29.3‰$ on average), respectively. However, Type I_2 and Type I_3 gases have higher $\delta^{13}C$ depletion levels than Type I_1 gases.

Inevitably, the natural gas in the Shunbei area was dominated by oil-associated gas, as shown by modified $\ln C_1/C_2$ vs. $\ln C_2/C_3$ plots, and oil cracking gas is present in the natural gas mixture. Carbon isotope ratios of the source rocks, natural gas, and oil in the Shunbei area suggest that the gases originated in the Ordovician source rocks.

The fault zone in the Shunbei area can be shown to control accumulation within reservoirs. As a new type of reservoir, ultra-deep fault-karst reservoir in the Shunbei area extended the theory of hydrocarbon accumulation in marine carbonates, shows a great exploration potential of ultra-deep marine carbonate formations, and is an important field for reserve increase in the future.

Author Contributions

Conceptualization, DH; methodology, ZJ; software, XZ and JB; review and editing, XM and ZJ.

Acknowledgments

All data and samples were generously provided by Northwest Oilfield Company, SINOPEC, which the authors gratefully acknowledge.

REFERENCES

1. Bai, G. P., and Cao, B. F. (2014). Global deep oil and gas reservoirs and their distribution. *Oil Gas. Geol.* 35 (1), 19–25. (in Chinese with English abstract). doi:10.11743/ogg20140103

2. Bernard, B. B., Brooks, J. M., and Sackett, W. M. (1978). Light hydrocarbons in recent Texas continental shelf and slope sediments. *J. Geophys. Res.* 33, 4053–4061. doi:10.1029/JC083iC08p04053

3. Berner, U., and Faber, E. (1996). Empirical carbon isotope/maturity relationships for gases from algal kerogens and terrigenous organic matter, based on dry, open-system pyrolysis. *Org. Geochem.* 24, 947–955. doi:10.1016/S0146-6380(96)00090-3

4. Cao, Y. H., Wang, S., Zhang, Y. J., Yang, M., Yan, L., Zhao, J. L., et al. (2019). Petroleum geological conditions and exploration potential of Lower Paleozoic carbonate rocks in Gucheng area, Tarim, China. *Petrol. explor. Dev.* 46 (6), 1099–1114. doi:10.11698/PED.2019.06.08

5. Chen, H. H., Wu, Y., Feng, Y., Lu, Z. Y., Hu, S. Z., Yun, L., et al. (2014). Timing and chronology of hydrocarbon charging in the ordovician of tahe oilfield, Tarim Basin, NW China. *Oil Gas. Geol.* 35 (6), 806–819. doi:10.11743/ogg20140608

6. Chen, Q. L., Yang, X., Chu, C. L., Hu, G., Shi, Z., Jiang, H. J., et al. (2015). Recognition of depositional environment of Cambrian source rocks in Tarim Basin. *Oil Gas. Geol.* 06, 880–887. doi:10.11743/ogg20150602

7. Cheng, H. G., Wei, G. Q., Ran, Q. G., Wu, D. M., Liu, L. W., Xiao, Z. Y., et al. (2013). Relationship between hydrocarbon accumulation and solid bitumen characteristics of the Lower Paleozoic in the eastern Tarim Basin. *Nat. Gas. Ind.* 33 (10), 40–46. doi:10.3787/j.issn.1000-0976.2013.10.006

8. Chung, H. M., Gormly, J. R., and Squires, R. M. (1988). Origin of gaseous hydrocarbons in subsurface environments: Theoretical considerations of carbon isotope distribution. *Chem. Geol.* 71, 97–104. doi:10.1016/0009-2541(88)90108-8

9. Dai, J., Ni, Y., Zhang, W., Huang, S., Gong, D., Liu, D., et al. (2016). Relationships between wetness and maturity of coal−derived gas in China. *Petrol. explor. Dev.* 43 (5), 737–739. doi:10.1016/S1876-3804(16)30088-X

10. Dai, J. X. (1989). Composition characteristics and origin of carbon isotope of liuhuanantan natural gas in tengchong county, Yunan Province. *China Sci. Bull.* 34, 690–692.

11. Dai, J. X., Song, Y., Dai, C. S., and Wang, D. R. (1996). Geochemistry and accumulation of carbon dioxide gases in China. *AAPG Bull.* 80, 1615–1626. doi:10.1306/64EDA0D2-1724-11D7-8645000102C1865D

12. Dai, J. X., Zou, C. N., Liao, S. M., Dong, D. Z., Ni, Y. Y., Huang, W. H., et al. (2014). Geochemistry of the extremely high thermal maturity longmaxi shale gas, southern Sichuan basin. *Org. Geochem.* 74, 3–12. doi:10.1016/j.orggeochem.2014.01.018

13. Deng, S., Li, H. L., Zhang, Z. P., Zhang, J. B., and Yang, X. (2019). Structural characterization of intracratonic strike-slip faults in the central Tarim Basin. *AAPG Bull.* 103 (1), 109–137. doi:10.1306/06071817354

14. Dutton, S. P., and Loucks, R. G. (2010). Diagenetic controls on evolution of porosity and permeability in lower Tertiary Wilcox sandstones from shallow to ultradeep (200–6700m) burial, Gulf of Mexico Basin, U.S.A. *Mar. Petrol. Geol.* 27 (1), 69–81. doi:10.1016/j.marpetgeo.2009.08.008

15. Gould, K. W., Hart, G. H., and Smith, J. W. (1981). Carbon dioxide in the southern coalfields a factor in the evaluation of natural gas potential. *Proceedings– Australasisn Inst. Min. Metall.* 279, 41–42.

16. He, D. F., Zhou, X. Y., and Yang, H. J. (2008). Formation mechanism and tectonic types of intracratonic paleo–uplifts in the Tarim Basin. *Ear. Sci. Fron.* 15 (2), 207–221.

17. Huang, B. J., Tian, H., Li, X. S., Wang, Z. F., and Xiao, X. M. (2016). Geochemistry, origin and accumulation of natural gases in the deepwater area of the Qiongdongnan Basin, South China Sea. *Mar. Petrol. Geol.* 72, 254–267. doi:10.1016/j.marpetgeo.2016.02.007

18. Huang, D. F., Liu, B. Q., Wang, T. D., Xu, Y. C., Chen, S. J., and Zhao, M. J. (1996). Genetic types and maturity identification of natural gas in Eastern Tarim Basin. *Sci China Ser. D.* 36 (4), 365–372. doi:10.1016/S0009-2541(99)00053-4

19. Huang, J., Ye, D. L., and Han, Yu. (2016). Petoleum geology features and accumulation controls for ultra-deep oil and gas reservoirs. *Pet. Geo. Exp.* 5 (38), 635–640. (in Chinese with English abstract). doi:10.11781/sysydz201605635

20. Jia, C. Z., and Pan, X. Q. (2015). Research processes and main development directions of deep hydrocarbon geological theories. *Acta Pet. Sin.* 36 (12), 1457–1469. doi:10.7623/syxb201512001

21. Jia, C. Z. (1997). Tectonic Characteristics and Petroleum of Tarim Basin China. *Petrol. Ind. beijing.* 1997, 205–389. (in Chinese with English abstract).

22. Jiao, F. Z. (2018). Significance and prospect of ultra-deep carbonate fault-karst reservoirs in Shunbei area, Tarim Basin. *Oil Gas. Geol.* 39 (02), 208–216. doi:10.11743/ogg20180201

23. Jin, Z. J., Liu, Q. Y., Yun, J. B., and Tenger, B. (2017). Potential petroleum sources and exploration directions around the Manjar Sag in the Tarim Basin. *Sci. Chi. Ear. Scie.* 2, 235–245. doi:10.1007/s11430-015-5573-7

24. Lan, X. D., Zhu, Y. M., Rang, Q. G., and Cheng, H. G. (2009). A discussion on the geochemical characteristics and migration and accumulation of natural gas in the eastern Tarim Basin. *Pet. Geol. Exp.* 30 (3), 324–329.

25. Li, J., Li, Z. S., Wang, X. B., Wang, D. L., Xie, Z. Y., Li, J., et al. (2017). New indexes and charts for Genesis identification of multiple natural gases. *Pet. Explor. Dev.* 44 (4), 535–543. doi:10.1016/S1876-3804(17)30062-9

26. Li, J. Z., Tao, X. W., Bai, B., Huang, S. P., Jiang, Q. C., Zhao, Z. Y., et al. (2021). China's marine ultra-deep oil and gas geological conditions, accumulation evolution and favorable exploration direction. *Pet. Geol. Exp.* 48 (1), 52–67. doi:10.11698/PED.2021.01.05

27. Ma, A. L., He, Z. L., Yun, L., Wu, X., Qiu, N. S., Chang, J., et al. (2021). The geochemical

characteristics and origin of Ordovician ultra–deep natural gas in the North Shuntuoguole area, Tarim Basin, NW China. *Nat. Gas. Geosci.* 32 (7), 1047–1060. doi:10.11764/j.issn.1672-1926.2021.03.012

28. Ma, N. B., Jin, S. L., Yang, R. Z., Meng, L. B., Wang, L., and Hu, Y. Z. (2019). Seismic response characteristics and identification of fault-karst reservoir in Shunbei area, Tarim basin. *Oil. Geo. Pros.* 54 (2), 398–403. doi:10.13810/j.cnki.issn.1000-7210.2019.02.019

29. Ma, Y. S., Li, M. W., Cai, X. Y., Xu, X. H., Hu, D. F., Qu, S. L., et al. (2020). Mechanisms and exploitation of deep marine petroleum accumulations in China: Advances, technological bottlenecks and basic scientific problems. *Oil Gas. Geol.* 41 (4), 655683. (in Chinese with English abstract).

30. Mikov, A. V., and Etiope, G. (2018). revised genetic diagrams for natural gases based on a global dataset of > 20,000 samples. *Org. Geochem.* 125, 109–120. doi:10.1016/j.orggeochem.2018.09.002

31. Ni, Y. Y., Liao, F. R., Gao, J. L., Chen, J. P., Yao, L. M., and Zhang, D. J. (2019). Hydrogen isotopes of hydrocarbon gases from different organic facies of the Zhongba gas field, Sichuan Basin, China. *J. Petrol. Sci. Eng.* 179, 776–786. doi:10.1016/j.petrol.2019.04.102

32. Pan, J. P., and Jiao, Z. L. (2022). Study on China's development strategy for oil & gas industry toward the goal of carbon peaking and carbon neutrality. *Tra. For.* 30 (8), 01–15. (in Chinese with English abstract).

33. Pang, X. Q., Wang, W. Y., Wang, Y. Y., and Wu, L. Y. (2015). Comparision of otherness on hydrocarbon accumulation conditions and characteristics between deep and middle-shallow in petroliferous basins. *Acta Petro Sin.* 36 (10), 1167–1185. doi:10.7623/syxb201510001

34. Prinzhofer, A., and Huc, A. Y. (1995). Genetic and post–genetic molecular and isotopic fractionations in natural gases. *Chem. Geol.* 126, 281–290. doi:10.1016/0009-2541(95)00123-9

35. Qi, L. (2021). Structural characteristics and storage control function of the Shun I fault zone in the Shunbei region, Tarim Basin. *J. Petrol. Sci. Eng.* 203, 108653. doi:10.1016/j.petrol.2021.108653

36. Ren, Z. L., Cui, J. P., Qi, K., Yang, G. L., Chen, Z. J., Yang, P., et al. (2020). Control effects of temperature and thermal evolution history of deep and ultra-deep layers on hydrocarbon phase state and hydrocarbon generation history. *Nat. Gas. Indus (B)* 7 (5), 453–461. doi:10.1016/j.ngib.2020.09.003

37. Schoell, M. (1980). The hydrogen and carbon isotopic composition of methane from natural gases of various origins. *Geochim. Cosmochim. Acta.* 44, 649–661. doi:10.1016/0016-7037(80)90155-6

38. Shang, G. Z., and Gao, S. (1990). The CO_2 discharges and earthquakes in Western Yunnan. *Acta Seismol. Sin.* 12, 186–193.

39. Song, D. F., Wang, T. G., and Li, J. M. (2016). Geochemistry and possible origin of the hydrocarbons from Wells Zhongshen1 and Zhongshen1C, Tazhong Uplift. *Sci. China Earth Sci.* 46, 840–850. doi:10.1007/s11430-015-5226-z

40. Stahl, W. J., and Carey, J. B. D. (1975). Source-rock identification by isotope analyses of natural gases from fields in the Val Verde and Delaware basins, west Texas. *Chem. Geol.* 16, 257–267. doi:10.1016/0009-2541(75)90065-0

41. Tassi, F., Fiebig, J., Vaselli, O., and Nocentini, M. (2012). Origins of methane discharging from volcanic–hydrothermal, geothermal and cold emissions in Italy. *Chem. Geol.* 310–311, 36–48. doi:10.1016/j.chemgeo.2012.03.018

42. Thompson, K. F. M. (1979). Light hydrocarbons in subsurface sediments. *Geochim. Cosmochim. Acta.* 43, 657–672. doi:10.1016/0016-7037(79)90251-5

43. Tissot, B. T., and Welte, D. H. (1984). *Petroleum Formation and occurrences*. Berlin: Springer.

44. Wang, T. G., Song, D. F., Li, M. j., Ynag, C. Y., Ni, Z. Y., Li, H. L., et al. (2014). Natural gas source and deep gas exploration potential of the Ordovician Yingshan Formation in the Shunnan-Gucheng region, Tarim Basin. *Oil Gas. Geol.* 12 (06), 753–762. doi:10.11743/ogg20140602

45. Wang, T. G., Wang, C. J., and Zhang, W. B. (2003). *Geochemical study on formation of the Ordovician oil/gas reservoirs in Tahe oil field*. Beijing, China: Sinopec Xinxing Northwest China Branch.

46. Wang, X., Liu, W., Shi, B., Zhang, Z., Xu, Y., and Zheng, J. (2015). Hydrogen isotope characteristics of thermogenic methane in Chinese sedimentary basins. *Org. Geochem.* 83-84, 178–189. doi:10.1016/j.orggeochem.2015.03.010

47. Whiticar, M. J. (1999). Carbon and hydrogen isotope systematics of bacterial formation and oxidation of methane. *Chem. Geol.* 161, 291–314. doi:10.1016/S0009-2541(99)00092-3

48. Whiticar, M. J., Faber, E., and Schoell, M. (1986). Biogenic methane formation in marine and freshwater environments; CO_2 reduction vs. acetate fermentation; isotope evidence. *Geochim. Cosmochim. Acta.* 50, 693–709. doi:10.1016/0016-7037(86)90346-7

49. Wu, F. Q., and Xian, X. F. (2006). Current state and countermeasure of deep reservoirs exploration. *Sedi Geol Teth Geol* 26 (2), 68–71. (in Chinese with English abstract).

50. Xiao, X., Wilkins, R. W. T., Liu, D. H., Liu, Z. F., and Fu, J. M. (2000). Investigation of thermal maturity of lower Palaeozoic hydrocarbon source rocks by means of vitrinite-like maceral reflectance – a Tarim Basin case study. *Org. Geochem.* 31, 1041–1052. doi:10.1016/S0146-6380(00)00061-9

51. Xie, Z. Y., Li, J., Li, Z. S., Guo, J. Y., Li, J., Zhang, L., et al. (2017). Geochemical characteristics of the upper Triassic Xujiahe formation in Sichuan Basin, China and its significance for hydrocarbon accumulation. *Acta Geol. Sin.* 91, 1836–1854. doi:10.1111/1755-6724.13414

52. Yang, F. L., Yu, L., Wang, T. G., Ding, Y., and Li, M. J. (2017). Geochemical characteristics of the Cambrian source rocks in the Tarim Basin and oil-source correlation with typical marine crude oil. *Oil Gas. Geol.* 38 (05), 851–861. doi:10.11743/ogg20170503

53. Yun, J. B., Jin, Z. J., and Xie, G. J. (2014). Distribution of major hydrocarbon source rocks in the Lower Paleozoic, Tarim Basin. *Oil Gas. Geol.* 35, 827–838. doi:10.11743/ogg20140610

54. Yun, L., and Cao, Z. C. (2014). Hydrocarbon enrichment pattern and exploration potential of the Ordovician in Shunnan area, Tarim Basin. *Oil Gas. Geol.* 35 (6), 788–797. doi:10.11743/ogg20140606

55. Zhai, G. M., and He, W. Y. (2004). An important petroleum exploration region in Tarim Basin. *Acta Pet. Sin.* 25 (1), 1–7.

56. Zhai, G. M., Wang, S. H., and He, W. Y. (2012). Hostop trend and enlightenment of global ten-year hydrocarbon exploration. *Acta Pet. sin.* 33, 14–19. (in Chinese with English abstract).

57. Zhan, Z. W. (2016). *De-convoluting the marine crude oil mixtures in the Tabei uplift, Tarim basim, NW China*. Beijing, China: Guangzhou Institute of Geochemistry, Chinese Academy of Sciences.

58. Zhang, B. S., Gu, Q. Y., Zhang, H. Z., Zhao, Q., and Yin, F. L. (2010). Genesis and Study Significance of High CO 2 Content in Carbonate Rocks in Tazhong Area, Tarim Basin. *Mari. Ori. Petro. Geol.* 15 (3), 70–73.

59. Zhang, H., Xiong, Y., Liu, J. Z., Liao, Y. H., and Geng, A. (2005). Pyrolysis kinetics of Pure n–$C_{18}H_{38}$ (I): gaseous hydrocarbon and carbon isotope evolution. *Acta Geol. Sin.* 79, 569–574.

60. Zhang, S. C., Su, J., Wang, X. M., Zhu, G. Y., Yang, H. J., Liu, K. Y., et al. (2011). Geochemistry of Palaeozoic marine petroleum from the Tarim Basin, NW China: Part 3. Thermal cracking

of liquid hydrocarbons and gas washing as the major mechanisms for deep gas condensate accumulations, NW China: Part 3. Thermal cracking of liquid hydrocarbons and gas washing as the major mechanisms for deep gas condensate accumulations. *Org. Geochem.* 42, 1394–1410. doi:10.1016/j.orggeochem.2011.08.013

61. Zhang, S., Zhang, B., Wang, F., Liang, D., and He, Z. (2000b). Middle-Upper Ordovician: the main source of the oils in the Tarim Basin. Mar. *Oil. Gas. Geo.* 5, 16–22. (in Chinese with English abstract).

62. Zhang, Z. P., Kang, Y., Lin, H. X., Han, J., Zhao, R., Zhu, X. X., et al. (2021). A study on the reservoir controlling characteristics and mechanism of the strike slip faults in the northern slope of Tazhong uplift, Tarim Basin, China. *Arab. Jour. Geo.* 14 (8), 735–762. doi:10.1007/s12517-021-07076-5

63. Zhao, J. Z., Zhang, W. Z., Li, J., Cao, Q., and Fan, Y. F. (2014). Genesis of tight sand gas in the Ordos Basin, China. *Org. Geochem.* 74, 76–84. doi:10.1016/j.orggeochem.2014.03.006

64. Zhao, M. J., Zeng, F. G., Qin, S. F., and Lu, S. F. (2001). Two pyrolytic gases found and proved in Talimu Basin. *Nat. Gas. Indus* 21 (1), 35–39. (in Chinese with English abstract).

65. Zhao, W. Z., Hu, S. Y., Wang, Z. C., Zhang, S. C., and Wang, T. S. (2018). Petroleum geological conditions and exploration importance of Proterozoic to Cambrian in China. *Pet. Geo. Exp.* 45 (1), 1–14. doi:10.1016/S1876-3804(18)30001-6

66. Zhao, W. Z., Zhu, G. Y., Su, J., Yang, H. J., and Zhu, Y. F. (2012). Study on the Multi−stage Charging Accumulation Model of Chinese Marine Petroleum: Example from Eastern Lungu Area in the Tarim Basin. *Acta Pet. Sin.* 28 (3), 709–721. (in Chinese with English abstract).

67. Zheng, J. F. (2018). Significance and Prospect of ultar−deep carbonate fault−karst reservoirs in Shunbei area, Tarim Basin. *Oil Gas. Geol.* 39 (2), 207–216. doi:10.11743/ogg20180201

68. Zhou, X, X., Lü, X. X., Zhu, G. Y., Cao, Y. H., Yan, L., and Zhang, Z. Y. (2019). Origin and formation of deep and superdeep strata gas from Gucheng-Shunnan block of the Tarim Basin, NW China, NW China. *J. Petrol. Sci. Eng.* 177, 361–373. doi:10.1016/j.petrol.2019.02.059

69. Zhu, D., Meng, Q., Jin, Z., Liu, Q., and Hu, W. (2015). Formation mechanism of deep Cambrian dolomite reservoirs in the Tarim basin, northwestern China. *Mar. Petrol. Geol.* 59, 232–244. doi:10.1016/j.marpetgeo.2014.08.022

70. Zhu, G., Milkov, A. V., Chen, F., Weng, N., Zhang, Z., Yang, H., et al. (2018). Non-cracked oil in ultra-deep high-temperature reservoirs in the Tarim basin, China. *Mar. Petrol. Geol.* 89, 252–262. doi:10.1016/j.marpetgeo.2017.07.019

71. Zou, Y. R., Cai, Y., Zhang, C., Zhang, X., and Peng, P. A. (2007). Variations of natural gas carbon isotope−type curves and their interpretation a case study. *Org. Geochem.* 38 (8), 1398–1415. doi:10.1016/j.orggeochem.2007.03.002

Controlling Hydrocarbon Dew Point and Water Dew Point of Natural Gas Using Aspen HYSYS

M. A. El Maghraby[1], N. A. El Moniem[2] and Amr Abdelghany[2]

[1]Engineering for Petroleum and Process Industries, ENPPI, Cairo, Egypt
[2]Chemical Engineering Department, Faculty of Engineering, Cairo University, Cairo, Egypt

ABSTRACT

A great attention is subjected to the environmentally friendly natural gas. Compared to other fossil fuels, natural gas is a cleaner burning due to the lower emission of carbon dioxides into the air. Removal of associated hydrocarbons from natural gas streams plays an important role to sell and to achieve the pipeline specification of natural gas. To satisfy the specification of pipelines, the hydrocarbon dew point and water dew point of natural gas must be controlled below the pipeline operating conditions to prevent many problems: two-phase flow and hydrate formation in the system. The main purpose of this paper is to simulate the gas plant process to study the effect of natural gas composition and changing in differential pressure of Joule–Thomson expansion valve on the obtained values of hydrocarbon, water dew points, and cricondentherm temperature.

The results of process simulation using Aspen HYSYS have shown that the control of hydrocarbon dew point, water dew point, and cricondentherm of natural gas is achieved through increasing the Joule-Thomson valve differential pressure. There is an inverse relation between increasing Joule-Thomson valve differential pressure (Δp) and hydrocarbon dew point, water dew point, and cricondentherm to meet the specification of gas pipeline transmission. Increasing differential pressure (Δp) from 14 bar to 24 bar causes a decrease in hydrocarbon dew point, water dew point from −1 to −26°C and from 0 to −18°C, respectively. Cricondentherm is also decreased from 4 to −12°C by increasing differential pressure (Δp) from 14 to 24 bars. The operating conditions at differential pressure below 14 bar is not advisable because cricondentherm temperature does not meet the specification of gas pipeline transmission and hence lead to many problems. Careful adjustment of the operating conditions of gas processing plant is very important by making such simulations to choose the optimum operating conditions which meet gas pipeline transmission.

Keyword: *Natural gas, Process simulation, Control, Hydrocarbon dew point, Water dew point, Cricondentherm*

INTRODUCTION

The production of natural gas and derivatives play an extremely important role in Egypt. Natural gas consumption is about 53% of the total energy used. Gas total production peak was in 2020 that reached an average rate of 85 BCM/year produced from three areas in Egypt which are Nooros field, West Delta Deep Marine, and Zohr. Currently in 2022, Egypt has three areas of production of natural gas which are Nooros field, West delta deep marine, and Zohr. In 2027, it is expected that gas production will be produced from two areas which are West Nile Delta and Zohr. Natural gas is used in various sectors such as electricity, industry, petroleum, residential, and CNG (compressed natural gas) sectors.

The electricity sector is the largest gas consumer, as natural gas consumption reached 62.3% of the total local gas consumption. The industry sector consumes around 22.5% of the total local gas consumption. The petroleum sector consumes about 10.1% of total local consumption. After that, the residential and CNG sectors come at the least sectors that consume natural gas which reached 5.1% of total local natural gas consumption [1,2,3,4].

Natural gas, a highly efficient form of energy, produces a lot of energy and emits fewer pollutants than many other energy sources. It has an increasing demand to provide energy in heating homes, cooking food, and generating electricity. It is considered as a source of hydrocarbon needed in petrochemical feedstocks. It also provides the main ingredients for such varied products as plastics, fertilizers, anti-freezes, and fabrics [5, 6]. Industrial consumers get advantages from operating natural gas combined heat and power (CHP) and combined cooling, heat, and power (CCHP) systems, similar to those used in commercial settings. Natural gas has different compositions depending on the well type and location [5]. Natural gas is formed from methane mainly and smaller amounts of ethane, propane, butane, and heavier hydrocarbons along with varying amounts of water vapors, carbon dioxide, sulfur compounds, and other non-hydrocarbons [7].

Ethane, propane, and butane are known as associated gases or (NGL) [8,9,10,11,12]. They have a variety of different purposes including the improvement of oil recovery in oil wells, providing raw materials for oil refineries or petrochemical plants, and as sources of energy. These NGL components must be recovered to control the dew point of the natural gas stream and also to earn revenue by selling out the separated components. Refrigeration is applied using a direct expansion Joule-Thomson technique or turboexpander to control the dew point of both water and hydrocarbons of natural gas in order to improve gas quality and satisfy the specification of pipelines to obtain saleable and useful energy forms to be used in a wide variety of applications [11,12,13,14]. The hydrocarbon liquid dropout causes some difficulties in gas transmission systems including the increase in pressure drop, reducing in line capacity and some equipment problems [15, 16]. Avoiding liquid dropout, the operating current specifications of gas transmission lines require to be operated above the hydrocarbon dew point or cricondentherm temperature. The achievable control of hydrocarbon dew point and water dew point depends on the differential pressure available and the composition of the feed gas. In industry, there are many widely applied different methods used for hydrocarbon dew point control. Joule-Thomson (J-T) expansion technique is the most preferable method rather than mechanical refrigeration if enough pressure is available [17].

This work aims to simulate the gas processing plant in order to illustrate the optimum operating conditions using Joule–Thomson expansion technique. The effect of feed composition of natural gas and changing in Joule–Thomson valve differential pressure (Δp) on hydrocarbon dew point, water dew point, and cricondentherm temperature is studied to meet the specification of pipeline gas transmission Table 1.

Table 1. Pipeline specifications of natural gas [11]

Parameter	Pipeline specifications
Water dew point, °C	< 0 @ 70 bars
Hydrocarbon dew point, °C	< 5 @ 70 bars
Cricondentherm, °C	< 5
Gross calorific value, BTU/SCF	> 1000

METHODS

Gases, coming from the wells located in North Nile Delta, contain mainly methane and other hydrocarbons. The feed composition of two wells (C1 and C2) are listed in Table 2. Aspen HYSYS steady-state simulation software version 11 is used to study the effect of different process variables on hydrocarbon dew, water dew point, and cricondentherm in the gas processing plant and choose the optimum process condition. The selected physical property package for the HYSYS model developed is the Peng-Robinson Equation-of-State [18, 19]. The gas processing plant is shown in Fig. 1 and described as follows:

Table 2. Feed compositions of different wells (C1 and C2) of natural gas

	C1, mass %	C2 mass %
N_2	0.20	0.05
CO_2	0.70	0.46
Methane	60.00	61.27
Ethane	5.00	5.49
Propane	3.92	6.48
i-Butane	2.00	3.16
n-Butane	1.51	2.77
C_5	6.50	1.25
C_6^+	13.77	15.00
H_2O	6.00	3.66
Methanol	0.40	0.40

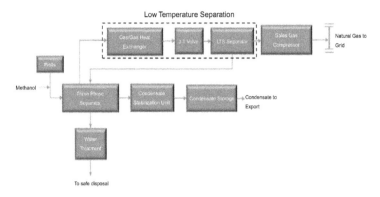

Figure 1. Gas plant block flow diagram [15].

Plant General Description

- Gas streams from the wells are gathered and delivered to the inlet manifold, and methanol solution is injected to prevent hydrate buildup at low temperatures [20].
- Gases, condensate, and produced water are separated in three-phase separator.
- Gases are treated in a low temperature separation train which contains gas/gas heat exchanger for cooling, Joule–Thomson (J-T) valve for reducing pressure and a low temperature three-phase separator to separate the condensate liquid, water, and sale gas.
- Sale gas stream is then recycled to the heat exchanger to cool the feed gas and collected the sale gas as the main product with certain conditions.
- Condensate is stabilized via a two-stage condensate stabilization unit, stored in tanks, and exported via pumps and pipeline to the national condensate grid.
- Produced water is degassed and stored in tanks where it is transported by trucks to a safe disposal.
- The actual plant inlet pressure varies from 51 bars to 66 bars related to the required Joule–Thomson valve differential pressure to ensure high quality of sales gas.

RESULTS AND DISCUSSION

The results are divided into four main parts: the first part studies the effect of changing differential pressure of Joule–Thomson expansion valve on the specifications of the natural gas such as hydrocarbon dew point, water dew point, and cricondentherm temperature using composition (C1). The second part illustrates the effect of compositions (C1 and C2) of wells on hydrocarbon dew point, water dew point, and cricondentherm. The third part includes the mass balance of LTS train for different feed gas compositions. The fourth part explains the effect of Joule–Thomson valve differential pressure on sale gas gross calorific value using different compositions of natural gas. The conditions of each stream of LTS train are obtained using Aspen HYSYS and the block flow diagram of the gas processing plant is previously shown in Fig. 1.

Effect of Joule–Thomson valve differential pressure (Δp) on the specifications of natural gas using composition (C1)

Effect of (J-T) valve Differential Pressure (Δp) on Hydrocarbon Dew Point of Natural Gas

Hydrocarbon dew point plays an important role in the specifications of gas pipeline transmission. Hydrocarbon dew point is the temperature at which the condensation of natural gas occurs when it is cooled at constant pressure [15]. It is necessary to control the hydrocarbon dew point for economical, operational, and safety reasons [20]. The feed of natural gas composition used is from well (1), C1. The effect of differential pressure (Δp) of Joule–Thomson expansion valve on hydrocarbon and water dew points obtained from the process simulation using HYSYS is shown in Fig. 2. There is an inverse relation between increasing in Δp and the values of hydrocarbon dew point and water dew point. Increasing Δp from 12 bars to 25 bars causes a decrease in hydrocarbon dew point from −1 to −26.5°C which normally indicates a lower proportion of heavy hydrocarbon components included in this composition of natural gas. This is an important parameter for pipeline transmission specifications. If the natural gas contains a high proportion of heavy hydrocarbons, there is a greater risk of liquid condensate forming in the pipelines. These condensates cause an increase in pressure drop and introduce operational problems resulting from a two-phase formation. These condensates can cause harmful damage such as blockage of pipelines.

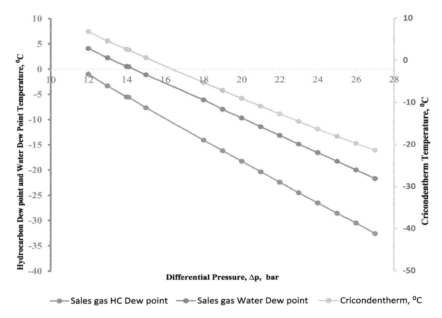

Figure 2. Effect of (J–T) valve differential pressure (Δp) on hydrocarbon dew point, water dew point, and cricondentherm using composition of natural gas, (C1).

Effect of (J-T) Valve Differential Pressure (Δp) on Water Dew Point of Natural Gas

Water dew point is the temperature at which water vapor begins to condense. Controlling water dew point of gas prevents the condensation and accumulation of water at low points in the pipelines. The water dew point specification is usually achieved by removing water vapor from the process gas plant stream using different dehydrations or other technologies. Methanol is used as hydrate inhibitor and applied in sufficient quantities.

The injected inhibitor absorbs water in the gas to prevent freezing or hydrate formation. The effect of the Joule–Thomson valve differential pressure (Δp) is estimated in Fig. 2. It is clear that increasing the differential pressure obtained from J–T expansion from 14 bars to 24 bars causes a reduction in water dew point from 0 to $-18°C$ which meet the specification of pipeline transmission.

Effect of (J-T) Valve Differential Pressure (Δp) on Cricondentherm Temperature of Natural Gas

Cricondentherm can be defined as the maximum temperature at which liquids and vapors can coexist. One phase is present at any pressure at higher temperatures than cricondentherm. The liquid–vapor boundary terminates at a critical point with a critical temperature and critical pressure. By simulating the effect of Joule–Thomson valve differential pressure (Δp) on the cricondentherm temperature as shown in Fig. 2, it is found that increasing differential pressure (Δp) from 14 bars to 24 bars causes a reduction in cricondentherm temperature from 4 to $-12°C$. This means that operating at values of differential pressure (Δp) lower than 13 bars is not safe because cricondentherm records values greater than $5°C$ which does not meet gas pipeline transmission.

Effect of Different Compositions of Natural Gas on Hydrocarbon Dew Point, Water Dew Point, and Cricondentherm

The results of this part illustrate the effect of different compositions of natural gas obtained from wells. Gas compositions mentioned in Table 2 contains well 1 (C1) and well 2 (C2) with various concentrations of different components. The results are given in Figs. 3, 4, and 5. It is obvious that hydrocarbon dew point, water dew point, and cricondentherm are affected by changing the composition of natural gas. A natural gas with a certain composition (C1) listed in Table 2 gives lower values of hydrocarbon dew point and cricondentherm compared to these values obtained using natural gas with composition (C2) which contains more heavier hydrocarbons C_6^+. This result explained as follows: increasing the concentration of heavier hydrocarbons, especially C_6^+ causes an increase of hydrocarbon dew point which is very sensitive to the specific components of the gas stream and is strongly influenced by the concentration of the heavier hydrocarbons.

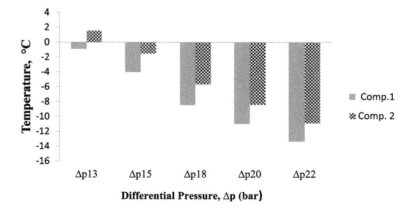

Figure 3. Effect of (J–T) valve differential pressure (Δp) on hydrocarbon dew point using different composition of natural gas, C1 and C2.

The results listed in Table 3 shows that at differential pressure (Δp) equals to 15 bars, the estimated values of hydrocarbon dew point, water dew point, and cricondentherm using composition (C1) are −4.0°C, −1.2°C, and 0.5°C, respectively, whereas those obtained using composition (C2) are −2.0°C, −1.80°C, and 1.0°C, respectively. All these results meet pipelines specification of natural gas transmission.

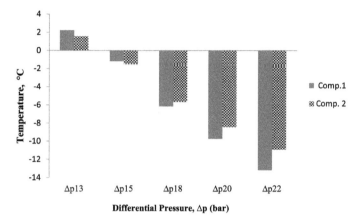

Figure 4. Effect of (J–T) valve differential pressure (Δp) on water dew point using different composition of natural gas, C1 and C2.

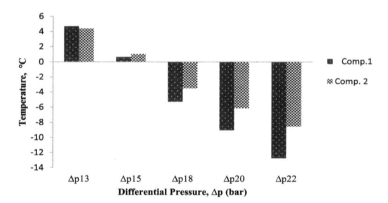

Figure 5. Effect of (J-T) valve differential pressure (Δp) on cricondentherm using different composition of natural gas, C1 and C2.

Table 3. Hydrocarbon dew point, water dew point, and cricondentherm using different compositions (C1 and C2)

	C1	**C2**
J–T valve differential pressure, (Δp), bar	15	15
Hydrocarbon dew point, °C	−4.0	−2.0
Water Dew Point, °C	−1.2	−1.80
Cricondentherm, °C	0.50	1.0

Mass Balance of LTS Train

Mass balance of each stream of low temperature separation train unit is listed in Table 4 for each composition C1 and C2. The conditions of each stream are listed in Table 5.

Table 4. Mass balance of low temperature separation train streams

	Feed gas		Sales gas		Condensate	
	C1, mass %	C2, mass %	C1, mass %	C2, mass %	C1, mass %	C2, mass %
N_2	0.24	0.07	0.24	0.07	0.00	0.00
CO_2	0.93	0.56	0.95	0.58	0.14	0.10
Methane	80.66	75.51	82.77	77.35	4.62	5.33
Ethane	6.24	6.79	6.38	6.92	2.05	2.63
Propane	4.33	7.37	4.38	7.43	5.04	9.77
i-Butane	1.85	3.23	1.84	3.19	5.26	10.23
n-Butane	1.48	2.67	1.44	2.60	5.94	11.84
C_5^+	2.87	2.49	2	1.84	76.89	60.00
H_2O	0.35	0.33	0.00	0.01	0.00	0.00
Methanol	1.05	0.97	0.00	0.01	0.05	0.10

Table 5. Conditions of low temperature separator train unit

	Feed gas		Sales gas		Condensate	
	C1	C2	C1	C2	C1	C2
Vapor fraction	0.99	0.99	1.00	1.00	0	0
Temperature, °C	30.72	30.67	0.62	2.00	0.62	2.00
Pressure, bar	51.00	50.89	35.97	36.77	35.97	36.77
Molar flow, kg mole/h	2692.34	2801.5	2675.6	2783.36	9.11	10.34
Mass flow, kg/h	48783.57	52802.52	47918.75	51928.34	605.08	608.91
Liquid volume flow, m^3/h	151.36	160.32	150.12	159.03	0.98	1.03

Effect of (J–T) Valve Differential Pressure on Sale Gas Gross Calorific Value Using Different Composition of Natural Gas, C1 and C2

Gross calorific value of sale gas ranges from 1092 Btu/SCF to 1078.5 Btu/SCF using composition C1 whereas it varies from 1137 Btu/SCF to 1122 Btu/SCF using composition C2 as Δp increases from 12 bar to 25 bar. These values meet the specification of sale gas listed in Table 1.

CONCLUSIONS

The hydrocarbon and water dew points may cause concerns in gas pipelines during transportation. The problem comes from the possibility of liquid condensation in pipelines, leading to issues in metering, pressure drop, and safe operation. It must be controlling hydrocarbon dew point, water dew point, and cricondentherm to meet the specification of pipelines and avoid various problems. Hydrocarbon dew point is a function of gas composition and pressure. The natural gas composition includes the lighter hydrocarbons that reduce the values of hydrocarbon dew point and vice versa. Controlling water dew point can be achieved by elimination of water condensation through pipelines. It is necessary to control the dew points to be below the pipeline operating conditions to prevent two-phase flow and hydrate formation in the system. Natural gas process simulation is very important to get the optimum operating condition that meet the specification of the pipeline as follows: hydrocarbon dew point lower than 5°C at pressure < 70 bars and water dew point equals 0 at 70 bars. Lower values of hydrocarbon dew point, water dew point, and cricondentherm temperature are obtained using raw natural gas composition contains lower content of heavier hydrocarbons whereas the presence of heavier hydrocarbon causes an increase in the hydrocarbon dew point. Also, the optimal operation conditions to meet the specification of pipelines are obtained at differential pressure (Δp) of Joule–Thomson ranging from 14 to 24 bars.

Acknowledgements

The authors acknowledge Cairo University, for providing support and for funding the publication of the paper. The authors also acknowledge the Process Department at ENPPI (engineering for petroleum and process industries), for the support provided during the methodology phase.

Abbreviations

BCM: Billion cubic meter unit
BTU: British thermal unit
CNG: Compressed natural gas
CHP: Combined heat and power
CCHP: Combined cooling, heat, and power
NGL: Natural gas liquids
J-T: Joule–Thomson
LTS: Low temperature separation
SCF: Standard cubic feet

REFERENCES

1. Natural gas - proved reserves, Indexmundi (2020). http://www.indexmundi.com/g/r.aspx?v=98

2. EGAS Annual Report (2019) https://www.egas.com.eg/annual-reports/2019

3. EIA, U.S (2021) Energy information administration, natural gas explained. https://www.eia.gov/energyexplained/natural-gas

4. WORLDOMETERS, Energy (2021) https://www.worldometers.info/energy/egypt- energy.

5. Abbas N S, Assfour H M, Abdel Wahhab M Z and Ashour E A (2020) About the Egyptian natural gas. An overview, history and prospects. 39: 109 - 116

6. Xiaomei Z, Fengxia H, Liming Z and Tumeng G (2021) Discussion on water dew point and hydrocarbon dew point of natural gas. 3rd International Conference on Green Energy and Sustainable Development. IOP Conf. Series: Earth and Environmental Science 651. https://doi.org/10.1088/1755-1315/651/3/032090

7. Elsheemy AA, Ashour FH, Gadalla MA (2018) Maximization of condensate production by revamping of gas-oil separation plant in gulf of Suez. Chem Eng Transact 70:343–348

8.   Ebrahiem EE, Ashour IA, Nassar MM, Abdel Aziz AA (2021) A comparison of natural gas dehydration methods. Yanbu J Eng Sci 15(1):1–16. https://doi.org/10.53370/001c.24332

9.   Sabbagh O, Fanaei MA, Arjomand A (2020) Optimal design of a novel NGL/LNG integrated scheme: economic and exergetic condition. J Thermal Anal Calorimetry 145:5

10. Gaihuan L, Lin Z, Jinmen H, Huimin L (2022) Technical, economical, and environmental performance assessment of an improved triethylene glycol dehydration process for shale gas. ACS Omega 7(2):1861–1873. https://doi.org/10.1021/acsomega.1c05236

11. Devold H (2010) Oil and gas production handbook, Edition 2.3. ABB, Oslo

12. Ahmed OB, Souad A (2021) Energy efficiency improvement of debutanizer column, for NGL separation. Int J Environ Sci Dev 12:255–260

13. Housam B and Ahmed B (2013) Simulation of the separation of industrially important hydrocarnon mixtures by different distillation techniques using mathematica. Chapter 3:47–78

14. Xia W, Changjun Li, Yufa He and Wenlong Jia (2018) Operation optimization of natural gas transmission pipelines based on stochastic optimization algorithms: a review. J. Mathematical Problems in Engineering. Article ID 1267045:18. https://doi.org/10.1155/2018/1267045

15. Noaman A, Ebrahiem E (2021) Comparison of natural gas hydrocarbon dewpointing control methods. J Adv Eng Trend 40:99–116

16. Poling BE, Prausnitz JM, Connell JP (2001) The properties of gases and liquids, 5th edn

17. Waele AT (2017) Basics of Joule–Thomson liquefaction and Joule–Thomson cooling. J Low Temp Physics 186:385–403

18. Peng D Y and Robinson D B (1976) A new two-constant equation of state, industrial and engineering chemistry: fundamentals 15:59-64.

19. Mondal S K, Uddin M R, Majumder S and Pokhre J (2015) HYSYS simulation of chemical process equipments. Research Gate at: https://www.researchgate.net/publication/281608946

20. Chatterjee N, Kinard G E and Geist J M(1983) Maximizing production in propane precooled mixed refrigerant LNG plants. Seventh Conference on Liquefied Natural Gas, Jakarta, Indonesia, May 15-19.

10

A Robustness Evaluation Method of Natural Gas Pipeline Network Based on Topological Structure Analysis

Xueyi Li[1], Huai Su[1], Jinjun Zhang[1] and Nan Yang[2]

[1]National Engineering Laboratory for Pipeline Safety/ MOE Key Laboratory of Petroleum Engineering /Beijing Key Laboratory of Urban Oil and Gas Distribution Technology, China University of Petroleum-Beijing, Beijing, China
[2]Natural Gas Marketing Company, PetroChina Co. Ltd., Beijing, China

ABSTRACT

As the total mileage of natural gas pipeline network continues to increase, the topological structure of natural gas pipeline network will become more and more complex. The complicated topological structure of natural gas pipeline network is likely to cause inherent structural defects, which have serious impacts on the safe operation of natural gas pipeline network. At present, related researches mainly focused on the safe and reliable operation of natural gas pipeline network, which has become a research hotspot, but few of them considered the complexity of natural gas pipeline network and its potential impacts. In order to understand the complexity of natural gas pipeline network and its behaviors when facing structural changes, this paper studied the robustness of natural gas pipeline network based on complex network theory. This paper drew on the methods and experience of robustness researches in other related fields, and proposed a robustness evaluation method for natural gas pipeline network which is combined with its operation characteristics. The robustness evaluation method of natural gas pipeline network is helpful to identify the key components of the pipeline network and understand the response of the pipeline network to structural changes. Furthermore, it can provide a theoretical reference for the safe and stable operation of natural gas pipeline network. The evaluation results show that natural gas pipeline network shows strong robustness when faced with random disturbances represented by pipeline accidents or component failures caused by natural disasters, and when faced with targeted disturbances represented by terrorist disturbances, the robustness of natural gas pipeline network is very weak. Natural gas pipeline network behaves differently in the face of different types of random disturbances.

Natural gas pipeline network is more robust when faced with component failures than pipeline accidents caused by natural disasters.

Keywords: *Natural gas pipeline network, Robustness evaluation, Topological structure analysis, Operation risk, Random disturbances*

INTRODUCTION

As the total mileage of natural gas pipeline network continues to increase, the topology of natural gas pipeline network will become more and more complex, and then gradually show a trend of system complexity (Ayala and Leong, 2013; Su et al., 2018; Lustenberger et al., 2019). The complicated topological structure of natural gas pipeline network is likely to cause inherent structural defects in natural gas pipeline network, which has serious impacts on the safe operation of natural gas pipeline network (Beyza et al., 2019; Chen et al., 2019; Cavalieri, 2020).

At present, related researches mainly focused on ensuring the safe and reliable operation of natural gas pipeline network which has become a research hotspot (Loktionov, 2018; Su et al., 2018; Almoghathawi et al., 2019; Chen et al., 2019; Chi et al., 2020; Hu et al., 2021). However, a detailed analysis of the current researches reveals that few studies have considered the complexity of natural gas pipeline network and its potential impacts. Therefore, the research on the complexity and robustness of natural gas pipeline network is not in-depth. The accidents that have occurred over the years have also highlighted the fragile side of the modern large-scale natural gas pipeline network system structure, and it objectively shows that the complexity and robustness research of natural gas pipeline network is imperative (Su et al., 2018; Munikoti et al., 2021).

Complexity is an inherent property of a large-scale network topology. Knowing this property not only helps to better grasp the controllability of the network system, but also helps to understand the dynamic behaviors that occur on the network, such as cascade effects, robustness, etc. Robustness evaluation is to evaluate the ability of a system to maintain its inherent functions in the case of structural changes. In related research fields, such as the electricity field, the research momentum of robustness is in the ascendant. Robustness researches mainly focus on changes in capabilities caused by changes in the system structure, and have scientific judgments on the fragility of natural gas pipeline network system, which can be used as a part of reliability researches (Carvalho et al., 2014; Wang et al., 2017; He et al., 2018; Sacco et al., 2019; Liu et al., 2020; Ramos and Batista, 2020).

As a combination of statistical physics and graph theory, complex network theory is an important method for studying complex systems which focus on the topological structure formed by the interaction of all units in the system and the dynamic behaviors that occur in the system. The view that structure determines function is the basis for understanding the researches of complex systems. At the beginning of the 21st century, the development of complex network theory has reached its own golden age. In recent years, its effective application in the fields of sociology, biology, etc. provides theory and technical support for the study of complexity and robustness of natural gas pipeline network (Ayala and Leong, 2013; Rădulescu and Nedelcu, 2017; Su et al., 2017, 2018, 2019; Lustenberger et al., 2019; Beyza et al., 2020).

There are few research materials related to robustness in the field of natural gas pipeline network. Therefore, the few references in the field of natural gas pipeline network have been referred to in this paper's research process, and the ideas and methods of robustness researches in other fields have also been used for reference.

In the field of natural gas pipeline network, (Munikoti et al., 2021) proposed a modeling framework based on heterogeneous function graph theory (HFGT) for integrated infrastructure such as natural gas pipeline network, and analyzed the robustness of the network. This method quantifies the impact of full/partial and random/targeted disturbances on the system as a whole, simulates various disturbance scenarios, and uses several robustness indicators to comprehensively evaluate the robustness of the system. The research results show that protecting system information and reducing disturbance intensity are feasible measures to enhance the robustness of integrated infrastructure. In view of the uncertainties of wind power, electric load and gas load, (Wang et al., 2019) proposed a two-stage robust day-ahead dispatch model for the Integrated Electricity and Natural Gas System (IEGS). The simulation results show that the uncertainty level and uncertainty budget directly affect the worst case selected in the test system. The two-stage robust day-ahead scheduling model can be extended to other uncertain application scenarios, such as the interruption of power transmission lines and pipelines.

The current theories have become an effective analysis tool for the robustness evaluation of natural gas pipeline network. Each research property has proposed its own natural gas pipeline network robustness (vulnerability) analysis model or method, but the current research is insufficient: 1) these researches rarely consider the source of network vulnerability, and the network performance when the network structure changes; 2) these researches rarely consider the complex system characteristics of natural gas pipeline network.

In contrast, in the field of power grids and transportation networks, robustness research materials are relatively abundant. Crucitti (Crucitti et al., 2004) took the Italian power grid as the research object and established the robustness evaluation system of the power grid. The results show that the Italian power grid is very vulnerable under targeted disturbances, and its robustness is weak; Albert (Albert et al., 2004) analyzed the robustness of North American power grid. The robustness evaluation results show that North American power grids are weaker in robustness when facing targeted disturbances. The main steps of robustness research are as follows: building network model, establishing robustness evaluation indicators, simulating disturbances to change the network structure, and analyzing the results of evaluation indicators, and all of the above steps need to take into account the operation characteristics of the network itself. Due to the similarities among natural gas pipeline network, power grid and transportation network, it is feasible to study the robustness of natural gas pipeline network, whose system function is natural gas supply capacity, but the robustness evaluation method of natural gas pipeline network must be combined with the operation characteristics of natural gas pipeline network.

This research is an exploration of applying the emerging complex network science to the robustness analysis of natural gas pipeline network. This paper draws on the methodological experience of network robustness analysis in other research fields, and proposes a robustness evaluation method for natural gas pipeline network, combined with the operation characteristics of natural gas pipeline network. The robustness evaluation method can be used to distinguish key system components and understand the response of natural gas pipeline network to structural changes, so as to provide a theoretical reference for the safe and stable operation of natural gas pipeline network.

METHODS AND MATERIALS

Changes in the network structure will affect the function of the network and the dynamic behavior on the network. Therefore, it is of great theoretical significance to study the ability of the network to maintain its function when the structure is disturbed. This chapter proposes a method for evaluating the robustness of a natural gas pipeline network. This method focuses on analyzing the ability of the pipeline network to resist excessive changes in its gas supply capacity after the structure of the pipeline network is changed.

Definition of Robustness of Natural Gas Pipeline Network

As a large-scale complex system, the robustness of natural gas pipeline network needs to be defined with its own characteristics. The robustness of natural gas pipeline network refers to the ability of the pipeline network system to maintain its gas supply function without excessive changes when the topological structure changes due to changes in the internal or external environment. In the concept of the robustness of natural gas pipeline network, the factors that cause the change in the gas supply capacity need to be determined in conjunction with the operating characteristics of natural gas pipeline network:

1) Pipeline Accidents

Pipeline accidents refer to the general term for all incidents in which natural gas leaks and causes pipeline failure. According to relevant statistical data, the main causes of pipeline failure are external interference, construction or material defects, pipeline maintenance errors, and pipeline corrosion.

After carefully analyzing the causes of pipeline accidents, this paper divides the causes into two categories: accidental causes which is represented by natural disasters and pipeline aging, and purposeful causes which is represented by deliberate damage by a third party. According to the above two types of reasons, this study divides pipeline accidents into accidental pipeline accidents and purposeful pipeline accidents. When a certain pipeline in the pipeline network fails due to an accidental pipeline accident or a purposeful pipeline accident, the pipeline can be considered to have no gas transmission capacity, which means that the pipeline exits the pipeline network and causes structural changes, thereby affecting the supply of the pipeline network.

2) Component Failures

In addition to natural gas pipelines, a long-distance natural gas pipeline network also consists of a first station, a gas compressor station and other parts. These components themselves have a certain failure rate. When the external or internal environment changes, these components may fail, which will affect the gas supply capacity to a certain extent.

Method Framework

The framework of studying the robustness of natural gas pipeline network in this paper is shown in Figure 1. The first step to evaluate the robustness of natural gas pipeline network is to determine the robustness definition of natural gas pipeline network. The second step is to summarize robustness research models in related fields. The third step is to establish an index system for identifying key components of the pipeline network model and establish a complex network model for the pipeline network. The fourth step is to determine the robustness evaluation indexes and scenarios. The fifth step is to propose a robustness evaluation system and algorithm. And the last step is to draw conclusions by case studies.

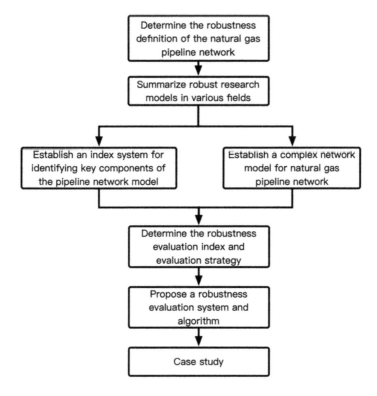

Figure 1. The research framework of natural gas pipeline network's robustness evaluation method.

Modeling Method for Complex Network Model of Natural Gas Pipeline Network

The first step of the robustness evaluation method is the complex network modeling of the network topology. The modeling method of this part is briefly summarized in this section. Each element in the pipeline network is mapped to the complex network model according to the corresponding relationship in Table 1. The network structure changes caused by each element are different. For example, the failure of the transmission station is equivalent to the node exiting the network, which causes the structure to change and the function is reduced, and the failure of the pipeline section is equivalent to the edge exiting the network, resulting in structural changes and service performance reduce.

Table 1. The relationship between the complex network and pipeline network table

Natural gas pipeline network	Complex network model
Gate station, first station, transmission station, receiving station	Node
Pipeline section, valve chamber, compression station	Edge

Other simplification principles and steps are as follows:
- Only the network topology is considered, and the operating hydraulic and thermal conditions of each pipeline section in the network are not considered for the time being.
- Establish an undirected graph with a weight of 1, assuming that the length of each pipeline section is the same, the pipeline diameter is the same, the design pressure is the same, the relative roughness of the pipeline section is the same, and the undirected graph is at the network level.
- Ignore the internal structure of the valve chamber, compression station, etc., and treat them as part of the pipeline section.
- For a given piece of pipeline network, traverse the pipeline network information in turn, transform each element into the corresponding part of the complex network according to the above principles, and then number the nodes and edges according to certain rules and store them in the corresponding data table.

After the above simplifications and steps, the actual natural gas pipeline network can be transformed into a complex network with N nodes and K edges. A large sparse matrix can be used to represent the network, and a series of calculations and statistics can be performed.

Key Node and Key Edge Identification Method Based on Pipeline Network Topological Structure

The criticality of each element in natural gas pipeline network is not only related to the properties of each element, such as pipeline length, pipeline diameter and other parameters, but also related to the gas supply task to which each element is "allocated" during the operation of the pipeline network. This research assumes that the attributes and tasks of each component are almost the same. Based on this assumption, the importance of each component is related to its topological structure attributes.

Key Node Identification Method

There are many indicators for judging the importance of nodes, which can be summarized into three categories: degree category, center category, and betweenness category. The degree indicators reflect the importance of the component at the connection level, the central indicators reflect the influence of the component in the entire network, and the betweenness indicators reflect the degree of contribution of each component to the network efficiency. The indicators constructed in this paper is an improvement or combination of one or more of the above three categories and they are as follows:

1) Central value of local proximity

This paper defines the local proximity center value as the sum of its own proximity center value and the proximity center value of adjacent nodes, as shown in Eq. 2.1:

$$localC_{ci} = C_{ci} + \sum_j C_{cj}$$

(2.1)

where C_{ci} represents the central value of the proximity of the node$i$, j represents the neighboring node of the node$i$, and C_{cj} represents the central value of the proximity of the node$j$.

2) Local node betweenness

On the basis of node betweenness, local node betweenness is defined as its own node betweenness plus the node betweenness of adjacent nodes, as shown in Eq. 2.2:

$$localB_i = B_i + \sum_j B_j \tag{2.2}$$

where Bi represents the node betweenness of the nodei, jrepresents the neighbor node of the nodei, and Bj represents the node betweenness of the nodej.

3) Local node degree

The local node degree is defined as its own node degree plus the node degree of adjacent nodes, as shown in Eq. 2.3:

$$localk_i = k_i + \sum_j k_j \tag{2.3}$$

where ki represents the node degree of the nodei, j represents the neighbor node of the node i, and kj represents the node degree of the node j.

4) Comprehensive evaluation index

This paper proposes a comprehensive evaluation indicator to consider the importance of nodes, as shown in Eq. 2.4:

$$synindex\,(v_i) = localk_i \cdot localC_{ci} \cdot localB_i \tag{2.4}$$

where $localk_i$ is the local node degree of the node i, $localC_{ci}$ is the local proximity centrality of the nodei, and $localB_i$ is the local node betweenness of the node i.

The above indicators not only take into account the importance of the nodes themselves, but also consider the importance of adjacent nodes. However, the above indicators do not incorporate the operating characteristics of natural gas pipeline network. Next, improvements will be made to each indicator.

Natural gas pipeline network is characterized by directional flow, and the nodes have functional differences, which can be divided into gas source nodes and gas demand nodes. The calculation basis of the original proximity centrality and node betweenness is all possible node pairs in the network. However, due to the characteristics of directional flow, only consideration can be taken when calculating the proximity centrality and node betweenness of natural gas pipeline network. For some node pairs, not all node pairs can be included in the calculation, so this research changes the central value of proximity and node betweenness.

The changed central value of proximity is shown in Eq. 2.5:

$$C_c^P\,(v_i) = \frac{N-1}{\displaystyle\sum_{\substack{j=1,j\neq i \\ i\in M, j\in T}}^{N} d_{ij}} \tag{2.5}$$

where C_c^P is the modified central value of the proximity, the gas source node set *M* and the gas demand node set *T*, N is the order of the network, and d$_{ij}$ is the shortest path length between a certain gas source node and a certain gas demand node.

The changed node betweenness is shown in Eq. 2.6:

$$B_i^P = \sum_{\substack{1\leq j<l\leq N \\ j\neq i\neq l \\ i\in M, j\in T}} \frac{n_{jl}\,(i)}{n_{jl}} \tag{2.6}$$

where B_i^P is the changed node betweenness, gas source node set M and gas demand node set T, N is the order of the network, n_{jl} is the number of the shortest path between a certain gas source node and a certain gas demand node, njl(i) is the number of the shortest path that passes v_i between the source node and a certain gas demand node.

Therefore, the improved central value of local proximity is shown in Eq. 2.7:

$$localC_{ci}^P = C_{ci}^P + \sum_j C_{ci}^P$$

(2.7)

where C_{ci}^P is the center value of the improved proximity of the representative node i, j is the neighbor node of the node i, and C_{ci}^P is the center value of the improved proximity of the node j. The improved local node betweenness is shown in Eq. 2.8:

$$localB_i^P = B_i^P + \sum_j B_j^P$$

(2.8)

where B_i^P represents the improved node betweenness of the node i, j represents the neighbor node of the node i, and B_i^P represents the improved node betweenness of the node j.

The improved comprehensive index of node importance is shown in Eq. 2.9:

$$synindex^P (v_i) = localk_i \cdot local\ C_{ci}^P \cdot local\ B_i^P$$

(2.9)

The improved evaluation index of key nodes takes into account the importance of the node itself and the importance of adjacent nodes, and also combines the operating characteristics of natural gas pipeline network.

Key Edge Identification Method

At present, the indicators for judging key edges in various fields are relatively uniform. A common judgment index is the betweenness number. According to the operating characteristics of natural gas pipeline network, its improvement can better analyze the importance of the connection of natural gas pipeline network. With reference to the method for improving the evaluation index of key nodes, the changes to the evaluation index of key edges are as follows:

$$B_{ij}^P = \sum_{\substack{1 \le l < m \le N \\ (l,m) \ne (i,j) \\ i \in M, j \in T}} \frac{N_{lm}(e_{ij})}{N_{lm}}$$

(2.10)

where B_{ij}^P is the modified edge betweenness, M is the gas source node set, T is the gas demand node set is, N is the number of nodes in the network, N_{lm} is the number of the shortest path between the nodevl and the node vm, and $N_{lm}(e_{ij})$ is the number of the shortest path that passes e_{ij} between the node v_l and the node v_m.

THE ROBUSTNESS EVALUATION METHOD OF NATURAL GAS PIPELINE NETWORK

Evaluation Index

There are many indicators for evaluating changes in network functions. In this study, combined with the operating characteristics of natural gas pipeline network, the following indicators are used:

1) Relative efficiency ratio of pipeline network

Pipeline network efficiency refers to its own transmission efficiency under the condition that the pipeline network meets the gas supply requirements within a certain range. The pipeline network efficiency in this paper is defined as follows:

$$E = \frac{1}{M \times T} \sum_{i \in M, j \in T} \frac{1}{d_{ij}}$$

(2.11)

where M is the number of nodes in the gas source node set, T is the number of nodes in the gas demand node set, d_{ij} is the shortest path length between the node i and the node j.

The relative efficiency ratio of the pipeline network used in this study reflects the degree of change in the transmission efficiency of the pipeline network, and its expression is shown in Eq. 2.12:

$$Ec = \frac{E}{E_0}$$

(2.12)

where E_c represents the relative efficiency ratio of the pipeline network, E is the pipeline network efficiency of the remaining pipeline network, E_0 is the pipeline network efficiency of the original pipeline network. When the network is not destroyed, the relative efficiency ratio of the network is 1, and when the network is completely destroyed, the relative efficiency ratio of the network is 0.

2) The largest subgraph ratio of the pipeline network

The failure of a certain component of natural gas pipeline network is equivalent to the temporary withdrawal of the component from the network, which causes a change in the network structure, and even changes the connected network to a disconnected network. In this study, the maximum subgraph ratio of the pipeline network is used to reflect the degree of change in the gas supply range of the pipeline network, which is defined as follows:

$$Nc = \frac{N}{N_0}$$

(2.13)

where N_c represents the maximum subgraph ratio of the pipeline network, N is the number of nodes in the maximum subgraph of the pipeline network, and N_0 is the number of nodes in the initial network.

Disturbance Scenarios

Natural gas pipeline network robustness evaluation method chooses two disturbance scenarios including random disturbances and targeted disturbances. Random disturbances mainly correspond to accidental pipeline damage caused by pipeline aging and natural disasters, while targeted disturbances mainly correspond to planned pipeline damage or shutdown caused by terrorist disturbances and pipeline construction. The changes reflected in the network structure after any disturbance on the pipeline network needs to be improved based on the operating characteristics of natural gas pipeline network.

In the pipeline network model of this study, pipeline sections, valve chambers, compression stations, etc. are all components of the edge, so the disturbance on the edge is equivalent to the actual pipeline accident or the original failure of the compressor.

When a pipeline accident occurs, the pipeline needs to be inspected and repaired. The pipeline section does not have any gas supply capacity, which is equivalent to completely removing the pipeline section from the network, as shown in Figure 2.

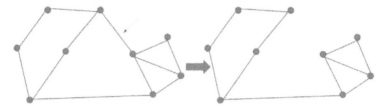

Figure 2. Edge's disturbance schematic diagram.

When the compressor and other components fail, the entire connection side will act as a gas storage. From a structural point of view, the network structure has not changed, but the gas supply capacity has changed. This study believes that any failure can be equivalent to a certain network structure change, and the structure change leads to a decrease in its gas supply capacity. Therefore, in this case, this study does not delete the connected edge where the compressor fails, but changes the weight of this edge from 1 to 100, as shown in Figure 3. In fact, the edge of the network that is removed due to a failure is equivalent to the weight of the edge changes from one to $\infty\infty$.

Figure 3. Edge's disturbance schematic diagram.

Algorithm Design of Robustness Evaluation Method for Natural Gas Pipeline Network

The above sections have elaborated the research ideas of the robustness evaluation method in detail, and designed the robustness research algorithm according to the research ideas.

　　1) Disturbance modes

　　① Pipeline accidents: delete the corresponding connection from the network.

　　② Compressor and other components failures: the side is not deleted, but the weight is changed from 1 to 100.

　　2) Disturbance scenarios

　　① Random disturbances: randomly select edges from the network to delete or change the weight to 100.

　　② Targeted disturbances: purposefully select an edge to delete or change its weight to 100.

　　3) The overall algorithm flow chart and simulation flow charts

The overall algorithm flow chart is shown in Figure 4. The first step is to establish a complex network model of the pipeline network. The second step is to calculate the network size and the number of connected edges. The third step is to evaluate the critical nodes and critical paths of the network. The fourth step is to choose disturbance mode. The fifth step is to choose disturbance scenario. The sixth step is to run a simulation. The seventh step is to calculate changes in the network. The eighth step is to check if it is less than the predetermined number of nodes. The nineth step is to draw the corresponding evaluation index change curve. The last step is to evaluate the robustness of the pipeline network.

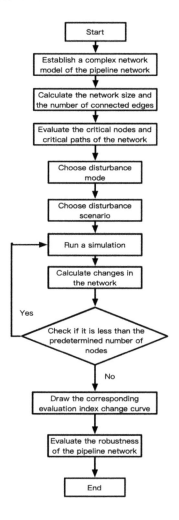

Figure 4. The overall algorithm flow chart.

The disturbance mode one simulation algorithm flow chart in the overall flow chart is shown in Figure 5. The first step is to use edge betweenness to rank the importance of connecting edges. The second step is to choose disturbance scenario. The third step is to remove edges from the network according to the disturbance mode. The fourth step is to check whether the network is connected. The fifth step is to calculate the network efficiency ratio. And if the network is disconnected, calculate the maximum subgraph ratio. The sixth step is to check whether the number of deleted nodes is less than the set valued. The seventh step is to draw the network efficiency ratio change curve.

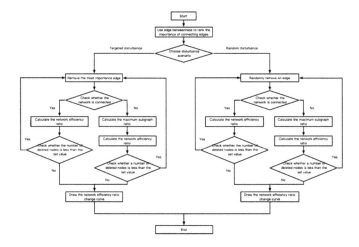

Figure 5. Disturbance model one simulation algorithm flow chart.

The disturbance mode two simulation algorithm flow chart in the overall flow chart is shown in Figure 6. The first step is to use edge betweenness to rank the importance of connecting edges. The second step is to choose disturbance scenario. The third step is to set the edge weight according to the disturbance mode. The fourth step is to calculate the network efficiency ratio. The fifth step is to check whether the number of deleted nodes is less than the set value. The last step is to draw the network efficiency ratio change curve.

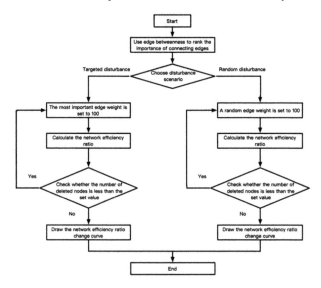

Figure 6. Disturbance model two simulation algorithm flow chart.

RESULTS AND DISCUSSIONS

This section uses natural gas pipeline network robustness evaluation method proposed in this paper to evaluate the robustness of the actual natural gas pipeline network, and identifies the key components in the network according to the key component identification method.

The Complex Network Modeling of Natural Gas Pipeline Network

According to the modeling rules, simplification principles and modeling steps in the evaluation method, the actual natural gas pipeline network is abstracted into a complex network, as shown in Figure 7.

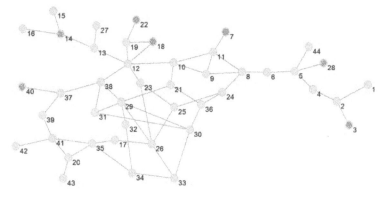

Figure 7. The complex network model diagram of natural gas pipeline network.

In this paper, the pipeline network robustness evaluation focuses on the connection relationship at the topological structure level, so it is assumed that the length of each pipeline section is the same, the pipeline diameter is the same, the design pressure is the same, and the relative roughness of the pipeline section is the same. The network is an undirected graph with a weight of 1.

The network has a total of 44 nodes and 59 edges. All nodes are divided into two categories. The node classification information of all nodes of gas source node and gas demand node (gate station) is shown in Table 2.

Table 2. The node classification table

Type of nodes	Number of nodes	Color of nodes
Gas node	3, 7, 14, 18, 22, 28, 40	Green
Demand node	Others	Yellow

Identification of Key Nodes

Node Influence

The improved central value of local proximity is used as a part of evaluating the criticality of each node. The central value of local proximity can well reflect the influence of the node. The central value information of the local proximity of each node is shown in Figure 8. The central value of the local proximity of the node 12, the node 31, and the node 29 is obviously larger than that of other nodes.

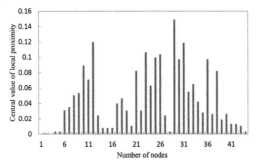

Figure 8. The statistical diagram of each node's local closeness centrality value.

According to the relative size of the central value of the local proximity of each node, the influence of each node is sorted. Table 3 lists the top 10 nodes with the central value of the local proximity.

Table 3. The node's influence degree sorting table

Sequence	Number of nodes	Sequence	Number of nodes
1	29	2	12
3	31	4	23
5	26	6	25
7	30	8	36
9	10	10	21

The Degree of Contribution of Nodes to Network Efficiency

The improved local node betweenness is used as a part of the critical degree of the evaluation node. The betweenness of local nodes reflects the contribution degree of nodes to network efficiency. The local node betweenness value of each node is shown in Figure 9. The contribution of node 38, node 41, and node 42 to network efficiency is obviously higher than that of other nodes.

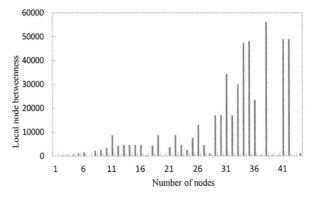

Figure 9. The statistical diagram of each node's local betweenness centrality value.

According to the relative size of each node's local betweenness, the efficiency contribution degree of each node is ranked. Table 4 lists the top 10 nodes.

Table 4. The node's efficiency contribution sorting table

Sequence	Number of nodes	Sequence	Number of nodes
1	38	2	41
3	42	4	35
5	34	6	31
7	33	8	36
9	30	10	32

The Importance of Node Location

The local node degree is used as a part of evaluating the criticality of nodes. The node degree reflects the importance of the position of the node in the network. The local node degree information of each node is shown in Figure 10. The local node degree of node 29, node 12, and node 11 is significantly higher than other nodes.

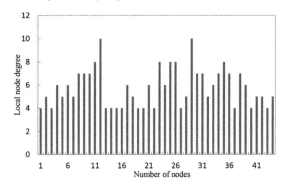

Figure 10. The statistical diagram of each node's local degree.

According to the relative size of the local node degree of each node, the position importance degree of each node is sorted. Table 5 lists the top 10 nodes in terms of importance degree.

Table 5. The node's position importance sorting table

Sequence	Number of nodes	Sequence	Number of nodes
1	12	2	29
3	11	4	23
5	25	6	26
7	35	8	8
9	9	10	10

Comprehensive Indicators to Judge Key Nodes

The importance of the position of the node, the influence of the node in the network, and the contribution of the node to the network efficiency are considered at the same time.

Using the comprehensive index proposed in this paper, sorting according to the value of the comprehensive index, the top 14 important nodes are listed in Table 6.

Table 6. The node's importance sorting table

Sequence	Number of nodes	Sequence	Number of nodes
1	38	2	31
3	29	4	36
5	34	6	33
7	30	8	35
9	26	10	25
11	12	12	11
13	32	14	23

It can be seen from Table 6 that node 31, node 29, and node 38 are the three most critical nodes and need to be protected.

Identification of Critical Path

The improved edge betweenness number is used to measure the relative importance of each edge. The greater the betweenness of an edge, the more critical it is. According to the value of each edge, the edges in the pipeline network are sorted. The sorting results are shown in Table 7 (due to the large number of edges, this paper only lists the top 20 edges).

Table 7. The edge's importance sorting table

Sequence	Edge (node---node)	Sequence	Edge (node---node)
1	6–8	2	5–6
3	10–12	4	12–13
5	12–38	6	8–24
7	4–5	8	37–38
9	17–26	10	24–25
11	10–11	12	2–4
13	13–14	14	17–35
15	25–26	16	9–10
17	8–11	18	12–23
19	37–39	20	8–9

Evaluation of Pipeline Network Robustness

According to the operating characteristics of natural gas pipeline network, different disturbances have different effects on the pipeline network structure.

Analysis of the Robustness Performance of the Pipeline Network Under Random Disturbances

Firstly, the robustness of natural gas pipeline network in the face of pipeline accidents caused by natural disasters is analyzed. The pipeline accident caused by a natural disaster in the pipeline network is equivalent to a random disturbance on the pipeline network model.

In this case, any pipeline section where the accident occurred will not have the ability to transport gas, which means that any disturbed side will completely exit the network.

Figure 11 and Figure 12 are graphs showing the change of the pipeline network robustness evaluation index as the degree of network damage increases. In the random disturbance mode, as the number of deleted edges increases, the efficiency ratio of the pipeline network continues to decrease. When the number of deleted connections is less than 10, the rate of decrease of the pipeline network efficiency ratio is slower, and when the number of deleted connections is between 10 and 20, the rate of decrease of the pipeline network efficiency ratio increases significantly. When the scale of damage is small, the pipeline network can maintain its ability. In other words, the pipeline network has a threshold phenomenon, which has strong robustness. When the number of deleted edges reaches half of the total number of network connections, the network's efficiency has dropped to 0.2. As the number of deleted connections increases, the scale of the network changes step by step, but when the number of deleted nodes reaches 25, the maximum subgraph order of the network changes significantly. At this time, the network has been divided into multiple subgraphs.

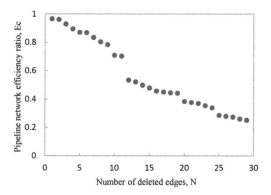

Figure 11. The diagram of pipeline network efficiency ratio.

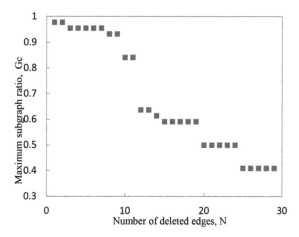

Figure 12. The diagram of pipeline network maximum subgraph ratio.

Secondly, analyze the robustness of natural gas pipeline network in the face of component failures. A component failure in the pipeline network is equivalent to a random disturbance on the pipeline network model. In this case, any pipeline section where the accident occurred has gas storage capacity. The disturbanceed edges were not deleted from the network, but only affected the network's gas transmission function.

Figure 13 is a graph showing the change of the pipeline network robustness evaluation index as the degree of network damage increases. In the random disturbance mode, as the number of deleted edges increases, the rate of decrease of the pipeline network efficiency ratio is slower. There is a threshold phenomenon in the pipeline network, that is, it has strong robustness. When the number of deleted edges reaches half of the total number of connected edges in the network, the efficiency of the network has dropped to 0.4, and a certain gas supply capacity can still be maintained. As the network structure remains unchanged, the largest subgraph of the network does not change.

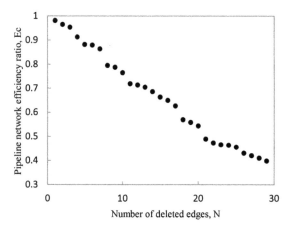

Figure 13. The diagram of pipeline network efficiency ratio.

The Robustness Evaluation of the Pipeline Network Under Targeted Disturbances

The following analyzes the robustness of natural gas pipeline network in the face of terrorist disturbances. When the pipeline network is disturbanceed by a terrorist disturbance, it is equivalent to a targeted disturbance on the pipeline network model. The core of a targeted disturbance lies in purpose. In this case, it is equivalent to any side that is 'targeted disturbance' will completely withdraw from the network. In the targeted disturbance mode, this paper only considers the situation of completely exiting the network.

Figure 14 and Figure 15 are graphs showing the changes of the pipeline network robustness evaluation index as the degree of network damage increases. In the targeted disturbance mode, the pipeline network does not show a threshold phenomenon. When the number of deleted edges of the network is less than 3, the efficiency ratio of the pipeline network drops sharply, and the maximum subgraph ratio has an obvious step. As the number of deleted edges continues to increase, the pipeline network efficiency ratio has shown a relatively stable rate of decline. When the number of deleted edges reaches half of the total number of connected edges in the network, the pipeline network efficiency ratio is close to 0.2. As the number of deleted connections increases, the scale of the network changes step by step, but when the number of deleted nodes reaches 15, the maximum subgraph order of the network obviously changes, and the network at this time has been divided into multiple subgraphs.

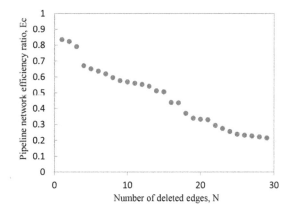

Figure 14. The diagram of pipeline network efficiency ratio.

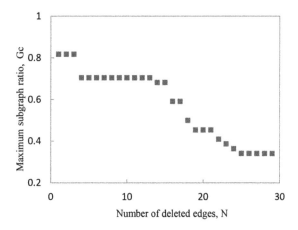

Figure 15. The diagram of pipeline network maximum subgraph ratio.

Analysis of Robustness Evaluation Results of Natural Gas Pipeline Network

First, compare and analyze the robustness of the pipeline network when faced with pipeline accidents caused by natural disasters and the robustness of the pipeline network when faced with component failures, as shown in Figure 16.

Pipeline accidents or component failures caused by natural disasters in the pipeline network are equivalent to random disturbances on the pipeline network. When the number of disturbanceed nodes is less than 7, the gas supply capacity of the pipeline network is less affected, indicating that the pipeline network has a threshold phenomenon under random disturbances, and the pipeline network has better robustness. When the number of disturbanceed nodes is between 7 and 10, the robustness of the pipeline network is similar. When the number of disturbanceed nodes is greater than 10, the impact on the pipeline network is significantly different. The impact of pipeline accidents caused by natural disasters on the pipeline network has undergone a step change, and the rate of decline in the efficiency of the pipeline network has gradually increased. When the number of disturbanceed nodes reaches half of the total number of nodes, the efficiency of the pipeline network has lost about 80%. The impact of component failure on the pipeline network is relatively stable, and the rate of decrease in the efficiency of the pipeline network is gradually reduced. When the number of disturbanceed nodes reaches half of the total number of nodes, the efficiency of the pipeline network loses about 60%.

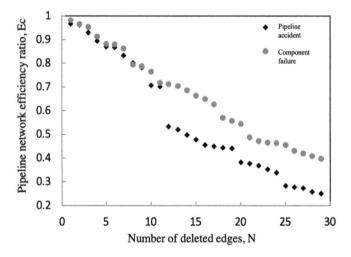

Figure 16. The network robustness diagram under the random disturbance caused by different reasons.

There are similarities and differences between the robustness evaluation results of natural gas pipeline network facing pipeline accidents caused by natural disasters and the robustness evaluation results of natural gas pipeline network facing component failures. The same point is that the pipeline network can show strong robustness. The difference is that when the number of disturbanceed nodes is greater than a certain value, the impact of pipeline accidents caused by natural disasters on the gas supply capacity of the pipeline network will gradually expand, while component failures have a gentler impact on the gas supply capacity of the pipeline network. Therefore, on the whole, the robustness of the pipeline network when faced with pipeline accidents caused by natural disasters is weaker than that of the pipeline network when faced with component failures.

Secondly, the robust performance of the pipeline network facing random disturbances and the robust performance of the pipeline network facing targeted disturbances are compared and analyzed, as shown in Figure 17.

The pipeline network reacts differently to random disturbances and targeted disturbances. When the pipeline network faces a targeted disturbance, there is no threshold effect. When the number of disturbanceed nodes is less than 3, the gas supply capacity of the pipeline network drops quickly. When the number of disturbanceed nodes is greater than 3, the gas supply capacity of the pipeline network has a "cliff-breaking" drop, losing about 10% of its capacity. As the number of disturbance nodes continues to increase, the gas supply capacity of the pipeline network continues to decline. Compared with the response of the pipeline network to a targeted disturbance, the pipeline network has a threshold effect when facing a random disturbance and is more robust. When the number of deleted nodes is less than 10, the gas supply capacity of the pipeline network decreases slowly, and 70% of the original gas supply capacity can still be maintained. Therefore, the robust performance of the pipeline network facing random disturbances is stronger than the robust performance of the pipeline network facing targeted disturbances.

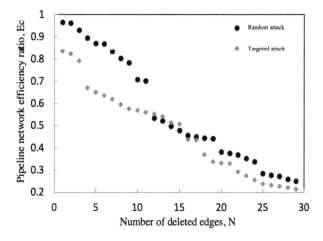

Figure 17. The network robustness diagram under the random disturbance and the targeted disturbance.

CONCLUSION

As the scale of the pipeline network continues to expand, natural gas pipeline network gradually shows the characteristics of a complex network. At present, researches aimed at ensuring the safe and reliable operation of natural gas pipeline network has become a research hotspot, but very few studies have considered the complexity of natural gas pipeline network and its possible impacts. In order to understand the complexity of natural gas pipeline network and its behaviors when facing structural changes, this paper studies the robustness of complex natural gas pipeline network based on complex network theory.

Based on the complex network theory and combined with the operating characteristics of natural gas pipeline network, this paper proposes a method for evaluating the robustness of natural gas pipeline network. The method includes a method for identifying key components of natural gas pipeline network, through which key components in the pipeline network can be identified, so as to strengthen the understanding of the vulnerability of the pipeline network and take effective measures to prevent accidents before they occur.

Based on the above method, this paper evaluates the robustness of natural gas pipeline network. The evaluation results show that natural gas pipeline network can show strong robustness when facing random disturbances represented by pipeline accidents or component failures caused by natural disasters, and when facing targeted disturbances represented by terrorist disturbances, the performance of natural gas pipeline network is vulnerable. Natural gas pipeline network behaves differently when facing different random disturbances. The pipeline network performs more robust when facing random disturbances represented by component failures than when facing random disturbances represented by pipeline accidents caused by natural disasters.

In this study, the hydraulic and thermal conditions of natural gas pipeline network were not considered, and only a preliminary exploration of the robustness of natural gas pipeline network was done. In order to make researches on the robustness of natural gas pipeline network better serve the engineering, it is indispensable to study the combination of hydraulic and thermal analysis of the pipeline network.

Author Contributions

The authors contributed to the paper in the following capacities: methods and materials, HS, JZ; results, XL; discussion, XL and NY.

REFERENCES

1. Albert, R., Albert, I., and Nakarado, G. L. (2004). Structural vulnerability of the North American power grid. *Phys. Rev. E* 69, 1–4. doi:10.1103/PhysRevE.69.025103

2. Almoghathawi, Y., Barker, K., and Albert, L. A. (2019). Resilience-driven restoration model for interdependent infrastructure networks. *Reliability Eng. Syst. Saf.* 185, 12–23. doi:10.1016/j.ress.2018.12.006

3. Ayala H., L. F., and Leong, C. Y. (2013). A robust linear-pressure analog for the analysis of natural gas transportation networks. *J. Nat. Gas Sci. Eng.* 14, 174–184. doi:10.1016/j.jngse.2013.06.008

4. Beyza, J., Garcia-Paricio, E., and Yusta, J. M. (2019). Ranking critical assets in interdependent energy transmission networks. *Electric Power Syst. Res.* 172, 242–252. doi:10.1016/j.epsr.2019.03.014

5. Beyza, J., Ruiz-Paredes, H. F., Garcia-Paricio, E., and Yusta, J. M. (2020). Assessing the criticality of interdependent power and gas systems using complex networks and load flow techniques. *Physica A: Stat. Mech. its Appl.* 540, 123169. doi:10.1016/j.physa.2019.123169

6. Carvalho, R., Buzna, L., Bono, F., Masera, M., Arrowsmith, D. K., and Helbing, D. (2014). Resilience of natural gas networks during conflicts, crises and disruptions. *PLoS One* 9, e90265. doi:10.1371/journal.pone.0090265

7. Cavalieri, F. (2020). Seismic risk assessment of natural gas networks with steady-state flow computation. *Int. J. Crit. Infrastructure Prot.* 28, 100339. doi:10.1016/j.ijcip.2020.100339

8. Chen, W., Lou, X., and Guo, C. (2019). A Robust Formulation Model for Multi-Period Failure Restoration Problems in Integrated Energy Systems. *Energies* 12, 1–23. doi:10.3390/en12193673

9. Chi, L., Su, H., Zio, E., Zhang, J., Li, X., Zhang, L., et al. (2020). Integrated Deterministic and Probabilistic Safety Analysis of Integrated Energy Systems with bi-directional conversion. *Energy* 212, 118685. doi:10.1016/j.energy.2020.118685

10. Crucitti, P., Latora, V., and Marchiori, M. (2004). A topological analysis of the Italian electric power grid. *Physica A: Stat. Mech. its Appl.* 338, 92–97. doi:10.1016/j.physa.2004.02.029

11. He, C., Dai, C., Wu, L., and Liu, T. (2018). Robust network hardening strategy for enhancing resilience of integrated electricity and natural gas distribution systems against natural disasters. *IEEE Trans. Power Syst.* 33, 5787–5798. doi:10.1109/TPWRS.2018.2820383

12. Hu, J., Khan, F., and Zhang, L. (2021). Dynamic resilience assessment of the Marine LNG offloading system. *Reliability Eng. Syst. Saf.* 208, 107368. doi:10.1016/j.ress.2020.107368

13. Liu, K., Biegler, L. T., Zhang, B., and Chen, Q. (2020). Dynamic optimization of natural gas pipeline networks with demand and composition uncertainty. *Chem. Eng. Sci.* 215, 115449. doi:10.1016/j.ces.2019.115449

14. Loktionov, V. I. (2018). Energy Resilience Assessment in the Period of Transition to Sustainable Energy. *Int. Multi-conference Ind. Eng. Mod. Technol. Fareastcon*, 2018. doi:10.1109/FarEastCon.2018.8602622

15. Lustenberger, P., Schumacher, F., Spada, M., Burgherr, P., and Stojadinovic, B. (2019). Assessing the performance of the European natural gas network for selected supply disruption scenarios using open-source information. *Energies* 12, 1–30. doi:10.3390/en12244685

16. Munikoti, S., Lai, K., and Natarajan, B. (2021). Robustness assessment of Hetero-functional graph theory based model of interdependent urban utility networks. *Reliability Eng. Syst. Saf.* 212, 107627. doi:10.1016/j.ress.2021.107627

17. Ramos, E. S., and Batista, L. S. (2020). Natural gas pipeline network expansion under load-evolution uncertainty based on multi-criteria analysis. *Appl. Soft Comput.* 96, 106697. doi:10.1016/j.asoc.2020.106697

18. Rădulescu, R., and Nedelcu, C. (2017). Finding optimal route in the Romanian natural gas network. *Proc. Int. Conf. Bus. Excell.* 11, 131–137. doi:10.1515/picbe-2017-0014

19. Sacco, T., Compare, M., Zio, E., and Sansavini, G. (2019). Portfolio decision analysis for risk-based maintenance of gas networks. *J. Loss Prev. Process Industries* 60, 269–281. doi:10.1016/j.jlp.2019.04.002

20. Su, H., Zio, E., Zhang, J., Chi, L., Li, X., and Zhang, Z. (2019). A systematic data-driven Demand Side Management method for smart natural gas supply systems. *Energ. Convers. Manag.* 185, 368–383. doi:10.1016/j.enconman.2019.01.114

21. Su, H., Zio, E., Zhang, J., and Li, X. (2018). A flow-based method for identifying critical pipelines in complex natural gas supply systems. *Saf. Reliab. - Safe Soc. A Chang. World - Proc. 28th Int. Eur. Saf. Reliab. Conf. ESREL*, 2051–2057. –2058. doi:10.1201/9781351174664-258

22. Su, M., Zhang, M., Lu, W., Chang, X., Chen, B., Liu, G., et al. (2017). ENA-based evaluation of energy supply security: Comparison between the Chinese crude oil and natural gas supply systems. *Renew. Sust. Energ. Rev.* 72, 888–899. doi:10.1016/j.rser.2017.01.131

23. Wang, C., Wei, W., Wang, J., Liu, F., Qiu, F., Correa-Posada, C. M., et al. (2017). Robust Defense Strategy for Gas-Electric Systems Against Malicious Attacks. *IEEE Trans. Power Syst.* 32, 2953–2965. doi:10.1109/TPWRS.2016.2628877

24. Wang, X., Bie, Z., Liu, F., and Kou, Y. (2019). Robust dispatch for Integrated Electricity and Natural Gas System Considering Wind Power Uncertainty. *Energ. Proced.* 159, 130–135. doi:10.1016/j.egypro.2018.12.030

Fossil Capitalism's Lock-ins: The Natural Gas-Hydrogen Nexus

John Szabo[1,2]

[1]Department of Environmental Sciences and Policy, Central European University, Budapest, Hungary;
[2]Institute of World Economics, Centre for Economic and Regional Studies, Budapest, Hungary

ABSTRACT

This paper investigates the hypothesis that power relations in the current, fossil fuel-based capitalist system allow the natural gas industry to appropriate the notion of a hydrogen energy utopia and substitute a natural gas-based vision for a renewable-based one. Although the uptake of hydrogen as a fuel is still in its infancy, the push to decarbonise natural gas-consuming regions has spurred action by natural gas industry actors to capture future markets. In doing so, they are able to maintain their capital accumulation practices based on unsustainable resource exploitation. This paper looks at how the domains of economic competitiveness, infrastructures, (geo)politics, and ideology all underpin the power of the natural gas industry to the detriment of their renewable competitors. The European Union is discussed in more detail, since this is the first region where ambitious climate policy targets and natural gas consumption collide.

Keywords: *Fossil capitalism, Hydrogen, Natural gas, European Union, Lock-in*

INTRODUCTION

A looming threat of climate change has pushed global society to begin to decarbonise its energy system. Electrification and renewables are the key disruptors, but technical hurdles remain *en route* to the consolidation of a low carbon economy. Experts have touted hydrogen as the missing link: a non-emitting, high power density, transportable fuel that can replace fossil fuels in applications ranging from industry to transportation. It can also store energy over longer periods of time, while potentially allowing firms to utilise existing natural gas infrastructure to transport and distribute it. Upon first reading, hydrogen offers a solution to our climate woes; especially, if we consider that it can be produced from renewables via power-to-gas technologies. Most have been excited about hydrogen's ability to shift our economies to sustainable ones by relying on renewable-based electricity generation. This paper proposes an alternative hypothesis: the current disposition of fossil fuel-based capitalism is set to pave the way for fossil fuel interests to capture hydrogen energy markets. The natural gas industry is especially well-positioned to appropriate the idea of a sustainable hydrogen utopia for a hydrocarbon-based one. We explore the various lock-ins that support a fossil fuel-based hydrogen society and assess this nascent market's developments in the European Union.

Scholars have only gradually reflected on the unique role energy plays in relations of production. Classical political economists were preoccupied with land's and labour's role in production, although the industrial revolution shifted their thinking to include raw materials as well. Karl Marx, for instance, paraphrases William Petty in stating that "labour is its [material wealth's] father and the earth its mother" (Marx 1887, n.p.). Energy resources are key inputs in industrial production, leading fossil fuels to mediate the social relations of fossil fuel-based capitalism, or simply *fossil capitalism* (Altvater 2006). This ever-expanding mode of social organisation faces planetary boundaries, as fossil fuels are non-renewable and their combustion has introduced the looming threat of climate change (IPCC 2018). Environmental constraints have not arrested the expansion of fossil capitalism, as fossil fuels continue to offer lucrative returns and mediate our modes of social organisation (Bellamy and Diamanti 2018; Szeman 2019). Social pressure is nonetheless mounting for climate action. The climate crisis offers us the opportunity to instate radical change by recalibrating fossil capitalist social relations predicated on exploitation. Alternatively, it could lead to incumbent actors stymieing the buds of transformation and maintaining prevalent social relations with a slight techno-fix – essentially substituting one fuel for another, *ceteris paribus*.

Hydrocarbon interests have begun to appropriate the notion of a sustainable hydrogen energy utopia for one based on natural gas. This paper traces the initial steps of this strategy and untangles how existing lock-ins empower the hydrocarbon sector. We first explore how the utopia of hydrogen has developed over the course of history. Then, we map the competing modes of hydrogen production, the power relations they encode, and the fuel's revolutionary potential. We then turn to the European case, where the fossil fuel industry has already leapt into action. This paper is based on the critical discourse analysis of policy and position papers issued by policy-makers, analysts, and energy industry incumbents (Fairclough 2013). It also draws on the analysis of presentations and discussions at the European Commission's (2018) prime natural gas industry event, The Madrid Forum. The author also conducted thirty-eight expert interviews with policy-makers, advocacy group representatives, industry experts, and academics to inform this paper's assessment of unfolding events.

FOSSIL CAPITALISM'S LOCK-INS

Marx wrote that the earth is material wealth's mother a century and a half ago, but the scale of its exploitation has considerably changed since then. Pre-industrial societies had relatively modest energy demands. They established *organic economies*, where source-fuels comprised of power extracted from phytomass, hydro, wind power, and limited quantities of coal (Wrigley 2010). The rise of industrial capitalism in the late-18th century rewrote these arrangements. Producers turned to coal to meet their demand for a steady supply of power dense energy resources enabling the proliferation of capital accumulation. Capitalist social relations were forged through the mediation of fossil fuels, paving the way for fossil capitalism (Malm 2016). Coal essentially constituted all additional energy demand growth between 1800 and 1900, and its role in global energy supply grew from 2 percent to 47 percent during that century (Smil 2010). Industrial production continued to rapidly expand in the 20th century, yielding an average annual economic growth rate of more than 3 percent – double the preceding century's average (Piketty 2017). Industrialising societies quickly conflated economic growth, industrialisation, and fossil fuel consumption to structurally institute fossil capitalist relations (Bellamy and Diamanti 2018).

The 20th century brought a rapid expansion of the oil and natural gas industries. Hydrocarbons proved to be an even more condensed and convenient source of energy, while allowing for the substitution of labour with technology during their production (Mitchell 2009). Their role rapidly grew in the global circuits of production. The tentacles of fossil capitalism expanded with the launch of electrification, motorisation, and the ascent of the petrochemicals industry (Malm 2018). Energy demand increased eleven-fold during the 20th century, with 81 percent of this met via fossil fuels (Fouquet 2016). A social structure predicated on expanding fossil capitalism also brought with it the rising concentration of wealth through control of resources in the hands of a limited number of entities. Monopoly capitalism accelerated (Lenin 1970). Oil and natural gas companies grew to become the largest and most profitable corporations in the world, controlling vast deposits of resources and underpinning industrial output. Currently, six of the largest ten companies by consolidated revenue are oil and gas corporations, according to the Fortune (2019) Global 500 tally. The power these entities have accrued allows them to exert a disproportionately large influence over the structures that maintain fossil capital's economic, political, ideological, and cultural relations in contemporary society (Wilson, Carlson, and Szeman 2017).

Fossil capitalism's disposition is reified through what Unruh (2000) identifies as a *carbon lock-in*. This is comprised of *scale economies* (decreasing costs with increasing production), *learning economies* (specialised skills reducing production costs), *adaptive expectations* (consumers and producers assume the stability of the system), and *network economies* (the development of interrelated technological systems). Unruh focuses on the economic and socio-technological dimensions of a lock-in, but these aspects should be extended to include the political and ideological factors that reproduce of fossil capitalism (Boyer 2014). This paper argues that fossil fuel interests depend on four heavily intertwined analytical dimensions of power to maintain their lock-in: (1) they can exploit resource bases economically; (2) infrastructure, including hard (e.g. pipelines) and soft infrastructure (e.g. the legal-technical means to produce, trade, etc.); (3) (geo)political factors; and (4) ideological inscription. These facilitate the continuation of a structural setting, where fossil fuel interests can continue to capitalise on their resource bases and impede a radical shift away from *fossil monopoly capitalism*. Stakeholders' claims and ability to exploit energy resources, as well as their push to utilise existing infrastructure, hinders their willingness to pursue a radical shift. (Geo)political factors are also crucial, insofar as those operating in fossil capitalism will look to uphold political stability to ensure capital accumulation. And lastly, society's widely adopted practices and ethical judgements pertaining to the desirability of fossil capitalism maintain and reify the system's structures.

Proliferating fossil fuel combustion has led to heightened greenhouse gas emissions, ushering in an era of anthropogenic climate change. This has turned into a climate crisis that poses a rupture to the dominant power relations predicated on fossil fuels, since most of global society's efforts to decarbonise will have to be directed at its energy system (Scrase et al. 2009). Renewables, such as solar photovoltaics and wind power plants, carry disruptive potential that recalibrate carbon lock-ins. However, they are unable to institute all-encompassing change, in-part due to technological limitations. We are unable to (economically) electrify social practices currently in place, while electricity storage to enable electrification on a grand scale is also lacking (Sivaram 2018). This is further inhibited with the existing lock-ins of fossil capitalism. Key fossil fuel actors have drawn on the carbon lock-in to promulgate their vision of the future. Hydrogen is at the heart of this strategy, since it is a source of energy that sustains *decarbonised fossil capitalism*.

THE UTOPIA OF A HYDROGEN SOCIETY

Hydrogen has a long-standing history of being a sustainable fuel utopia. This vision is based on the ability to use renewable-based electricity for the electrolysis of water, yielding *green hydrogen*. Verne (1874, ch. 11) was among the first who wrote about the idea in *The Mysterious Island*:

"And what will they burn instead of coal?"

"Water," replied Harding.

"Water!" cried Pencroft, "water as fuel for steamers and engines! Water to heat water!"

"Yes, but water decomposed into its primitive elements," replied Cyrus Harding, "and decomposed doubtless, by electricity, which will then have become a powerful and manageable force, for all great discoveries, by some inexplicable laws, appear to agree and become complete at the same time. Yes, my friends, I believe that water will one day be employed as fuel, that hydrogen and oxygen which constitute it, used singly or together, will furnish an inexhaustible source of heat and light, of an intensity of which coal is not capable. Some day the coalrooms of steamers and the tenders of locomotives will, instead of coal, be stored with these two condensed gases, which will burn in the furnaces with enormous calorific power."

The narrative of a *hydrogen society* became a staple of science fiction writers and technocrats by the middle of the 20th century, despite society making little progress on the fuel's wide-scale adoption (Zubrin 2007). These narratives strengthened the fuel's positive connotation and reified its ideological lock-in.

Experts saw hydrogen as the *ultimate fuel* (Dell and Bridger 1975) by the 1970s, but the oil crises did not disrupt the lock-ins of a fossil fuel economy. Environmentalism's rising momentum and the growing awareness of climate change beginning in the 1980s pushed some countries and corporations to explore fossil fuel alternatives. Car manufacturers and the U.S. navy took steps to deploy fuel cells in the 1980s and 1990s, but ultimately halted these undertakings (Romm 2004). Oil's role in transportation was too pervasive to substitute. In 1998 the Icelandic Parliament was the first to lead a large-scale inquiry into what a hydrogen society might look like (Hultman 2009). This is a still-ongoing experiment, but its impact has been limited. Hydrogen has not displaced oil consumption and is being crowded out by electricity's use as an energy carrier in Iceland. President George W. Bush reinvigorated the discourse of hydrogen as the *future energy source* in the U.S.A. when he launched the National Energy Policy Development Group (2001) to explore and promote the fuel's potential. This was followed by the U.S. Department of Energy's (2002) report arguing that hydrogen is the only energy form that can help sustain current modes of living, while averting climate change. U.S. efforts to promote hydrogen's uptake were thwarted by the shale gas revolution that offered the country ample supplies of a relatively clean fuel and was supported by existing lock-ins.

Europe had also been a front-runner in developing a hydrogen economy, given its vast reliance on imported fossil fuels and its bid to lead global climate action (Oberthür and Kelly 2008; Eurostat 2019). The European Commission launched the High Level Group on Hydrogen and Fuel Cell technologies in the early-2000s. Research Commissioner Philippe Busquin claimed that

[u]p until now in the 'fossil fuel civilisation,' we have been trying to strike a balance between the need to foster economic growth and at the same time to ensure this has a minimum impact on the environment. With an extensive use of hydrogen as an energy carrier, this conflict will be resolved. (European Commission 2002)

The Group argued that member states of the European Union should shift to an energy system based on renewable electricity generation, nuclear-based energy, as well as fossil fuel combustion paired with carbon capture and storage technologies, and use hydrogen as an energy carrier (European Commission 2003). The report was followed by the European Council's decision to establish the Fuel Cells and Hydrogen Joint Undertaking in 2008, providing a platform to explore hydrogen's future role (Council of the European Union 2008). The leaders of the EU reconfirmed their commitment to exploring hydrogen's potential at an informal meeting in Linz, Austria in September 2018, when they launched the non-binding Hydrogen Initiative (EU Energy Ministers 2018) and the European Commission (2020) has followed up on this with a Hydrogen Strategy. Initiatives in the U.S. and Europe reflect the deep-seated culturally-inscribed understanding that hydrogen could underpin a sustainable utopia, but the fuel's inability to gain momentum reflects the fact that we have not witnessed a sufficiently strong rupture in fossil capitalism's lock-ins.

WHY HYDROGEN?

Researchers have long understood hydrogen to be a high power density energy carrier that yields no pollutants when combusted, and an element that can be produced via the electrolysis of water (IEA 2019). It can also be stored for longer periods of time without degrading – in contrast to most currently available energy and electricity storage technologies. Historically, hydrogen was consumed as a component of manufactured gas since the beginning of the 19th century – typically produced from coal or oil (Thomas 2018). Urban residents and industrial consumers in Western Europe quickly adopted its coal-based variant, town gas, due to the availability of coal, its convenience for lighting and other applications, and the fuel's ability to alleviate air pollution by moving combustion sites outside urban areas. The 20th century brought the demise of town gas, as high coal prices and discoveries of large natural gas deposits led most European consumers to switch from coal-based town gas to natural gas (Peebles 1980). Meanwhile, European companies and governments undertook large-scale infrastructure upgrades necessary to enable a rapid switch from one fuel to the other (Williams 1981).

These actions show that policy-makers, the energy industry, and the wider population saw gas as a key and favourable source of energy. Countries were willing to adapt their infrastructure to accommodate the transit and distribution of the new fuel. This disrupted town gas' lock-in, but reinforced the lock-in of gas more broadly. The natural gas industry argues that many of these actions can essentially be reverse-engineered, allowing hydrogen to be transited and distributed through natural gas infrastructure (once again). This would yield tremendous economic savings for society, since with such a transition alternative infrastructure does not have to be constructed, with gas transmission system and other gas infrastructure operators kept in business. Legal-technical lock-ins also surface, as policy-makers expect that they can anchor hydrogen's regulations into those of natural gas. Policy-makers have extensive experience with engineering natural gas markets, which streamlines their approach to developing hydrogen markets.

The feasibility and the costs of the shift from natural gas to hydrogen infrastructure are not clear yet, as the industry is only beginning to conduct related experiments. Expert findings are promising, but much work still has to be done (IEA 2019). A methane-hydrogen admixture between 5 and 15 vol percent in existing natural gas infrastructure has been proven possible, but factors ranging from the age of the infrastructure to national regulations shape these figures (Ogden et al. 2018). Interviewees also pointed out that many unresolved issues remain with regards to the pipelines, for example the extremely high costs of switching pipeline fittings to suit the requirements of hydrogen. Moreover, Meng et al. (2017) find that "[t]he fatigue life of the X80 steel pipeline [a popular natural gas pipeline choice] was dramatically degraded by the added hydrogen" (7411). Various companies and researchers are also exploring how hydrogen can be stored in different geological formations. Salt caverns offer the most promise; although, researchers are heavily engaged in understanding how depleted natural gas and oil fields can store hydrogen, since they constitute the bulk of current natural gas storage capacities (Tarkowski 2019). Lastly, adapting end-user appliances to hydrogen or hydrogen-methane admixtures is a further crucial challenge (de Vries, Mokhov, and Levinsky 2017). Such experiments are at the top of the agendas of both company executives and policy-makers, indicating how great a lock-in investment into infrastructure yields.

The invention of the fuel cell allows hydrogen's applications to go beyond that of an energy carrier capable of producing heat and light. Fuel cells use hydrogen to generate electricity by converting the energy of a chemical reaction between hydrogen and an oxidant into electrical energy. Its application has been most promising in transportation, where engineers have sought a carbon neutral source of energy that has a power density higher than the lithium ion batteries – currently limiting the range of electric vehicles. KPMG's (2018) authoritative automotive survey indicated that executives in major companies expected that the future of personal vehicles may be hydrogen fuel cells, as opposed to electric. The surprising development reflects the lock-ins predicated on systemic interconnections between the transportation sector and a fuel that behaves similar to oil. Hydrogen offers similar power density, range, transmission and distribution system to its hydrocarbon counterparts. And, as we will argue below, it relies on the power relations prevalent in fossil capitalism.

THE DIFFERENT COLOURS OF HYDROGEN

Hydrogen is already a key feedstock in the circuits of global production. 2018 dedicated pure hydrogen output amounted to 73.9 million tonnes, which was consumed by the oil refining (52 percent), ammonia production (43 percent), and other (5 percent) sectors (IEA 2019). Additionally, industries such as steel and methanol production consumed a further 45 million tonnes of hydrogen which was not separated from other gases – this is primarily sourced from non-dedicated hydrogen output. 76 percent of dedicated hydrogen production is reliant on natural gas, with the remainder on coal, while carbon capture and storage/utilisation (CCUS) technologies only playing an experimental role in the supply chain. As industrialisation continues in a large number of countries, the IEA (2019) anticipates that hydrogen demand for industrial uses will continue to grow, but this is not the domain that we are concerned with in this paper. Instead, we are curious about the energy disposition into which hydrogen is being introduced: a fossil capitalist setting where global society needs to urgently decarbonise its energy system. This constitutes an undertaking much greater than current industrial consumption. Energy-specific applications of hydrogen may currently be scarce, but, as remarked by the Executive Director of the IEA, Birol (2019), "hydrogen offers tantalising promises of cleaner industry and emissions-free power: turning it into energy produces only water, not greenhouse gases. It's also the most abundant element in the universe. What's not to like?"

Experts such as Birol, build on the long-standing idea that a hydrogen utopia will be green, but the realities of our carbon lock-in suggest that it will be fossil fuel-based for the foreseeable future. Green hydrogen production is in its infancy, meaning that it is not yet economically viable, nor has it been scaled up to produce energy on a large scale. The largest hydrogen electrolyser has an installed capacity of 6 MW, which is set to be followed by other projects adding 5–30 MW apiece (Collins 2020). These are dwarfed by the existing hydrogen production capacities already used by oil refineries, for example. Dedicated pure hydrogen production is currently intimately linked to the hydrocarbon industry, since the oil refining industry is the prime user of hydrogen as a petrochemical for hydrocracking and desulphurisation. Industry incumbents carry the know-how and have already constructed vast hydrogen production infrastructures. The oil and ammonia industries predominantly rely on steam methane reformers to produce pure hydrogen, a natural gas-based process with a high operational efficiency and low production costs (IEA 2019).

Steam methane reforming offers the cheapest form of hydrogen, but it leads to emissions. Natural gas-based emitting hydrogen production yields so-called *grey hydrogen*. Other emitting forms of hydrogen include *black* and *brown*, for which producers rely on hard coal and lignite, respectively, as feedstock. Coal gasification is in use or being considered as source of energy production in coal-abundant regions such as China or Poland, and rely on a long-standing technology used for town gas production already popular two centuries ago. Governments have begun to frame the technology in a positive manner, with Polish MP Sitarski (2018) claiming at COP 24 in Katowice that Poland will become "hydrogen Kuwait." The fossil fuel industry can draw on both its access and ability to exploit natural resources and existing infrastructure to establish its role at the heart of a hydrogen society. Additionally, geopolitics comes into play, as the cases of Poland and China show, since their governments are laying the foundations to maintain their energy self-sufficiency.

The emissions of black, grey, and brown hydrogen have led involved industries to devise ways to decarbonise fossil fuel-based hydrogen. These still cannot offer sustainable modes of energy production, but they can potentially alleviate air pollution, eliminate greenhouse gas emissions, supply hydrogen in large quantities, and keep fossil capitalism intact. Emissions can be eliminated if producers apply carbon capture and utilisation/ storage (CCUS) technologies, leading to *blue hydrogen*. Oil and natural gas firms have a competitive edge in deploying CCUS, given their long-standing experience with the technology involved. Most CCUS projects currently in operation are linked to enhanced oil recovery (EOR), which oil and natural gas companies have been deploying since 1972 (Herzog 2011). The economics are also in favour of fossil fuel-based hydrogen production, since these are generally 2–4 times less expensive than green hydrogen, even with the costs of CCUS included (Götz et al. 2016; Zero Emissions Platfom 2017; IEA 2019). This competitive advantage hinges on numerous factors, ranging from the costs of renewables, their utilisation rates, location, and linkages to the grid, as well as the costs and utilisation rates of electrolysers. However, they depict the uphill battle green hydrogen faces against its grey and blue variants on solely economic grounds.

Green hydrogen's prospects are boosted by maturing renewables and electrolyser technologies, as well as the inability of private and public actors to develop and deploy CCUS. Glenk and Reichelstein (2019) surveyed cases in Germany and Texas, where wind-based power-to-gas production proved to be competitive on a small and medium scale. As electrolysers become more efficient, renewables become cheaper, and technology allows a more precise synchronisation of various systems, green hydrogen production may challenge its fossil fuel-based counterparts on economic grounds in the coming 10–15 years (Staffell et al. 2019). Additionally, large-scale CCUS has been very slow to materialise, despite it being a prerequisite to meeting commitments made in the Paris Agreement (Anderson 2015). The shaky economic foundations for it, the lack of coherent national, regional, or global strategies for its development, and barriers posed by social acceptability still hinder its expansion (Braun et al. 2018; European Court of Auditors 2018; Herzog 2018). The IEA (2017) claimed that "the global portfolio of CCS projects is not expanding at anything like the rate that would be needed to meet long-term climate goals" (61). In principle, green hydrogen could become economically competitive in the foreseeable future, but it will have to have a more forceful impact to disrupt the lock-ins of fossil capitalism.

EUROPE, THE FIRST BATTLEGROUND FOR HYDROGEN MARKETS

European Union policy-makers are taking action to establish hydrogen as a pillar of decarbonisation; an opportunity on which the hydrocarbon industry has been quick to pounce. At the root of this dynamic is the EU's leading role in the battle against climate change, which has become even more prominent following the 2015 Paris Climate Agreement and the European Commission's (2016) decision to accelerate the diffusion of renewables and electrification with the Clean Energy for All European policy package. This stands in contrast to the lock-in of natural gas EU member states have developed. They consume immense amounts of the fuel and have a vast infrastructure network traversing the continent to deliver the fuel to end-users (Alvera 2017; Eurostat 2019). The European Commission and national governments have also developed and implemented extensive rules and regulations to facilitate the trade of the fuel (Glachant, Hallac, and Vazquez 2013), which, in turn, have played a central role in maintaining the geopolitical stability between Europe and Russia (Gustafson 2020). The natural gas industry has a long-standing strong presence in the region, empowering industry incumbents to assert their power to capture hydrogen markets.

Natural gas industry actors have devised a relatively coherent message in response to the EU's climate ambitions: they can facilitate the energy transition by decarbonising natural gas and utilising available infrastructure. The industry pushed to be included in the EU's energy future. Their motion was supported by Eurelectric's (2018) – the EU electricity generators' advocacy group – influential position that existing technologies only allow a maximum of 60 percent electrification in the EU; therefore, additional source-fuels and energy carriers will be necessary in coming decades. Given the hydrocarbon industry's strategic interests to continue their capital accumulation based on the resource bases at their disposal, actors launched a campaign supportive of blue hydrogen. The matter was led by transmission system operators, since their businesses would default without any gas flowing through their pipelines. They were the leaders in devising and promulgating the message that Europe requires some form of natural gas to meet its energy needs (Stern 2019).

In principle, natural gas producers have slightly greater maneuverability, since they can export their resources to alternative geographies, but the European market is so vast, and its lock-ins so extensive, that major suppliers have taken a large interest in adapting to the EU's needs. Equinor has been a vocal proponent of hydrogen, since it is in a good position to capture this market (Eikaas 2017; Szalai 2017). It has vast natural gas deposits, expansive infrastructure, experience with steam methane reforming, and a long history in using CCUS. Not only has it fine-tuned CCUS for EOR, but most of its hydrocarbon production takes place offshore, providing it the opportunity to store CO_2 in a socially acceptable manner. Unsurprisingly, the company has become the leader of multiple hydrogen projects in Europe (e.g. H21, H-vision, Magnum, and the Net Zero U.K. partnership) (European Commission 2017; Equinor 2020).

The EU's largest natural gas supplier, Gazprom has looked to methane pyrolysis (methane cracking) to decarbonise its natural gas supplies (Shiryaevskaya 2018). This technology splits methane into carbon and hydrogen without combusting the molecule – avoiding CO_2 emissions. During methane pyrolysis, bubbles of methane (CH_4) rise through a plasma (various liquid metals can play this role), breaking the chemical bond between carbon and hydrogen. The reaction deposits carbon on the inner surface of the hydrogen bubbles. When the bubble pops at the surface of the plasma, the carbon – in the form of carbon black – is deposited on top of the plasma, while the hydrogen gas rises and is captured (Weger, Abanades, and Butler 2017). Methane cracking provides a palatable technology for Gazprom to continue the exploitation of its natural gas resources while meeting the EU's requirements to deliver a decarbonised gas. The technology may still be in its infancy, but it offers great promise and, in comparison to Equinor's strategy – reliant on CCUS, Gazprom would not have to develop and maintain costly CO_2 storage facilities. Furthermore, the Russian firm would have access to additional revenues from the sales of carbon black, which is used in industrial applications ranging from tire manufacturing to, potentially, carbon fibre production (Chung 2017; Duke University 2019). These companies have developed the contours of strategies allowing them to capture hydrogen energy markets as soon as they emerge.

POWER AND PLATFORM

A hydrogen society is still far from a sure thing and many still perceive it as mere hype. The industry and policy-makers have to overcome numerous technical hurdles before the fuel's consumption can take off. Irrespective of its future trajectory, we see how a threatened industry has mobilised to maintain its prominent role in fossil capitalism by capturing a new market that perpetuates its activities. Its actions are also coupled with attempts to shape policy agendas; most prominently, the industry has attempted to steer discussions of the European Commission's (2018) Madrid Forum. This has been annual convention of key natural gas stakeholders (policy-makers, producers, infrastructure owners, and a few academics), where discussions have focused on the technical codes regulating the EU's natural gas markets. The 2018 Forum reoriented this focus to the future of natural gas, and participants presented hydrogen as a palatable option to meet the region's energy demand in an economic manner, while maintaining that it would also sustain their businesses. The Fuel Cells and Hydrogen Joint Undertaking may still be a key platform to discuss the explicit applications and technical hurdles related to hydrogen, but the Madrid Forum's inclusion of the issue reflects the natural gas industry's push to include itself as a key stakeholder in the EU's hydrogen future. In doing so, it it is actively shaping the policy-making agenda, which, coupled with its political clout reliant on extensive lobbying (Balanya and Sabido 2017) and its lock-in, reflects its bid to maintain its role in the broader system by decarbonising the fuel it supplies. The natural gas industry has been eager to shape the hydrogen policy agenda, irrespective of the fuel's prospects amounting to mere hype or more, while advocacy groups of green hydrogen are notably left out of these discussions.

The European Commission requested that key stakeholders conduct studies to better understand the role of natural gas – and, by extension, natural gas-based hydrogen – in the EU's energy future during the 2018 Madrid Forum (Borchardt 2019). This both allows policy-makers to make informed decisions and grants industrial actors an opportunity to frame their fuel as a viable and desirable alternative. The International Association of Oil & Gas Producers, an oil and natural gas advocacy group, was commissioned to inquire about CCUS. SNAM, the Italian gas transmission system operator, will research how to blend various natural gas with other gases (e.g. biomethane, hydrogen, etc.) in the gas transmission system. Gas Infrastructure Europe (GIE), a storage advocacy group, will present a study on storing various gases in existing facilities. The European Network of Transmission System Operators for Electricity and Gas (ENTSO-E and ENTSO-G), the advocacy organisations of European electricity and natural gas transmission system operators, will explore the possibilities to integrate electricity and natural gas infrastructure. The Commission's bid to include these advocacy groups into the policy-making process is set to provide them with an opportunity to actively shape hydrogen's policy framework, most likely in their favour. Their research and findings will be crucial in identifying what is possible in the future, but it is fundamentally shaped by lock-ins pertaining to the exploitability of their resource bases, existing infrastructure, avoiding radical changes in consumer-producer relations, and drawing on the idea that society can continue to consume vast amounts of energy without exacerbating climate change through the adoption of a non-emitting fuel.

DECARBONISING NATURAL GAS TO ACCUMULATE CAPITAL

Global industrial capitalism relies on the wide-scale exploitation and consumption of fossil fuels. The rise of climate change rise as a paramount obstacle has pitted the survival of our civilisation and the interests of the fossil fuel industry – in its current form – against one another. Pressured by climate action, the hydrocarbon industry can maintain its relevance by capitalising on carbon-neutral fossil fuels. A power struggle is unfolding between green and grey/blue hydrogen to capture nascent hydrogen markets. The natural gas industry has a good chance at dominating this struggle, supported by factors stemming from four intertwined domains: (1) resource bases and production, (2) infrastructure, (3) (geo-) politics, and (4) ideology. Fossil fuel-based hydrogen remains economically competitive as it continues fossil capitalism's long-standing practice of exploiting *cheap nature* (Moore 2016). Natural gas prices have plummeted in recent years (BP 2019), enabling grey and blue hydrogen to maintain their competitive edge vis-à-vis green hydrogen production. The prices of renewables have also collapsed, but they are still frequently outcompeted by low natural gas prices. Additionally, steam methane reforming remains cheaper than hydrogen produced via electrolysers. However, not only does the combination of renewables and electrolysers have to be competitive, but they have to break lock-ins posed by long-term investment commitments that companies have already made in fossil fuel assets.

European actors have responded to the risk of a fossil fuel phase-out by emphasising the benefits of utilising existing infrastructure. Hard infrastructure owners – mostly transmission system operators, distribution system operators, storage facility operators, and liquified natural gas facility operators – responded by claiming that gas will be a part of the solution, but the form of this gas is yet to be identified. The form of the gas is not particularly important for them, since they can adapt to transit and distribute other fuels, although, the upstream, midstream, and downstream segments of the hydrocarbon industry maintain intimate and strong linkages optimised for oil and natural gas. Consequently, infrastructure operators will argue for the least change possible, so their ability to capitalise on existing resources is least affected. Biogas and green hydrogen jeopardise their existing models, since energy may be produced and consumed in a much more decentralised manner in comparison to the *status quo*. Soft infrastructure and the way it is designed also underpins fossil capital's lock-in. For instance, ENTSO-G functions as an advisory body for the European Commission in drafting codes, regulations, and policy. Green hydrogen faces a clear disadvantage in this domain, since professionals drafting the regulatory framework governing power-to-gas facilities have only began to clarify and develop the conceptual and legal definitions and tools necessary to integrate these facilities into the grid. The natural gas industry has developed a relatively united front and strategy to ensure the industry's survival, while renewables and green hydrogen producers are both fairly small and convey fragmented interests.

Political dimensions of a lock-in surface through the hydrocarbon industry's ability to shape government policy and its role in maintaining social stability. The fossil fuel industry is an immensely powerful political bloc shaping the actions of the state (Johnstone and Newell 2018), carrying the ability to influence policy via lobbying, shaping agendas (e.g. the Madrid Forum), drafting studies that will form the basis of policy, and so on. Simultaneously, fossil capitalism has maintained established consumer-producer relations, which has entrenched certain domestic (e.g. by providing jobs) and international links (e.g. through EU-Russia relations) that fortify lock-ins. Lastly, fossil capitalism provides an ideology that has normalised human practices pertaining to the widescale use of natural resources for gain, irrespective of the environmental and social impacts. An industrial capitalist regime that places capital accumulation on the back of labour and resource exploitation has been constantly reproduced by society, especially since the industrial revolution. The shock of climate change may force society to introduce techno-fixes that mitigate emissions, but buds of systemic transformation are not (yet) in sight. Fossil capitalism has proved to be an extremely flexible system that promulgates the desirability of fossil fuel-based practices irrespective of their sustainability. Hydrogen is the perfect energy carrier that enables fossil fuel-based relations of production and consumption to remain in place. The natural gas industry has taken the opportunity to offer the convenient solution of substituting a gas for another gas. Natural gas may be swapped for hydrogen, but apart from the technocrats directly involved with this undertaking, broader society will barely notice the change.

FINAL THOUGHTS

This paper proposed to reflect on the hypothesis that power relations of fossil capitalism will allow the natural gas industry to appropriate the notion of a hydrogen utopia and substitute a natural gas-based vision for one based on renewables. This ultimately allows natural gas interests to dominate (future) hydrogen markets. Green and blue hydrogen only offer techno-fixes to climate change, but the latter carries the potential to perpetuate current capital accumulation practices that rely on the exploitation of our natural resources in an unsustainable manner. In doing so, fossil capitalism is set to prevail in a slightly altered form. The carbon lock-in based on economic, infrastructural, political, and ideological elements is sustained through blue hydrogen. Even if green hydrogen does not offer an opportunity to supersede capital accumulation as the governing principle of our society, the more equitable distribution of renewable energy resources, as well as the potential to decentralise and ensure a sustainable form of energy production, introduces significant change to social power relations. However, hydrocarbon interests will deploy all means at their disposal to limit the extent of this change, a move society seems willing to accept. To rephrase Jameson (2003) quoting *someone, it is easier to imagine an end to the world than to end fossil capitalism.*

Acknowledgements

Many thanks for the work and input of the editors, the two reviewers, and the colleagues that had commented on previous drafts.

REFERENCES

1. Altvater, Elmar. 2006. "The Social and Natural Environment of Fossil Capitalism." In Coming to Terms with Nature: Socialist Register, edited by Leo Panitch, and Colin Leys, 37–60. London, UK: Merlin Press.

2. Alvera, Marco. 2017. "Gas Infrastructure in the EU towards 2050, Challenges and Opportunities." In The Role of Gas in the EU's Energy Union, EU Energy Law, XI, edited by Christopher Jones, 21–32. Deventer, Netherlands: Claeys and Casteels Law Publishers.

3. Anderson, Kevin. 2015. "Talks in the City of Light Generate More Heat." Nature News 528 (7583): 437. doi:https://doi.org/10.1038/528437a.

4. Balanya, Belén, and Pascoe Sabido. 2017. "The Great Gas Lock-in: Industry Lobbying Behind the EU Push for New Gas Infrastructure." Corporate Europe Observatory. https://corporateeurope.org/en/climate-and-energy/2017/10/great-gas-lock.

5. Bellamy, Brent Ryan, and Jeff Diamanti, eds. 2018. Materialism and the Critique of Energy. Chicago, USA: MCM' Publishing.

6. Birol, Fatih. 2019. "How Hydrogen Can Offer a Clean Energy Future." Financial Times, June 4. https://www.ft.com/content/8d0b818c-81f6-11e9-a7f0-77d3101896ec.

7. Borchardt, Dieter. 2019. "Exclusive! Borchardt (EU Commission) | From the Latest Madrid Forum to the next Gas PackageVideo." https://www.youtube.com/watch?v=qHCAc_5Yrh4.

8. Boyer, Dominic. 2014. "Energopower: An Introduction." Anthropological Quarterly 87 (2): 309–333. doi:https://doi.org/10.1353/anq.2014.0020.

9. BP. 2019. BP Statistical Review of World Energy 68. London, UK: BP. https://www.bp.com/content/dam/bp/business-sites/en/global/corporate/pdfs/energy-economics/statistical-review/bp-stats-review-2019-full-report.pdf.

10. Braun, Carola, Christine Merk, Gert Pönitzsch, Katrin Rehdanz, and Ulrich Schmidt. 2018. "Public Perception of Climate Engineering and Carbon Capture and Storage in Germany: Survey Evidence." Climate Policy 18 (4): 471–484. doi:https://doi.org/10.1080/14693062.2017.1304888.

11. Chung, Deborah D. L. 2017. "4-Polymer-Matrix Composites: Mechanical Properties and Thermal Performance." In Carbon Composites, 2nd ed., edited by Deborah D. L. Chung, 218–

255. Butterworth-Heinemann. doi:https://doi.org/10.1016/B978-0-12-804459-9.00004-X.

12. Collins, Leigh. 2020. "World's Largest Green-Hydrogen Plant Begins Operation in Austria | Recharge." Recharge | Latest Renewable Energy News. https://www.rechargenews.com/transition/worlds-largest-green-hydrogen-plant-begins-operation-in-austria/2-1-708381.

13. Council of the European Union. 2008. "Council Regulation (EC) No. 521/2008 of 30 May 2008 Setting up the Fuel Cells and Hydrogen Joint Undertaking." Official Journal of the European Union L153 (1): 20. https://www.fch.europa.eu/sites/default/files/documents/regulation_521-2008__en_1.pdf.

14. Dell, Ronald M., and Nevill J. Bridger. 1975. "Hydrogen—The Ultimate Fuel." Applied Energy 1 (4): 279–292. doi:https://doi.org/10.1016/0306-2619(75)90029-X.

15. de Vries, Harmen, Anatoli V. Mokhov, and Howard B. Levinsky. 2017. "The Impact of Natural Gas/Hydrogen Mixtures on the Performance of End-use Equipment: Interchangeability Analysis for Domestic Appliances." Applied Energy 208 (December): 1007–1019. doi:https://doi.org/10.1016/j.apenergy.2017.09.049.

16. Duke University. 2019. "RFI: Upgrading Carbon Derived from Methane Pyrolysis | Research Funding." https://researchfunding.duke.edu/rfi-upgrading-carbon-derived-methane-pyrolysis.

17. Eikaas, Steinar. 2017. "Statoil – Strategic Fit of Hydrogen." Paper Presented at the Oil and Gas Seminar. https://www.loyensloeff.com/media/1477760/presentation-oil-gas-seminar-2017-strategic-fit-of-hydrogen-by-steinar-eikaas-statoil.pdf.

18. Equinor. 2020. "Renewables and CCS – Actively Investing in Renewables – Equinor.com." https://www.equinor.com/en/what-we-do/new-energy-solutions.html.

19. EU Energy Ministers. 2018. The Hydrogen Initiative. Linz: Federal Ministry Republic of Austria Sustainability and Tourism. https://www.eu2018.at/dam/jcr:9b0c0051-2894-4bc6-86ba-ea959dc82c0d/The%20Hydrogen%20Initiative%20(not%20available%20in%20an%20accessible%20format)%20(EN%20only).pdf.

20. Eurelectric. 2018. Decarbonisation Pathways. Brussels: Eurelectric. https://cdn.eurelectric.org/media/3457/decarbonisation-pathways-h-5A25D8D1.pdf.

21. European Commission. 2002. "Commission to Launch High Level Group on Hydrogen and Fuel Cell Technologies." European Commission Press Releases. http://europa.eu/rapid/press-release_IP-02-1282_en.htm.

22. European Commission. 2003. Hydrogen Energy and Fuel Cells: A Vision of Our Future. EUR 20719 EN. Brussels, BE: European Commission: Directorate-General for Research and Directorate-General for Energy and Transport. https://www.fch.europa.eu/sites/default/files/documents/hlg_vision_report_en.pdf.

23. European Commission. 2016. Communication from the Commission to the European Parliament, the Council, the European Economic and Social Committee, the Committee of the Regions and the European Investment Bank Clean Energy for All Europeans. COM(2016)860. Brussels, BE: European Commission. https://eur-lex.europa.eu/resource.html?uri=cellar:fa6ea15b-b7b0-11e6-9e3c-01aa75ed71a1.0001.02/DOC_1&format=PDF.

24. European Commission. 2017. "Projects of Common Interest – Energy – European Commission." Energy. https://ec.europa.eu/energy/en/topics/infrastructure/projects-common-interest.

25. European Commission. 2018. "31st Madrid Forum – Presentations." https://ec.europa.eu/energy/en/content/31st-madrid-forum-presentations.

26. European Commission. 2020. Communication from the Commission to the European Parliament, the Council, the European Economic and Social Committee and the Committee of the Regions - A Hydrogen Strategy for a Climate-Neutral Europe. COM(2020)301. Brussels, BE: European Commission. https://ec.europa.eu/energy/sites/ener/files/hydrogen_strategy.pdf.

27. European Court of Auditors. 2018. Special Report No. 24/2018: Demonstrating Carbon Capture and Storage and Innovative Renewables at Commercial Scale in the EU: Intended Progress not Achieved in the Past Decade. Luxembourg, LUX: European Court of Auditors. https://www.eca.europa.eu/en/Pages/DocItem.aspx?did=47082.

28. Eurostat. 2019. "Eurostat/Energy/Data/Database/Energy(Nrg)/Energy Statistics – Quantities, Annual Data (Nrg_quanta)/Energy Balances (Nrg_bal)/Simplified Energy Balances (Nrg_bal_s)." Eurostat. https://ec.europa.eu/eurostat/web/energy/data/database.

29. Fairclough, Norman. 2013. Critical Discourse Analysis: The Critical Study of Language. Oxon, UK and New York, USA: Routledge.

30. Fortune. 2019. "Fortune Global 500 List 2018: See Who Made it." Fortune. http://fortune.com/global500/list/.

31. Fouquet, Roger. 2016. "Path Dependence in Energy Systems and Economic Development." Nature Energy 1 (https://doi.org/10.1038/nenergy.2016.98): 16098. http://www.nature.com/nenergy.

32. Glachant, Jean-Michel, Michelle Hallac, and Miguel Vazquez. 2013. Building Competitive Gas Markets in the EU. Cheltenham, UK and Northampton, MA, USA: Edward Elgar Publishing.

33. Glenk, Gunther, and Stefan Reichelstein. 2019. "Economics of Converting Renewable Power to Hydrogen." Nature Energy 4 (3): 216–222. doi:https://doi.org/10.1038/s41560-019-0326-1.

34. Götz, Manuel, Jonathan Lefebvre, Friedemann Mörs, Amy McDaniel Koch, Frank Graf, Siegfried Bajohr, Rainer Reimert, and Thomas Kolb. 2016. "Renewable Power-to-Gas: A Technological and Economic Review." Renewable Energy 85 (January): 1371–1390. doi:https://doi.org/10.1016/j.renene.2015.07.066.

35. Gustafson, Thane. 2020. The Bridge: Natural Gas in a Redivided Europe. Cambridge, MA, USA and London, UK: Harvard University Press.

36. Herzog, Howard. 2011. "Scaling up Carbon Dioxide Capture and Storage: From Megatons to Gigatons." Energy Economics, Special Issue on The Economics of Technologies to Combat Global Warming 33 (4): 597–604. doi:https://doi.org/10.1016/j.eneco.2010.11.004.

37. Herzog, Howard. 2018. Carbon Capture. Cambridge, MA: The MIT Press.

38. Hultman, Martin. 2009. "Back to the Future: The Dream of a Perpetuum Mobile in the Atomic Society and the Hydrogen Economy." Futures 41 (4): 226–233. doi:https://doi.org/10.1016/j.futures.2008.09.006.

39. IEA (International Energy Agency). 2017. World Energy Outlook 2017. Paris, France: IEA/OECD.

40. IEA (International Energy Agency). 2019. The Future of Hydrogen. Paris: IEA/OECD. https://webstore.iea.org/the-future-of-hydrogen.

41. IPCC (International Panel on Climate Change). 2018. Global Warming of 1.5°C. Special Report. UNFCC. https://www.ipcc.ch/sr15/.

42. Jameson, Fredric. 2003. "Future City." New Left Review 21 (May–June). https://newleftreview.org/issues/II21/articles/fredric-jameson-future-city.

43. Johnstone, Phil, and Peter Newell. 2018. "Sustainability Transitions and the State." Environmental Innovation and Societal Transitions 27 (June): 72–82. doi:https://doi.org/10.1016/j.eist.2017.10.006.

44. KPMG. 2018. Global Automotive Executive Survey 2018. KPMG. https://assets.kpmg.com/content/dam/kpmg/nl/pdf/2018/sector/automotive/global-automotive-executive-survey-2018.pdf.

45. Lenin, Vladimir Ilich. 1970. "Imperialism: The Highest Stage of Capitalism: A Popular Outline." In Lenin Selected Works vol. I: 1897–1916. Moscow. USSR: Progress Publishers. https://www.marxists.org/archive/lenin/works/sw/index.htm.

46. Malm, Andreas. 2016. Fossil Capital: The Rise of Steam Power and the Roots of Global Warming. London, UK and New York, USA: Verso.

47. Malm, Andreas. 2018. "Long Waves of Fossil Development: Periodizing Energy and Capital." Mediations 31 (2 (Special Issue: Materialism and the Critique of Energy)). http://www.mediationsjournal.org/articles/long-waves.

48. Marx, Karl. 1887. "Book One: The Process of Production of Capital, Chapter One: Commodities, Section 2: The Two-fold Character of the Labour Embodied in Commodities." In Capital – A Critique of Political Economy, Volume I, translated by Samuel Moore and Edward Aveling, edited by Frederick Engels. Moscow, USSR: Progress Publishers. https://www.marxists.org/archive/marx/works/1867-c1/ch01.htm#S2.

49. Meng, Bo, Chaohua Gu, Lin Zhang, Chengshuang Zhou, Xiongying Li, Yongzhi Zhao, Jinyang Zheng, Xingyang Chen, and Yong Han. 2017. "Hydrogen Effects on X80 Pipeline Steel in High-Pressure Natural Gas/Hydrogen Mixtures." International Journal of Hydrogen Energy, Special issue on The 6th International Conference on Hydrogen Safety (ICHS 2015, 19–21 October 2015, Yokohama, Japan) 42 (11): 7404–7412. doi:https://doi.org/10.1016/j.ijhydene.2016.05.145.

50. Mitchell, Timothy. 2009. "Carbon Democracy." Economy and Society 38 (3): 399–432. doi:https://doi.org/10.1080/03085140903020598.

51. Moore, Jason W. 2016. "The Rise of Cheap Nature." In Anthropocene or Capitalocene? Nature, History, and The Crisis of Capitalism, edited by Jason W. Moore, 78–115. Oakland, CA: PM Press.

52. National Energy Policy Development Group. 2001. National Energy Policy. Washington, DC: National Energy Policy Development Group. https://www.nrc.gov/docs/ML0428/ML042800056.pdf.

53. Oberthür, Sebastian, and Claire Roche Kelly. 2008. "EU Leadership in International Climate Policy: Achievements and Challenges." The International Spectator 43 (3): 35–50. doi:https://doi.org/10.1080/03932720802280594.

54. Ogden, Joan, Amy Myers Jaffe, Daniel Scheitrum, Zane McDonald, and Marshall Miller. 2018. "Natural Gas as a Bridge to Hydrogen Transportation Fuel: Insights from the Literature." Energy Policy 115 (April): 317–329. doi:https://doi.org/10.1016/j.enpol.2017.12.049.

55. Peebles, Malcolm W. H. 1980. Evolution of the Gas Industry. London, UK and Basingstoke, UK: Macmillan International Higher Education.

56. Piketty, Thomas. 2017. Capital in the Twenty-first Century. Cambridge, UK: Harvard University Press.

57. Romm, Joseph J. 2004. The Hype about Hydrogen: Fact and Fiction in the Race to Save the Climate. Washington, DC, USA: Island Press.

58. Scrase, J. Ivan, Tao Wang, Gordon MacKerron, Francis McGowan, and Steven Sorrell. 2009. "Introduction: Climate Policy Is Energy Policy." In Energy for the Future: A New Agenda, edited by J. Ivan Scrase, and MacKerron Gordon, 3–19. Energy, Climate and the Environment Series. Basingstoke and New York: Palgrave Macmillan.

59. Shiryaevskaya, Anna. 2018. "Russia Looks to Hydrogen as Way to Make Gas Greener for Europe." Bloomberg, November 8. https://www.bloomberg.com/news/articles/2018-11-08/russia-looks-to-hydrogen-as-way-to-make-gas-greener-for-europe.

60. Sitarski, Krzysztof. 2018. "Poland Could Be a 'Hydrogen Kuwait' for Transport Needs – COP24." https://www.thefirstnews.com/article/poland-could-be-a-hydrogen-kuwait-for-transport-needs—cop24-3691.

61. Sivaram, Varun. 2018. Taming the Sun: Innovations to Harness Solar Energy and Power the Planet. Cambridge, USA: MIT Press.

62. Smil, Vaclav. 2010. Energy Transitions: History, Requirements, Prospects. California, USA: Praeger.

63. Staffell, Iain, Daniel Scamman, Anthony Velazquez Abad, Paul Balcombe, Paul E. Dodds, Paul Ekins, Nilay Shah, and Kate R. Ward. 2019. "The Role of Hydrogen and Fuel Cells in the Global Energy System." Energy & Environmental Science 12 (2): 463–491. doi:https://doi.org/10.1039/C8EE01157E.

64. Stern, Jonathan. 2019. "Narratives for Natural Gas in Decarbonising European Energy Markets." Oxford Institute of Energy Studies. doi:https://doi.org/10.26889/9781784671280.

65. Szalai, Pavol. 2017. "Statoil VP: 'Natural Gas Has a Home in the Zero-Carbon World.'" Euractiv.Com, December 18. https://www.euractiv.com/section/energy/interview/statoil-vp-natural-gas-has-a-home-in-the-zero-carbon-world/.

66. Szeman, Imre. 2019. On Petrocultures: Globalization, Culture, and Energy. 1st ed. Morgantown, USA: West Virginia University Press.

67. Tarkowski, Radoslaw. 2019. "Underground Hydrogen Storage: Characteristics and Prospects." Renewable and Sustainable Energy Reviews 105 (May): 86–94. doi:https://doi.org/10.1016/j.rser.2019.01.051.

68. Thomas, R. 2018. "The Development of the Manufactured Gas Industry in Europe." In History of the European Oil and Gas Industry, edited by Jonathan Craig, Francesco Gerali, Fiona MacAulay, and Rasoul Sorkhabi, 137–164. Bath, UK: Geological Society.

69. Unruh, Gregory C. 2000. "Understanding Carbon Lock-in." Energy Policy 28: 817–830.

70. U.S. Department of Energy. 2002. A National Vision of America's Transition to a Hydrogen Economy – To 2030 and Beyond. Washington, DC, USA. https://www.hydrogen.energy.gov/pdfs/vision_doc.pdf.

71. Verne, Jules. 1874. The Mysterious Island. Project Gutenberg. http://www.gutenberg.org/ebooks/1268.

72. Weger, Lindsey, Alberto Abanades, and Tim Butler. 2017. "Methane Cracking as a Bridge Technology to the Hydrogen Economy." International Journal of Hydrogen Energy 42 (1): 720–731. doi:https://doi.org/10.1016/j.ijhydene.2016.11.029.

73. Williams, Trevor Illtyd. 1981. A History of the British Gas Industry. Oxford, UK: Oxford University Press.

74. Wilson, Sheena, Adam Carlson, and Imre Szeman. 2017. Petrocultures: Oil, Politics, Culture. Montreal, Canada: McGill-Queen's Press.

75. Wrigley, E. A. 2010. Energy and the English Industrial Revolution. Cambridge, UK: Cambridge University Press.

76. Zero Emissions Platfom. 2017. "Commercial Scale Feasibility of Clean Hydrogen." European Zero Emission Technology and Innovation Platform. http://www.zeroemissionsplatform.eu/extranet-library/publication/272-cleanhydrogen.html.

77. Zubrin, Robert. 2007. "The Hydrogen Hoax." The New Atlantis Winter: 7–20. https://www.thenewatlantis.com/publications/the-hydrogen-hoax.

INDEX

The results obtained from the conventional exergetic analysis highlighted already that HE1 in Case A is the component with the highest exergy destruction, where approximately half of the exergy destruction could be avoided. The exergy destruction within HE3 is quite low, but it has a large potential for improvement, due to a relative high amount of avoidable exergy destruction.

In Case AD1, the MHE is the component with the highest exergy destruction, where just a small part could be avoided. The potetial for improvement is slightly higher for HE1 and HE2.

In Case AD2, the MHE and HE2 have the highest exery destruction with a relativ small potential for improvement. However, the components IC2 and IC3 could be improved.

Economic Analysis

Figure 18 shows the estimated purchased equipment costs for three discussed cases. In addition to this information, the distribution of PEC among the group of components is demonstrated in Figures 19–21. The purchased equipment costs of the air compression and purification block and the column block are approximately the same for all three cases. However, the distribution within each case varies. While the share of the overall costs of the air compression and purification block differs slightly (between 7% and 9%), the share of the column block is affected more and varies between 40% and 54% for the three cases.

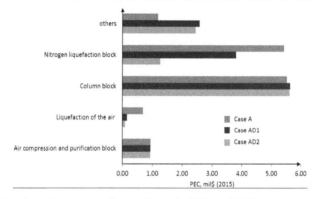

Figure 18. Purchased equipment costs for the Cases A, AD1, and AD2.

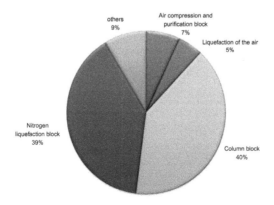

Figure 19. Distribution of the purchased equipment costs among the groups of components for Case A.

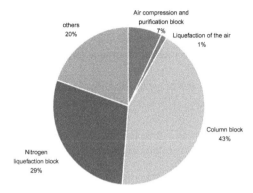

Figure 20. Distribution of the purchased equipment costs among the groups of components for Case AD1.

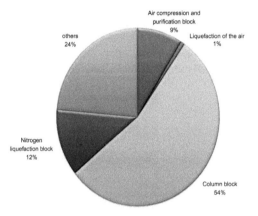

Figure 21. Distribution of the purchased equipment costs among the groups of components for Case AD2.

Table 4 shows the results of calculations of the fixed and total capital investment for the overall systems. The FCI and TCI of the Case AD1 is only slightly lower (3%) than the FCI and TCI of Case A. However, the difference between Case A and Case AD2 is far greater. Here, the FCI is 21.3% lower compared to Case A.

Table 4. Results obtained from the economic analysis of the overall systems

	Case A mil. US$ (2015)	Case AD1 mil. US$ (2015)	Case AD2 mil. US$ (2015)
Calculation of the fixed capital investment (FCI)			
Direct costs	41.4	39.9	32.6
Indirect costs	17.2	16.5	13.5
FCI	58.5	56.4	46.1
Calculation of the total capital investment (TCI)			
Plant facilities investment 1 (60% of FCI)	35.1	33.9	27.6